Principles of

Dynamic Psychiatry

Including an Integrative Approach to Experimental and Clinical Psychology

Jules H. Masserman, M.D.

Professor of Neurology and Psychiatry, Northwestern University, and Director of Education, Illinois State Psychiatric Institute, Chicago

SECOND EDITION

W. B. SAUNDERS COMPANY

Philadelphia · · London · · 1961

TO

CZERNA

who made this work possible

AND TO

CHRISTINE

who continues to inspire it

Let us (since life can little more supply

Than just to look about us and to die)

Expatiate free o'er all this scene of man:

A mighty maze! But not without a plan.

POPE—*Essay on Man*

Preface to the second edition

SECOND EDITIONS, like second thoughts, are not necessarily better than the original, but they signify, first, a recognition that all statements can be amended; second, an acknowledgment that there have been intervening events and changing concepts and, third, an attempt to utilize these to improve the initial formulations. In effect, I have not altered my view (Chapter VII of the first edition) "that the 'truth' about behavior, however penetrating our 'reasoning,' is eternally dependent on our current knowledge"—and that our knowledge is never complete, nor our reasoning ever absolute.

In accordance with this principle, about half the 1200 references in the original bibliography have been replaced by more recent and more comprehensive contributions, and their import has been incorporated into the sections on neurophysiology and pharmacology, comparative and experimental psychology, social psychiatry, and psychoanalysis. The discussions on combat neuroses and wartime morale have, happily and hopefully, been deleted. In their place are entirely new sections on ethology (Appendix 1), information and systems theory (Chapter 6), disturbances of communications (Chapters 6 and 7), and the evolution of psychotherapy (Chapter 14). As always, my expository purpose has been not only to sketch current outlines but to indicate beckoning vistas. However, references to illustrative clinical material in my *Practice of Dynamic Psychiatry* (W. B. Saunders Co., 1955) have been held to a minimum so that the text of the current volume would remain adequate to its own purposes of fundamental exposition.

As to style, I have continued to pay my respects to the reader's literary discernment by exploiting to the best of my ability the wealth of subtleties, nuances and resonances of the English language.

I wish to thank my friends and colleagues in many countries who, by their teachings, publications and personal examples, have helped me improve my own knowledge, thinking and writing. May this version of the book, now in its adolescence of fifteen years, be treated as gently and as generously by them and by others as was the first.

Northwestern University   JULES H. MASSERMAN, M.D.

Preface to the first edition

WHY ADD another book on psychiatry to a field that, many may contend, is already overburdened with a diffuse and contentious literature? Since no reply to this question can be completely impersonal, the author may state that he has embarked upon this work for the immediate purpose of getting into print certain fundamentals of modern dynamic psychiatry now being taught by his colleagues and himself only through lecture and precept. With these fundamentals available in book form, he could then divert his perennial efforts to those tasks of clinical teaching and guidance to which reading alone must forever remain supplementary.

And yet this question of an introductory text is in itself highly important. During many years of lectures to undergraduate physicians, nurses, psychologists and social workers, the author has sought for books which, breaking with tradition, would present the fundamentals of dynamic psychology and clinical psychiatry briefly, clearly and systematically, and so prepare the student for clinical training in diagnoses and therapy through direct work with patients. In this search the author was often rewarded by the discovery of brilliant chapters and pedagogic excellencies in many volumes: a comprehensive case-taking outline here, a striking clinical description there, an eclectic and dynamic exposition of various modes of therapy somewhere else. Why, then, not cull these references and construct the usual "required" and "recommended" reading lists?

Experienced instructors and harassed students alike well know the difficulties of such a course. To begin with, the neophyte who has had only a scattering of reading in fields allied to psychiatry may share one or more of the popular misconceptions which seem to have been little affected by thirty years of the "mental hygiene movement." To wit, he may approach psychiatry as a somewhat esoteric specialty concerned with those most awesome of afflictions—the "diseases" of the "mind"; then, after a little direct contact with psychiatric material which may touch off various emotionally charged prejudices of his own, he might either become compulsively and sometimes morbidly intrigued with some special and narrow approach (such as the "somatic," "reflexologic," "semantic," or "psychoanalytic") or he may fly from the wilderness of some of the current literature and from his own anxieties by deciding, not altogether correctly, that psychiatry is a contentious cacophony of fantastic dogmas, contradictory nosologies, and impractical theories somehow inserted into an otherwise "scientific" university or medical school curriculum.

Moreover, many students in the special disciplines often have specific difficulties. For example, the graduate in psychology may have had little acquaintance with biologic factors in behavior, and may in addition have been misled by outmoded preparatory courses in "abnormal psychology." The medical student, intrigued with his hard-won knowledge of anatomy, physiology and pathology, may also be resistant to less "exact" but more comprehensive formulations of behavior. However, perhaps most likely to be handicapped for an eclectic orientation is the student social worker, who runs the danger of becoming lost in the impersonal lore of budgeting, eleemosynary law and agency administration, or, in her avid seeking for "deeper" understanding of her clients' personal problems, may grow over-enthusiastic about some "school" or "system," adopt its specialized vocabulary, misapply its methods (e.g., "passivity," "semantic analysis" etc.) to her case work, and then rationalize her frequent failures with such limited techniques by persistent attitudes of diagnostic and therapeutic nihilism.

The above are only a few examples of how, in the author's experience, some students have been misled by their early readings in fields related to psychiatry, and of how necessary it is to forestall such misconceptions of the subject. Moreover, even were it practicable for the instructor to guide and discuss all of the student's contacts with the literature, it would still be more a pious hope than a sober expectation to think that students can spare time from their usually crowded curricula not only to seek out the scattered literature on psychobiology, descriptive psychiatry and dynamic therapy, but to emerge from their readings with an integrated understanding of behavior that would lead to useful clinical application and, possibly, fruitful research.

The purposes of this work are, then, to provide an orientative introduction to the principles of modern dynamic psychiatry, to outline their application to the techniques of clinical diagnoses, and to demonstrate the rationale and methods of effective therapy. Accordingly, the text of this volume has been divided as follows:

Part I defines the scope of psychiatry and presents a critical consideration of the various theories of behavior.

Part II attempts to re-formulate and integrate these theories into a biodynamic organon of behavior.

As a further orientation for the subject-matter of this book, it may be well to state that a companion text, entitled "Practice of Dynamic Psychiatry," is in preparation according to the following outline:

Part I applies to biodynamic principles of this organon to the rationale of the clinical examination of the patient by various special techniques.

Part II presents a description of clinical psychiatric syndromes. This section differs from the standard texts on psychiatry in emphasizing the dynamic over the purely nosologic and empiric approach, and in giving the neuroses and "character disorders" the extended consideration that their clinical importance deserves.

Finally, in Part III of this succeeding volume the various methods of influencing neurotic and psychotic behavior are presented and integrated into a rationale of treatment that transcends the limits implied by the word "psychotherapy," and rounds out the holistic and operational concepts of dynamic psychiatry.

Illustrative Material. Relatively simple dynamisms of behavior are exemplified in the text by accounts of typical laboratory experiments; more complex concepts and syndromes are illustrated by clinical "case histories." These vary in length and detail from thumb-nail sketches of specific "symptoms" to the description of a full-length psychoanalysis in Appendix I. The case histories have necessarily been altered in various ways to conceal the identity of the patient, but every effort has been made to keep the data of psychiatric significance intact.

Vocabulary. Despite the almost unbridgable semeiotic differences among the various fields that this book attempts to reintegrate, the author has resisted the temptation to create a new terminology, and has instead endeavored to redefine older diagnostic and operational concepts in terms of *biologic dynamisms*—hence "biodynamic," the only new word in the text, and one itself defined operationally throughout Part II. He has been guided in this course by the fact that previous unilateral attempts, however well-intentioned, to create a new psychiatric terminology (e.g., those of psychobiology and of psychoanalytic metapsychology) have, on the whole, introduced more confusion than they cleared, and have thereby demonstrated that the invention of scientific terms had better wait upon, rather than precede, accuracy of observation and clarity of theoretic concept. Nevertheless, to aid the student who may be completely unfamiliar with the vocabulary of psychiatry—a lexicon which, unfortunately, has in some respects vitiated the intuitive and cumulative insights of our everyday language of behavior—a fairly extensive glossary of psychiatric terms has been appended to this volume. To this glossary the student is implicitly referred during passages in the text that he may find terminologically obscure.

Acknowledgments of scientific indebtedness would, in complete justice, have to be made to every one of the many preceptors who have guided and inspired the author's training in neurology, experimental psychology, psychiatry and psychoanalysis. Special gratitude must be expressed to Dr. Adolf Meyer and to Dr. Franz Alexander who supervised my psychobiologic and psychoanalytic training respectively, and to Professor David Slight, under whose academic and clinical sponsorship the author has developed the theories and practiced the techniques expounded in this volume. To the University of Chicago, the Rockefeller Foundation and the Otho S. A. Sprague Memorial Institute I am indebted for a decade of support and freedom in clinical and experimental research, done in collaboration with my friends and colleagues of the Department of Medicine and the Division of Psychiatry. To the long-suffering amanuenses who deciphered my manuscripts I am also grateful for the fact that somehow they emerged in legible type. But perhaps those most deserving of any credit that may ensue from this collaborative work are first, the author's patients, who studiously disclosed in their behavior the facts and principles dealt with in this book, and second, the author's students, who patiently taught him the fundamentals of pedagogy.

J. H. M.

CHICAGO, ILLINOIS

Acknowledgments

THE AUTHOR wishes to express his thanks to the following publishers for permission to reproduce, in part, material previously published in articles under their copyright:

Grune and Stratton, Inc., for portions of Appendix 1.

Bailliére, Tindall and Cox, London, England, for portions of Appendix 2.

Psychoanalytic Quarterly, for portions of Appendix 4.

Other specific acknowledgments appear in the text.

J. H. M.

Contents

Part Two

Biodynamics

Appendices

Illustrative histories
and experiments

Case histories

Experiments

Plates

Part One

Development
of behavior theory

Chapter 1

Psychiatry, a science of behavior

Scope. *Psychiatry can be broadly defined as a science which deals with the determining factors of human behavior, its variations and vicissitudes, the methods of its analysis, and the means that may be employed to align behavior with optimal personal and social goals.*

Since a person's conduct is in part dependent on his physical state, every psychiatrist must be a physician thoroughly versed in the biologic and medical sciences. But inasmuch as behavior is also evolved through the unique experiences of the individual and is thus interwoven with his socio-cultural milieu, the psychiatrist must likewise know the ethnic, educational, economic, political, religious and other environmental influences that impinge on his patients. Since until recently it was in these fields that medical education was most deficient,* it was necessary for the physician, as part of his psychiatric orientation, to draw from his own life experiences and personal sensitivities the empathy needed to reconstruct his patient's background, ingrained attitudes, and accustomed patterns of conduct, and to supplement this "intuitive" (i.e., inwardly taught) understanding by background reading and a realistic awareness of current social processes and problems.

Contributory fields of knowledge

Essential to more formal training in behavior theory are the basic sciences of ethology and experimental biodynamics (cf. Appendix 1 and Chapter 8). Equally important are the various fields of psychology that deal with the modality, perception, retention and interpretation of sensations, Gestalt concepts of closure and field response, assays of the perceptive, mnemonic, associative and manipulative skills that comprise *intelligence* or the special mathematical, musical or other capacities called *talents*, the consistencies of spontaneity and action that constitute traits of personality, and the techniques that detect changes in any of these as a result of development, disease or therapy. Linguistics and kinesics (verbal and gestural communication), semantics (the science of meanings) and information theory have also clarified interpersonal communications that constitute the psychiatrist's most useful diagnostic and therapeutic tools (Chapter 13). Finally, psychoanalysis as a method of

* In the past decade, greater cognizance of the humanities has been taken in medical teaching, and Johns Hopkins, Northwestern, Western Reserve and other medical schools have introduced courses in history, philosophy, sociology and the humanities into a re-integrated six-year curriculum.

research, a theoretical system and an approach to therapy has become an integral (though not universally accepted) part of psychiatry, and has enriched it with a deeper understanding of the experientially determined development of motivations, personality traits and social adaptations (Chapters 3 to 8).

Historical development of behavior concepts

Mystic and quasi-organic concepts of "mental disease." The determinants and control of man's behavior have necessarily been topics of immediate interest to man ever since the prehistoric formation of familial and social groups, since if these groups were to survive, each person in them had to fit more or less efficiently into an organized hierarchy of responsibility and duty in relation to others; i.e., the behavior of each member had to conform predictably to certain implicit customs or formulated "laws" under which the group operated.

But primitive man could not trace the slow evolution of such customs and "laws"; instead, he assumed vaguely that his personal and social conduct was somehow governed by "powers" superior to both the individual and the group. An initial formulation of this phenomenon was to attribute these influences directly to awesome and uncontrollable agents: the sun, the lightning, the wind, or the "spirits"* of the dead that he saw in his dreams (Tyler). Later, these were embodied as totems or deities which could be more tangibly worshipped, propitiated, or even (somewhat fearfully) reprimanded by the mortals who had erected them. Everything was then governed by these Powers who, by their omnipotent caprice, could direct success or failure, plenty or want—and health and ease as opposed to evilness (illness) and dis-ease. Abnormalities of bodily function or conduct were considered to be visitations of devils or other malign beings which, by pervading the victim's body, caused him to develop various "symptoms" (Greek—anything that has befallen one) of an "attack" or a "seizure"—terms which persist in our current language. It mattered not whether these were expressed as specific physical disabilities (illness) or more generalized behavioral aberrations (neuroses and psychoses); in both cases the victim was supposed to be governed by external yet immanent influences which caused him to act abnormally—and which made it necessary for the group to regard him with a mixture of fear, awe and covert malice until either the supposed malignity was expelled or its victim perished. In medieval Europe such concepts attained a high degree of fantastic elaboration: the sick were starved, purged, cupped and bled white to rid them of an excess of "body humors," and the more grossly disturbed and vulnerable neurotics and psychotics were exorcised and tortured until the incubi and succubi which had "possessed" them were induced to leave the victim's body.

Unfortunately, so ingrained in our thinking and language did such traditions become that even today diseases are spoken of as deplorable

---

* Latin *spiritus*—breath or soul: the first sign of life in the child, joyous when we are *inspired,* depleted when we are *dispirited,* pervasive in *esprit de corps* and returned to the land of departed spirits when we *expire.*

visitations rather than processes of adaptation to bodily traumata. For instance, a patient is thought of as "catching" pneumonia rather than as reacting with every physiologic resource at his command—fever, leuko-cytosis, antitoxins, etc.—against a complex combination of circumstances that render him temporarily vulnerable to bacterial infection. And the same conceptual error is repeated when a physician diagnoses his patient as *having* a "hysterical seizure" or a "compulsion" rather than thinking of him as mobilizing various adaptive maneuvers, however "neurotic," against motivational conflicts to which, by virtue of individual vulnera-bilities accentuated by previous traumata, he has become especially sus-ceptible (cf. Chapter 3).

Early dynamic and psychosomatic concepts of behavior.   Interest-ingly, the viewpoint that all normal and abnormal behavior is a process of organismic adaptation between physiologic needs on the one hand and "external" circumstances on the other seems to have been expressed in enlightened Greek thinking more than two thousand years ago. In his concept of the "four humors" (yellow bile, black bile, phlegm and blood), Hippocrates postulated not only a balance of physiologic processes but also their respective expressions in the attitude and conduct of his pa-tients which we still characterize by the derived terms *choleric, melan-cholic, phlegmatic* and *sanguine*. Further, Hippocrates thought that when the humors were adversely mixed (i.e., when incompatible modes of be-havior were in conflict in an individual) physical and mental disease resulted—an etiology which, however crude, was scientifically far in advance of the superstitious mysticism of his day. Thus, it is reported that when "a dislocation of the humors" produced the symptoms of hys-teria in one of his female patients, Hippocrates recommended that the woman's illness be relieved "by indulging the intentions of nature and lighting the torch of Hymen," i.e., satisfying her inhibited erotic urges. Whether or not Hippocrates' biographer, Soranus, objected to this pre-scription on moral grounds is not clear, but in his own medical writings he cautioned against advising frank sexual indulgence as a specific for hysteria, since "It is folly to think of curing one fury by another . . . good counsel and persuasion alone can effect a cure." In effect, Hippocrates prescribed behavior designed to relieve the patient's repressed drives, whereas Soranus acknowledged the limitations set by fear and recognized that a wise and trusted physician can guide a patient out of a pathogenic dilemma.

Startlingly modern in tone, too, are some of the concepts of Plato who, two and a third millennia before Freud, taught that man as well as all other forms of life is actuated by physiologic needs and "natural appe-tites" collectively called Eros—a moving (conative) force expressed in all behavior from brute aggressiveness to intellectually sublimated "reason and love of truth." Plato, as did Heraclitus of Ephesus, anticipated Freud in his insight into the functions of fantasies and dreams as substituted satisfactions resorted to when man's goals and desires are otherwise frus-trated: "In dreams, desire tends to satisfy itself in imagery when the higher faculties no longer inhibit the passions." So also did Plato specifi-cally recognize "a stage at which desire and reason are in conflict"—a concept that parallels the Freudian formulation of a corresponding conflict between Id and Ego (Chapter 3). And to Plato's pupil, Aristotle, can be traced yet another modern idea: that the ethics which govern man's "rational" behavior and are counterposed to his "animal passions" are themselves not divine fiats, categorical imperatives or transcendent sociologic laws, but merely the distinctive *customs* developed by various social groups for the greater cohesion and distributive benefits of the individuals that comprise them. A "social conscience" is, then, a culturally adaptive process on the part of the individual; if it clashes excessively with more immediately selfish and asocial wishes, the resulting tensions can produce irrationally "neurotic" aberrations from the group norm.

These fragments of the early history of psychologic thought* are cited to illustrate how deep are the roots of the mystic, organic, social and holistic-dynamic formulations of behavior which, in various combinations and with various terminologies, still dominate our thinking.

Organic theories of behavior

The approach of pathology.   In essence, this position holds that since "normal" behavior depends on the optimal functioning of the organs of the body as regulated by the endocrines and by the central nervous system, "abnormal" conduct must be simply an expression of injury or disease affecting the body economy. The example most often cited is that of luetic general paresis, which had been regarded as a functional psychosis until Moore and Noguchi, in 1913, demonstrated the actual presence of *Treponema pallidum* in the brains of paretics.† With this as a paradigm, adherents of the exclusively organic school of psychiatry contend that when physiochemical methods have become sufficiently refined and precise, we shall discover that hysteria, schizophrenia and other such disorders are really caused by organic disturbances consequent upon dietary deficiencies, infections, dystrophies, or other hitherto unsuspected pathologic disturbances.

Because of the qualification "when methods become sufficiently refined" faithful adherents to this school are not deterred by the careful studies of Mott, Dunlap, Spielmeyer, Freeman and others which have failed to disclose pathologic changes in the central nervous system even in the advanced functional psychoses. Current studies include possible anomalies in the ascending reticular activating system (the RAS of Moruzzi and Magoun), preoccupations with metabolic and hormonal imbalances such as those of Osmond and Hoffer on adrenochrome, Himwich on serotonin, Ackerfeldt on ceruloplasmin (a blood monoamino-oxidase),

---

* For a more detailed account of the evolution of various psychiatric concepts, cf. *The Practice of Dynamic Psychiatry*, Chapters 21–23.

† Although the cerebral damage caused by the *Treponema* undoubtedly impairs cerebral functions, it can be shown that the affective lability, grandiose delusions and other manifestations of paresis either are due to the release of previously repressed personality characteristics, or represent the patient's attempts to overcompensate for inwardly sensed deficiencies.

Altshule on pineal secretions, and Heath on "taraxein" (a postulated schizophrenogenic cerebral toxin named from the Greek *tarassein*, to disturb), and Funkenstein's postulate that psychotics differ from normals in their reactions to epinephrine and Mecholyl. Nevertheless it remains true that decades of search everywhere, and particularly intensive recent studies at the National Institute of Mental Health in Washington (Elkes, Kety), have failed to confirm any consistent physiologic deviations that are demonstrably the cause rather than the accompaniments or results of neurotic or psychotic behavior. Of course, failure to find unequivocal proof does not refute a theory, so there can be none but economic objections to the continued attempts by this school of psychiatry to seek for the etiology of "mental disease" on purely chemical or physical grounds.*

Unfortunately, many organicists, disdaining proof on the plea of urgency, have proceeded with "specific" therapies—some of them drastic and regrettable—on false premises such as that all psychiatric disorders are caused by peculiar "dysjunctions" in the pathways of the central nervous system (Wernicke), focal infections (Cotton), metabolic imbalances (Berman), or "bad nervous inheritance" predisposing to "storms" in the hypothalamus (Alvarez). Accordingly, for many years psychiatric patients were subjected to multiple surgical operations, including nephrectomies and colectomies to remove non-existent "hidden infections" until Cheney, Kirby and others had the procedure interdicted; more recently, various toxic medicaments (e.g., colloidal gold, dinitrophenol, NP207, Iproniazid) have caused serious complications (nephritis, cataract, retinitis and hepatitis in the instances cited) before their use was discarded or modified. Why, then, does the organic theory of behavior disorders still claim so many adherents despite its conceptual deficiencies and therapeutic failures or tragedies? The reasons seem to be many, but the leading ones are in themselves of psychiatric interest.

First, a purely materialistic approach to all problems has been the accepted method in most sciences†, including medicine. Second, the advances in our knowledge of metabolic, neuroendocrine and other physiologic processes, the discovery of the infectious, toxic or anutrient causes of many previously mysterious illnesses, and the staggering increase in specialized technology literally clogged the medical curriculum. Third, psychiatry itself was until recently taught in so obscure, dehumanized and sterile a fashion that the student had little opportunity to anticipate that he would have to treat traumatic, infectious and metabolic disturbances not as isolated phenomena, but in every instance as affecting a

---

* Very recently it has been shown that schizophrenic serum adversely affects living cultures of cerebral neurons and oligodendroglia (Ruth Geiger), and the web-spinning of spiders (N. A. Bercel); so also, J. Gottlieb and his co-workers have evolved a refined technique for demonstrating altered carbohydrate metabolism in some forms of psychosis. However, this work, though better controlled than previous studies, may withstand closer scrutiny no better than many other initially promising leads.

† However, Planck, Dirac, Heisenberg and others point out that even in physics not only does the observer play a central role in recording events, but he also influences them through his very act and individual mode of observation.

uniquely organized individual concurrently responding to interrelated physical and experiential insults. A physician trained to think only in organic terms would, for instance, regard "a case of pneumonia" as an infectious disease characterized by pulmonary consolidations which cause cough, hemoptysis and fever, with little or no consideration given to equally important matters such as the habit patterns of the patient which rendered him susceptible to the infection, or his concurrent desires, attitudes and reactions that could profoundly influence the outcome of his illness, either toward a return to full health and function or toward chronic invalidism, regression and neurotic maladaption. Similarly such a physician, when confronted with behavior problems in which some of the precipitating factors are not as readily apparent as are those in pneumonia, may deny the possibility of "purely functional" disorders even though these usually comprise over half his practice, or may admit that the patient has a vague "neurosis" but seek obscure "somatopsychic" explanations in which mild and incidental somatic disturbances are once again postulated as the sole "cause" of the patient's difficulties. Therapy then consists of covertly punitive treatments such as rigid diets, unnecessary "rest cures," musculoskeletal manipulations, and even mutilating surgical operations; when these fail, the patient is either condemned as a deliberate "malingerer," or, more charitably, dismissed as "just a neurotic." On the other hand, if these procedures seem temporarily effective this is regarded as proof that the illness had all along been of somatic origin. This reasoning, of course, neglects the subtle but potent influences of the physician-patient relationship during therapy, and the multiple comforting and suggestive effects of any therapeutic procedure, reassuringly applied (cf. Part Two).

Nosologic approach to mental disorders.   Closely allied to such orientations is a tendency to classify psychiatric disorders into separate categories and to assume, as in general medicine, that each "disease entity" also follows a definite pattern of symptomatology, course and outcome. Little justification for this exists on etiologic, clinical or heuristic grounds; on the contrary, the prognosis and therapy in every behavior disorder depend on many factors impossible to include in any diagnostic label. True, in the early years of psychiatry it was convenient to organize clinical observations around various systems in which each "disease" was given a pseudo-Linneaian binome and fitted into an assigned niche in some arbitrary scheme, but conscientious and discerning taxonomists who followed this course (e.g., Kahlbaum, Kraepelin, Bleuler) eventually found it necessary to add subgroups, variants and "transitional forms" almost endlessly in an effort to retain artificially intact even their major diagnostic categories. As one consequence, an appalling number of hours was formerly spent in heated polemics as to the "differential diagnosis" between, for example, agitated depression, involutional melancholia or some other clinical entity equally vague as to etiology, prognosis and therapy. So also, attempts were made to assign the patient's "pre-psychotic constitution" and "personality type" to yet another set of categories. These were either covertly condemnatory, for example, the *constitutional inferior* or *degenerate* types of Lombroso, or else purported to correlate physique and temperament, for example, Kretschmer's "pyknic-syntonic type" (a stocky individual theoretically subject to mood disorders) as contrasted to the "dystrophic-schizoid type" (a tall, lanky individual likely to develop "dementia praecox").

More recently, Sheldon has attempted to revive interest in such correlations by proposing, on the basis of his own system for measuring full-length photographs of nude males, that there are three types of physique corresponding to the predominant development of one of the three embryonic layers. Sheldon classified these as *ectomorphic* (tall, thin, delicate), *mesomorphic* (muscular, solid) and *endomorphic* (splanchnically developed, usually stout), with conformations graded on a scale of 1 to 7. According to Sheldon, predominantly ectomorphic individuals are intellectual, aloof, compulsive or schizoid; mesomorphic ones, athletic, impulsive and inclined to "manic" aberrations; endomorphic, earthy and pleasure-seeking but inclined to mood swings, and so on. This scheme, like the preceding systems of Naccarratti, Jung and others (cf. Glossary), is open to the criticism that anthropometric measurements show a Gaussian rather than a trimodal distribution, that correlations with "personality types" may involve subjective imponderables, and that carefully controlled statistical studies (cf. Paterson) have shown no significant correlations between "constitution" on the one hand and either "personality" or type of mental disorder on the other. Nor would it be surprising if a man rendered thin and cachexic by some metabolic disorder secondarily became "morose" and "introspective," or one with uninhibited oral desires were stout and merry, or one with a strong musculature acquired athletic interests, and so on.

Fortunately, there is developing a healthy reaction away from the concept that the current nosologic terminology is useful for much more than convenience in the filing of case histories under crudely descriptive headings. (Cf. the *Practice,* Chapters 8 through 14). Even when the diagnosis concerns some specific etiologic agent, such as "alcoholic delirium" or "psychosis with meningovascular syphilis," it is recognized that any truly useful appraisal must include terms describing the patient's multiple and variably intense *reactions* and *adaptations* to these complexly meaningful traumata. True, it is still convenient—and certainly so for chapter writing—to distinguish major rubrics such as neuroses and psychoses with perhaps the principal syndromes under each, but in practice diagnostic statements must be made sufficiently broad to allow for almost every conceivable configuration of normal and abnormal patterns and fluid enough to cover multidirectional transitions even among the major categories. In any case, the most pertinent and meaningful clinical data are those relevant to the patient's motivations, his skills and capacities, his characteristic adaptive patterns, the environmental contingencies that precipitated his previous and present reactions, and the circumstances that militated for or against a change in his behavior in desired directions.

Heredity in behavior disorders. It is an ancient belief that the sins of the fathers shall be visited on the children in the form of madness "yea, even unto the fourth generation"; it is not surprising, therefore that, from ancient to modern times, many efforts have been made to prove either that "mental ill-ness" (evil-ness) was itself congenital or that susceptibility to it was determined by a dominant or recessive heredity. Such genetic studies generally took the following forms:

1. FAMILY HISTORIES (method of Galton) detailing the occurrence of supposedly familial "traits" or "diseases." Unfortunately, even when the biases of both the informants and the investigators could be minimized, this method of investigation rarely furnished reliable data, since really accurate descriptions could not be obtained, the environmental influences on a patient's antecedents could not be evaluated, and the adverse influences of criminal, neurotic or psychotic parents on the patient's early behavior were often underestimated or neglected. For instance, in purely medical genetic research, uncontrolled studies of this type led to fallacious conclusions such as that tuberculosis and pellagra were inherited. Even less reliable, therefore, were the inferences drawn as to the hereditary nature of feeblemindedness, criminality or mental diseases in a particular genealogy. Conclusions of this type, now completely disproved, were, for example, those of Goddard on the Kallikak family (cf. Penrose).

2. QUASI-MENDELIAN STUDIES of "pure strains" in isolated communities. These, too, have been fragmentary, unreliable and inconclusive (cf. Rosenberg).

3. STUDIES OF TWINS. These generally furnished better evidence, but again it was difficult to determine the *identity* of the twinship, or to eliminate the effects of similar early environments in such siblings. Certainly, in the few cases in which twins were raised in separate environments, wide differences of behavior occurred (Holzinger, et al.), and in 41 pairs of identical twins studied by Rosanoff, only one twin of a pair developed a psychosis (schizophrenia) in a third of the cases.

Nevertheless many of our capacities and proclivities (cf. Chapter 8) are undeniably inborn* and the field continues to be controversial. For example, Linus Pauling contends that "Mental disease is chemical in origin, and . . . the result of abnormalities in the genetic constitution of the individual." In contrast, J. L. Fuller sums up the more moderate views of Pollack, Kallmann, et al. in the operational dictum that "heredity is [merely] the *capacity to utilize our environment* in a particular way." All in all, genetic studies have shown that while certain defects in the helical templates of deoxyribonucleic acid in our genes (and consequent disturbances in protoplasmic ribonucleic acid) may transmit feeblemindedness, epilepsy, and possibly a few other disorders, there is no reliable evidence for definite hereditary factors in behavioral aberrations

---

* Benson Ginsberg vividly describes the unique genetic endowment of every organism as follows: "At the moment of fertilization [it] receives a distillate from each of two samples in an unbroken . . . evolutionary continuity. This distillate is an organized collection of potentially immortal biomolecules, none of which has known death and each of which has undergone innumerable replications and (presumably) mutations. In organization and structure, this microscopic collection of matter in the zygote nucleus represents a sampling from the accumulated experiences of countless ages of evolution. As such, it is a finely adjusted mechanism, although its components probably represent a unique qualitative combination that has never occurred before and will never occur again."

less directly dependent on somatic and neurologic functions. Rather, controlled genetic-environmental studies (cf. Rosenberg) indicate strongly that parents influence their children's patterns of behavior less by genes than by the nature of parental care, precept and example.

References*

Brinton, Crane: The Shaping of the Modern Mind.
Bromberg, W.: The Mind of Man.
Cameron, D. E.: Objective and Experimental Psychiatry.
Cobb, S.: Foundations of Neuropsychiatry.
Coghill, G. E.: Anatomy and the Problem of Behavior.
Dunbar, H. F.: Emotions and Bodily Changes.
Fuller, J. L.: Nature and Nurture, A Modern Synthesis.
Gesell, A. and Amatruda, C.: The Embryology of Behavior.
Hall, et al., Eds.: A Hundred Years of American Psychiatry.
Herskovitz, J. J.: Man and His Works.
Hunt, J. Mc.: Personality and the Behavior Disorders (Chapters 1, 2, 3, and 17).
Kraepelin, E.: Text-book of Psychiatry.
La Barre, W.: The Human Animal.
Masserman, J. H.: Behavior and Neurosis (Chapter I and appended references).
Paterson, D. G.: Physique and Intellect.
Rose, A. M. (Ed.): Mental Health and Mental Disorder; a Sociological Approach.
Sheldon, W. H.: The Varieties of Human Physique.
Stockard, C. R.: The Physical Basis of Personality.
Wertheimer, F. L., and Hesketh, F. E.: The Significance of the Physical Constitution in Mental Disease.
Whitehead, A. N.: Science and the Modern World.
Zilboorg, G., and Henry, G.: A History of Medical Psychology.

* The readings listed after each chapter are supplementary to the text or present contrary viewpoints. Full references by author, title and publication will be found in the Bibliography.

Chapter 2

Psychologic concepts of behavior

CURRENT schools of psychology (e.g., those of Lewin, Tolman, Hull, J. G. Miller) are arriving at truly holistic and dynamic formulations of human behavior, and we shall consider them in various connections later in this volume; however, certain more traditional psychologic concepts have so permeated psychiatric thought that they require preliminary reexamination.

Cognition

In some philosophic systems, man's "mind"* has, through introspection, been described as an "organ of reason" by which man senses his milieu, perceives and remembers its organization, consciously plans his own adaptations, and finally directs their effective execution. This complacent overevaluation of man's cognitive functions has classical sanction: Plato and Aristotle taught that man was distinguishable from animals only by the former's supposed rationality; Descartes, in his *cognito, ergo sum,* postulated thought as the very basis of existence, and some contemporary academicians, in a resurgence of neoscholasticism, still recommend "the cultivation of intellect" as the sole objective of education.

However, from more inclusive considerations of personal and social maturation and fulfillment, intelligence comprises only variously attuned and integrated *capacities* to perceive the environment through sense modalities, to appraise and integrate its significance in relation to past experience, and to manipulate relevant elements in that environment in accordance with the organism's predominant needs. Intellect, then, measures the range and complexity of behavior, but determines neither its direction nor its goal. The most immediate illustration of this statement is also its clinically most important one: highly intelligent people are at least as likely to develop neuroses or psychoses as are those with normal or moderately subnormal intellects, with the difference that the former will show more richly elaborate and versatile aberrations of ideation and conduct.

Sensations and perceptions. These were originally thought to be elementary sense data secondarily built into perception by a process of summation; however, as has been particularly emphasized by the Gestalt school of psychology, objects are not really recognized as assemblies of

---

* In the wisdom of pragmatic language the term *mind* is used literally in all three of its principal operational referents; "to keep in mind" (pay "conscious" attention to), "to mind" (obey), and "to put one's mind to it" (awareness of endeavor).

disparate sensory stimuli of sight, taste, touch, temperature or smell, but as integrated and interpreted *wholes*: e.g., "a cold, yellow orange," "a distant, forested mountain" or "a dancing woman." Even our seemingly most elemental "sensations" are implicitly referential to more complex previous experiences: a "knife-like" pain, a "gentle" touch or a "rotten" smell. In fact, whenever the cumulative evidence of a combination of sensations is inadequate, we employ *closure* to complete total precepts with which to operate: geometric solids, figures of animals, human physiognomies, etc. Solutions of problems, too, may be reached by relatively rapid closure-like "insights," although sometimes this so-called *ah-ah! experience* (W. Koehler) may be only the end-stage of prolonged, though only partly conscious, trial-and-error deliberation (v.i.). Perception, then, is not a compendium of multitudinous sensations each of which gives rise to an independent sensory-motor response; instead, perception itself is a dynamically organized process, influenced by previous experience and pre-charged with significance.

Apperceptions and meaning. To begin with, perceptions become relevant to an organism's behavior only when the perceived objects have some current or derived reference to the organism's needs—otherwise, the organism would neither become "cognizant" of nor "unconsciously" react to the object. For example, if a person is hungry—and not simultaneously distracted by more urgent influences such as pain, danger, or erotic desire—he will pay primary attention to the sight and smell of available food and temporarily ignore (though not delete) all other signals; conversely, if he were gastronomically and sexually satiated but physically fatigued, he would sleep undisturbed by the aroma of food, an importunate mistress or the earth-shaking rumble of passing trains until the faint tinkle of an alarm clock woke him to the renewed and urgent task of earning a living. But the "meanings" and relative effects of these signals, acquired only by dint of complex past associations, would continue to be modified by later experiences and contingencies. Thus, should our subject ever be seriously hurt or frightened in a railway accident, he could never again bear the noises of a moving train with complete equanimity, since they would now "mean" danger and call for a state of alertness, if only as a nightmare in his sleep; on the other hand, on a vacation he could ignore the alarm and rely on an inner anticipation to awaken him at an early hour to go fishing. Meaning, then, is the evaluation of a perceived situation with relation to the current balance of motivations of the percipient as correlated with past experience, whether consciously "remembered" or not. Moreover, as will be shown in Chapter 13, the same considerations apply to the influence of gestural, written, spoken, pictorial and other forms of communication in psychotherapy.

Resolution. As noted, classic cognitive theory also held that, after an appropriate comparison of meanings and weighings of possibilities, the "intellect" reaches a conscious conclusion as to a "reasonable" course of action. Obviously, this could be shown by introspection to be true only for man—hence the peculiar non sequitur that, among all animals, only man's actions are "reasoned." However, verbalized "resolves" are manifestly absent from most behavior, and, even when present, are accompaniments rather than prerequisites of action. Instead, thinking and determination may be regarded dynamically as more or less conscious ratiocinations between the perception of motivationally relevant situations and the crystallization of adaptive behavior. The latter may be as nearly instantaneous as the withdrawal of the body from a threatened injury, as intentful as a mother's dash into a burning house to rescue her child, or as delayed and deliberative as a decision to marry after long years of hesitation. However, the individual's behavior obviously remains adaptive to *his interpretation* of the situation: i.e., direct preservation of bodily integrity in the first instance, preservation of "her own flesh and blood" in the second, or familial security, social prestige, avoidance of military duty or other privately or publicly "reasoned" advantages of matrimony in the third. Conversely, verbalized resolves, no matter how "sincere" in intent, that do not really fit one's accustomed patterns of satisfaction are about as lasting and effective as the perennial crop of New Year's resolutions.

In summary, man's intelligence is not an organ by which he accurately determines the "reality" of the world about him, rationally inventories, compares and calculates the probabilities, and then "resolves" on a final course of action. Instead, man's cognitive processes are unconsciously driven by his inner needs, perceptions, judgments and anticipations and colored by symbolism and wishful fantasy; and his behavior is thereby made either as exquisitely adaptive as his culture requires, or as complexly deviant and symbolic as is seen in the neuroses and psychoses.

Conation

Speculations as to the role of "free will" in human behavior had also been the avocation of psychologically minded philosophers long before Descartes made explicit a doctrine (previously abandoned by Aristotle) to the effect that whereas animals were merely automatons governed by mechanical "reflexes," human beings were directed by an individual "soul" or "will" that made them responsible to social and divine judgment. From this traditional doctrine it could be argued that even the feebleminded, the neurotic and the psychotic were to be regarded as malefactors and sinners whenever they transgressed social law or religious dogma—unless they grew sufficiently powerful to impose laws and dogmas of their own. Indeed, society has continued to condemn and punish persons with psychiatric disorders—a sentiment implicit in many mutilatory and punitive measures administered under the guise of treatment for neurotic or psychotic behavior. However, inasmuch as will itself is but the direction an organism has learned to take in the hope of achieving its goals, and since human beings, whether they deny or glorify their objectives, cling stubbornly to accustomed patterns of achieving them, one clinically important consequence becomes apparent: it is generally useless to attempt to influence a person's behavior by exhorting him to apply his "will power," since such appeals, directed as they must be merely to verbal superficialities, can produce only evanescent results unless they are reinforced by therapeutic methods that more directly affect basic values and motivations.

Other concepts of conation shift the emphasis from its conscious aspects to "deeper" actuating forces in the organism variously labelled "instincts," "drives," "unconditioned reflexes," "libidinous tendencies," "valences," etc. according to the terminology indigenous to various schools of psychology. Unfortunately, this noumenal approach has in the past also been subject to at least two sources of error: first, that every pattern of behavior was attributed to a separate "instinct" or "stage of libidinal development"; second, that these were conceived as unidirectional and invariable in expression, in whatever combinations or in whatever circumstances the organism found itself. Thus, some animals and men were observed to fight for food or mates; ergo, a universal instinct of aggression was postulated and thereafter regarded as the initiator of all forceful and combative action, including the social phenomena of war. Conversely, if other animals and people were found who fed and mated in peaceful patterns, the "aggressive instinct" in them was supposed to be merely "latent" or "repressed." Such reasoning led either to a multiplication of autonomous "instincts" (McDougall eventually postulated some two dozen), or else to oversimplified dichotomies such as the Freudian contrast between Eros, representing the forces of life, and Thanatos, the supposedly universal tendency toward dissolution and death (Chapter 7). Instincts or their equivalents also became translated qualitatively into "character traits"; for example, Pasteur's extreme devotion to his work in later life and his neglect of almost every other kind of satisfaction would be attributed to an overwhelming "instinct for scientific exploration," rather than to the persistence of a complex pattern of learned behavior that had earlier won him fame, security and social acclaim. Obviously the former appraisal not only neglected channelizations and experiential modifications of conation, but was also therapeutically nihilistic. As will be seen in Part Two, conation can be formulated more profitably in biodynamic terms, and then integrated operationally into a comprehensive theory of behavior.

Affect

Basic considerations. Literally, emotion means simply "moving out"; i.e., we are "moved" to action only by situations which "affect" us insofar as they appear to be relevant to our own welfare. Grey Walter has recently illustrated the indissoluble meanings of *motivation, emotion* and *adaptation* (to be *apt* at) by constructing relatively simple automatons equipped with only one small battery (the life force), one transducer for sound and one for light (sensory receptors), four electrical relays (synapses) and two motors (skeletal effectors). So equipped, these creatures "perceive," "remember" and travel about their environment, respond to differentially learned "experiences," seek to repeat pre-set "pleasurable" ones and, when "tired," return "home" to recharge their batteries with such disconcerting individuality that, in Walter's words, "they resemble an animal [in] exploration, curiosity, freewill in the sense of unpredictability, goal-seeking, self-regulation, avoidance of dilemmas, foresight, memory, learning, forgetting, association of ideas, form recognition [including self] and the elements of social accommodation. . . . Such is life.

[If provisions are also made in the circuits for perceptive equations (symbolism) and for calculating the probabilities of effective vs. ineffective action—in effect, if misinterpretations, indecisions and conflicts are made possible—the machines] become temperamental . . . and recalcitrant [or freeze] into catatonic inaction." Significantly also, they can then be restored to "normal" function by temporarily disconnecting some circuits (rest or sleep), by establishing new connections (relearning) or by a forcible breakthrough of old systems (deliberate stress or shock). Walter draws further analogies between the spontaneities and responsivities of his *machinae speculatrices* and the electrical activities of the human brain, particularly its spontaneous cerebral rhythms,* and finally comments on the almost infinite resources of human behavior in these words: "In theory, a system with six richly interacting reflexive elements could get into over 10 billion different states. The human brain, with its ten billion nervous elements, could therefore . . . develop more patterns of behavior than there are particles in the galaxy."

Psychophysiologic formulations. But the obective investigations of modern biophysicists† have not yet eliminated from psychiatric and "psychosomatic" thought more traditional and complex concepts of the poignant subjective experiences called emotions, and these must still be considered. For example, in the hormic system of McDougall—later paralleled in psychoanalytic theory—an emotion is defined as a "felt excitement accompanying instinctive activity," and a separate "emotional quality" is postulated for each instinct: e.g., fear accompanies the "instinct to escape"; anger is the affective concomitant of aggression, and so on. In the James-Lange theory‡ emotions were considered with more specific organic reference to bodily and especially visceral activity; fear was part of the subjective appreciation of trembling or running, and anger was "felt" during aggressive action, much as preprandial gastric peristalsis is sensed as hunger.

However, Angell, and later Perry, contended that the James-Lange theory could hardly account for the infinitely variable combinations, subtleties and intensities of affect, and that the concept of the visceroceptive origin of emotions should be enlarged to include kinesthetic appreciations of various forms of "set" or skeletal muscular tonicity. In criticism of such formulations Kantor, Drever and others pointed out that instead of inspiring various emotions, many bodily activities actually serve to dissipate them; for example, fear is mitigated during the hurry of

---

* Walter divides human electroencephalographic frequencies into *delta* (0.5 to 3.5 per second), *theta* (4 to 7 per second), *alphoid* (7 to 8), *alpha* (8 to 13) and *beta* (14 to 32), and believes that compulsive behavior is accompanied by theta and alphoid rhythms, that alpha reflects auditory, tactile and kinesthetic but not visual imagery, and that various personality types with differing emotional and reactive proclivities correspond to specific rhythmic patterns. As a control observation, the superficial mimetic character of the pseudo-emotions induced under hypnosis (cf. the *Practice*, Chapter 35) produce "almost no significant change in the EEG . . . even when the trance is quite deep and behavior apparently much changed."

† Cf. J. Ashby, N. Weiner, J. Lilly, C. Pribram, et al.

‡ Cf William James' discussion (Chapter XXV of his *Principles of Psychology*, 1913) of C. Lange's *What Is an Emotion?* (Mind, 1884).

flight, and hot anger is replaced by cold ruthlessness or reckless abandon during the heat of battle. A corollary was therefore proposed that "emotions are felt only when the satisfaction of a need is suspended or checked," and that visceral and motor tensions are provocative of emotion only insofar as they are *not* relieved by consummatory activity. This formulation (first suggested by Dewey in 1894) likewise antedates many of the current psychoanalytic explanations of functional bodily disorder. Thus, in psychoanalytic theory, unrelieved "sex tension" may be *displaced* to various bodily organs to cause *conversion* symptoms; or a person with an unrequited "hunger for love" or repressed aggressivity may suffer various organic hypertonicities that result in gastric ulcer or spastic colitis.

THE HYPOTHALAMUS.   Closer scrutiny, however, indicated that the etiologic role of peripheral bodily "set" or tonicity in emotion had been overemphasized. Thus, Cannon demonstrated that emotions are perceived subjectively long before any significant visceromotor changes can be shown to occur, whereas the work of Sherrington and others indicated that emotions could be experienced even after a transection of the spinal cord had eliminated the visceroceptive, kinesthetic and muscular afferent impulses from most of the body. Cannon therefore inferred that, instead of being dependent on peripheral reactions, affects were perceived within the brain as an expression of thalamic-cortical interactions with or without visceral, hormonal or motor accompaniments. The role of other portions of the diencephalon in mediating and regulating the peripheral *expressions* of emotion was, meanwhile, confirmed by the experimental work of Karplus and Kreidl, Cannon and Britton, Ranson, Bard and Rioch. These and other investigators, including the author, showed that electrical or pharmacologic stimulation of the hypothalamus of experimental animals induced dramatic visceral and motor behavior appropriately described by Cannon as *sham rage,* whereas lesions of the hypothalamus resulted in a marked diminution in emotional sensitivity and expression. Unfortunately, this evidence, bolstered by certain questionably significant experimental and clinical observations in human subjects, was used in support of the proposition that the human hypothalamus controlled both motivation and "emotion"—or, as it was put in psychoanalytic terms, the "hypothalamus was the seat of the Id." Alvarez went so far as to propose that "nervous and mental diseases" were the result of "hypothalamic storms" or "bad nervous inheritance" in this tiny, but apparently all-important diencephalic substructure.

Unfortunately, this attractively simple psychosomatic formula did not stand the test of further experimentation and clinical observation. A special series of animal studies (cf. Chapter 8) showed that the supposed rage or fear produced in animals by direct hypothalamic stimulation differed from the normal expressions of the corresponding emotions in that the pseudo-affective reactions were stereotyped, undirected, unadaptive and stimulus-bound, and neither modified spontaneous behavior nor were directly influenced by external stimuli. Moreover, while gross injuries to the hypothalamus in experimental animals made them emotionally apathetic for variable periods, if the animals could be nursed through the severe postoperative fluctuations in temperature, fluid and ionic balance and other metabolic disturbances, they gradually recovered almost normal emotional reactivity despite the hypothalamic lesions and the secondary degeneration of their projection pathways.* The clinical observations of Dott, B. Wortis, Mowrer, Alpers, and others correspondingly indicated that the disturbances of function caused by hypothalamic disease in human beings are not accompanied by demonstrable changes in true affect. At present, therefore, the hypothalamus is generally regarded as a neural structure that may reinforce and coordinate the sympathetic, hormonal and motor mechanisms of the *expression* of emotion, but not as being itself the seat of either conation or affective experience.

Later neuropsychiatric correlations.   The failure of other attempts to localize on purely anatomic grounds the source and perception of affect led to a search for more comprehensive neurophysiologic and psychologic correlations. As long ago as 1878, Broca had noted that the limbic lobes were well developed in all mammals capable of manifold drives and versatile emotional responses, and von Economo, writing in 1929, had preceded Moruzzi and Magoun in attributing activating and regulatory functions to the peri-aqueductal central gray matter and mesencephalic reticulum. Papez, in 1927, therefore suggested that the rhinencephalon, which had originally mediated olfaction as the most primitive distance receptor concerned with escaping from danger, securing food and finding mates, now elaborated these functions as subjective "emotions" through its neural connections with the hippocampus, amygdalae, cingulum and cuneus.

MacLean, in 1955, proposed the concept of a *visceral brain* or *archipallium* which receives affectively significant signals through the brain stem and mid-thalamic nuclei, regulates their intensity through resonance with the reticular system, marshals appropriate visceral responses via the fornix and hypothalamus (with concurrent retroflexions to the thalamus by way of the mammillo-thalamic tract and hormonal regulation through the tuberal-pituitary circulation of Houssay) and then transmits these hitherto "unconscious emotions" to the neopallium for preconscious "evaluation." "Thought" and action are then evolved via the cingulate gyrus (aggression), uncus (sex), parietal lobes (orientation in space and time), temporal lobes (memory and speech) and prefrontal cortex (conscious judgment and execution).

More recently, Pribram, N. Miller, Olds and others have demonstrated that animals will repeatedly press switches which, through implanted electrodes, stimulate "pleasure-mediating" structures in the septum, lateral amygdalae and anterior hypothalamus. Delgado noted lesser stimulation-avidity for various areas in the cingulum and hippocampus, and specific avoidance of "displeasure points," far fewer in number, in the tegmentum, central gray matter, posteroventral thalamus, fornix and posterior hippocampus. The Killams and John have also observed that electrical rhythms imposed on the brain by intermittent sensory stimulation (e.g., a flickering light) recruit one structure after another in the

---

* The author's experimental work in this field, challenged only by Nakao, has been confirmed by Pribram, Delgado, Magoun and others.

archi-, meso- and neopallium into synchronous electroencephalographic rhythms as their functions become involved in conditioned responses to the original stimulus. Finally, Penfield and Jasper, on the basis of surgical observations in man, collated these structures into what they call the *centrencephalon,* and assigned to it the seat of consciousness.

As will be seen in Chapter 8, the neurophysiology and behavior of animals can be translated into that of humans only with due allowance for evolutionary encephalization, whereas neurophysiologic studies of the human brain itself present almost insuperable difficulties in recording, analysis and valid interpretation. Nevertheless, studies such as those outlined in this section give rich promise of progressive clarification of the neuropsychiatry of the so-called emotions and their dynamic role in human behavior.

Effects of stress on affective behavior. Hans Selye has proposed that physiologic and psychologic "stresses" are operationally indistinguishable, and that the body responds to both, first by general alarm reactions, then by specifically adaptive resistance, and finally, by exhaustion and degeneration. In psychiatry, these phases would correspond, first, to diffuse anxiety; next to effective (normal) or excessively symbolic (neurotic) fight, flight or dependence; and finally, if all socially oriented maneuvers failed, to affective emptiness and psychotic desuetude. In such parallelisms, however, *stress* must be defined not as an abstract quantity, but in terms of each patient's unique experiences and special sensitivities.

Whitehorn cites two striking military examples in this connection: an enlisted farmer who had shown unusual bravery in combat became severely neurotic when he was ordered to dig a latrine in an admirably cultivated strawberry bed; an artillery lieutenant remained a highly effective soldier until a prisoner saved his life and thereby personally and poignantly reminded him that, at long distance, he had all along been killing human beings. Groen reported that some German industrialists were simultaneously relieved of their business stresses and their gastric ulcers while confined to a concentration camp, but regained both when they returned to their harassed private lives after the war.

Psychoanalytic concepts of emotion. These vary considerably among various writers, some of whom (Fenichel) consider affective behavior merely as an avenue for "discharging libidinous energy," whereas others (Sterba, Federn) apparently elevate emotions to the rank of specific drives springing directly from the Id (cf. Chapter 3). In the latter sense, a distinction is often made between calm, considered, efficiently adaptive *rational* behavior, as contrasted to the impulsive, diffuse and recklessly uncontrolled expressions of "primary emotion." At the same time, an opposite distinction is drawn between "merely intellectual or verbal insight" as being superficial and transitory, *vs.* "emotional insight" which reaches to "deeper levels of the unconscious" and is therefore likely to be more lasting and effective (cf. Chapter 3). Fortunately, in practice most analysts do not take "emotional" behavior as elemental in the hormic sense of McDougall, but regard it correctly as expressive of unconscious motivations, conflicts and symbolic reactions themselves requiring detailed dynamic analysis.

Biodynamic concepts of emotion.   As will be shown in Part Two, emotions can be relegated to the ancillary status of "subjective" epiphenomena that accompany stressful adaptations, and are expressed in behavior patterns that range in complexity from the relatively simple and constant bodily expressions of anxiety to the highly elaborate and variable concomitants of subtle affective states such as pity, enthusiasm and esthetic inspiration. Further, the manifestations of emotion are determined not only by the cultural and experiential history of the subject but by his physical status, his current interpretation of his milieu, his relationships to the observer and many other contingencies. Clinically, indeed, "emotions" as usually conceived are far too vague, variable, complexly structured and difficult to interpret to be used as either diagnostic units or as etiologic determinants of behavior; instead, it is the motivational sources and adaptive functions of the affective states that are the more profitable objectives for dynamic analysis.

This brief discussion of some of the traditional psychologic approaches to behavior has not concerned itself with the numerous other contributions the various schools of psychology have made in the fields of perception, concept-organization, learning theory, imagery, individual differences, and so on. Some of these contributions, particularly with regard to percept-theory and clinical testing, are discussed in Chapter 6 of the *Practice;* others cannot at present be easily or profitably integrated with the clinical approaches in which psychiatry must be primarily interested. Nevertheless, students who have not had an opportunity to become more thoroughly acquainted with psychologic concepts should consul⁺ the supplementary references listed below.

References

Allport, F.: Social Psychology.
Allport, G. W.: Personality—A Psychological Interpretation.
Boring, E. G.: A History of Experimental Psychology [General Review].
Flügel, J. C.: A Hundred Years of Psychology (1833–1933).
Frank, J. D.: The Contributions of Topological and Vector Psychology to Psychiatry.
Freeman, F. S.: Individual Differences.
Gerard, R.: The Body Functions (Chapters II and X).
Hunt, W. A.: A Critical Review of Current Approaches to Affectivity.
Kluckhohn, C., and Murray, H. A. (Eds.): Personality in Nature, Society and Culture. 2nd ed.
Kohler, W.: Gestalt Psychology.
Lindsley, D. O.: Emotion.
McIlwain, H.: Biochemistry and the Central Nervous System.
Masserman, J. H.: Behavior and Neurosis (Chapter III).
Murchison, C., Ed.: Feelings and Emotions.
Penfield, W., and Jasper, H.: Epilepsy and the Functional Anatomy of the Human Brain.
Rivers, W. H.: Psychology and Ethnology.
Ruch, F. L.: Psychology and Life.
Thorndike, E. L.: Human Learning.
Tolman, E. C.: Purposive Behavior in Animals and Men.
Walter, W. Grey: The Living Brain.
Woodworth, R. S.: Contemporary Schools of Psychology.

Chapter 3

Psychoanalytic
concepts of behavior

General considerations

It is no longer disputable that the work of Freud and his followers has contributed significantly to our understanding of human behavior; in fact, certain basic psychoanalytic concepts, terms and formulations have so thoroughly permeated behavior theory that they are now used, with or without acknowledgment of their source, by nearly all psychologists and psychiatrists. However, it must be recognized that psychoanalysis, as a self-isolated body of formalized thought and practice, has influenced psychiatry in at least three separate ways as follows:

Psychoanalysis as a method of research in behavior. Under this rubric, psychoanalysis has introduced certain special techniques such as *free association* (the verbalization of relatively uninhibited thought sequences), the direct observation of *emotional catharsis* and *abreaction* (affective expressions and their sequences), the meaning of dreams and symbols, the sources of covert feelings and impulses, and the significance of various adaptive or maladaptive maneuvers, whether *autoplastic* (psychosomatic) or *alloplastic*, i.e., socially directed. These techniques and interpretations not only are used in the investigation of individual patients but have been applied—although not always with proper circumspection—to esthetics, biography and historical and sociologic data.

Psychoanalysis as a method of therapy. During psychoanalytic treatment the patient ostensibly uncovers pathogenic conflicts and their *cathexis* (charge) of anxiety or other affect, reexplores early events, relationships and symbol formations, acquires increasingly clear understanding of previously unconscious values and motivations, and converts his originally overdependent, aggressive, erotic or other irrational demands on the analyst into progressively more realistic interpersonal transactions (transference resolution); by generalizing these analytic *insights* and experiences, the patient also reorganizes his attitudes and *works through* his personal and social maladaptations to achieve more practicable and ultimately more satisfactory (*"mature"*) life patterns. These procedures—actually implicit in all effective psychotherapy—have profoundly influenced the formulation, if not the practice, of other psychiatric techniques.

Psychoanalysis as a theory of behavior. By the unique methods outlined above, Freud, over a period of almost fifty years, acquired a wealth of clinical observations which led him to propose a succession of new and dynamic formulations of human development and conduct. Freud himself, however, never regarded his *depth psychology* as a static and dogmatic system; on the contrary, he continued to amend, expand and even radically revise his concepts. Fortunately, too, psychoanalytic theory has continued to be elaborated, clarified and integrated—although sometimes only through an extravagant expenditure of dialectics—by Alexander, Grinker, Horney, Rado, Sullivan, Thompson and others until modern psychoanalysis can aspire to the dignity of a scientific discipline, based on a theory of behavior which can be translated into fundamental biodynamic terms. But, because of the rapid development of psychoanalysis, there has been at the same time a cultural lag in its teaching greater than that in other scientific fields, and as a result many lay and some professional workers still tend to identify psychoanalysis with a body of older and now partially discarded doctrine stemming from the exploratory confusions, extravagances and gaucheries likely to trouble the youth of any science. The following sections, therefore, will restate with a minimum of controversial elaboration those concepts of analytic metapsychology that govern most of the advanced thinking in the field today.

Development of the libido

The concept of the libido.   The term, *libido*, although still variously used by analytic writers, is by most equated with Bergson's *élan vitale* as a dynamic force which actuates all life processes. This generalized definition runs counter to the common misconception that libido has only the much narrower meaning of sexual drive. True, Freud in his earlier writings was frequently concerned with the role that sexuality played in behavior disorders, and criticisms of his theory became so often centered on this point that the specialized application of the term *libido* to sexuality became fixed in popular thought. However, Freud and others also recognized the following forms of "libidinal" expression:

PRIMARY NARCISSISM.   In operational terms, this may be equated with the tendency of the living organism—from germ cell to senile adult—to stay alive if at all possible.* In the early months of infancy "narcissistic" self-love is expressed in the child's *polymorphous perverse* delight in the various parts and functions of its own body; only later, and under necessity, does the infant's interest gradually include the outside universe. In fact, since no infant's concept of his surroundings can ever be dissociated from some body function, the distinction between the *I* and the *not-I* in his developing consciousness is made slowly and always in relative terms; it may be contended, indeed, that in the deeper unconscious

---

* The term "narcissism," or self-love, was born of Freud's own preference for (and not infrequent misapplication of) poetic euphemisms and cryptic allusions (e.g., "Oedipus complex," "Nirvana phantasy"). Narcissus was an Attic youth who, in the subtle sense of the Greek myth, fell so deeply in love with his own reflected *image* (not, as Freud would have it, *himself*) that he lost interest in all else, including his homosexual friend Almeinas and his aptly named female companion, Echo.

such distinctions are never made at all.* Further, the infant's universe seems completely subservient in such all-important matters as food, warmth and other care—a circumstance that gives rise to feelings of dominance which appear frankly in the play fantasies of the child and more covertly in all later behavior. As examples, infantile independence of space, time and mores is nightly reconstituted in our dreams; the peremptory service demanded and elicited by the cry of the child is projected into the magic attributed to the Voice and the Word; the normal duress of adult life is recurrently ameliorated by escapes ranging from weekly and yearly vacations (reverently cherished as *holy-days*) to the more deeply felt reunions with divine protectors during *religious* (Latin —to return with devotion) *retreats.* Or, under more seriously disruptive stresses, latent fantasies of universal being and power appear pathologically in the grandiosity of the paretic or the autistic delusions of the schizophrenic or paranoiac. In any of these phases or forms, objects or persons may be invested (*cathected*) with *secondary narcissism;* i.e., we value our possessions insofar as they represent our prestige and influence; we "love" the friend, child or wife who serves us, and we regard many a particularly precious man-made thing or thought as no less than divine.

ORAL EROTISM. From the mere circumstances of early mammalian development, the next important source of multiple satisfaction for the human child is its mother, who furnishes the nutriment and tender protection indispensable to the child's very existence. Even before the infant is able to distinguish various parts of its body, it must be aware through kinesthetic, thermal and other sense modalities of its relative security in its mother's arms,† and that its lips, mouth and tongue are the organs by which it obtains satisfaction of its nutritive needs. In addition, there is good evidence from animal experimentation (D. Levy) and clinical observation (E. Erikson, R. Spitz) that the adequate stimulation and exercise of the oral region of infants satisfies needs other than those of simple nutrition. This consideration makes all the more regrettable the practice, indulged in by many ill-advised or rejecting mothers, of placing

---

* BIRTH TRAUMA. In certain earlier psychoanalytic theories much was made of the fact that the first serious threat to the life of an organism occurs when it leaves the absolute security of the womb and is born precariously into the blaring, threatening confusion of the outside world. This *birth trauma,* according to Rank (and before him, Kierkegaard), constituted the deepest root of all subsequent anxiety, and underlay the ubiquitous longings of all mankind for a return to the "Nirvana" (not the *Nirvana of non*-being in the Hindu sense) of prenatal life. Among other offshoots of early analytic metapsychology may be placed Jung's concept of the *racial unconscious,* Ferenczi's equation of the supposed *latent period* (from age six to twelve) in human sexuality with the influence of the Ice Ages in human development, and most of Groddek's fantastic elaborations of *das Es* (the *Id,* v.i.).

† Harlow (1959) has shown that baby monkeys cling to furry inanimate "mothers" with greater avidity than they seek food; so also, on the basis of clinical evidence, Bowlby (1959) believes that maternal bodily contact is the single most important source of security in infancy and of amity in later life. The "Cornelian Corner" (named for Cornelia, the Roman noblewoman who proclaimed "my only jewels are my children") is a national organization dedicated to promoting such essential early intimacies between mother and child (C. Moloney).

even the youngest infants on a rigid schedule of artificial, impersonal feedings—an arrangement convenient to her own desires rather than those of the child. Whether or not the infant's "oral needs" are adaquately satisfied, the functions of the oral region become linked with the regressive dependent longings that lie not far beneath the apparent self-sufficiency of human beings of every age. Certainly when, through weaning, the child is deprived of the maternal breast, it begins to seek substitutively symbolic satisfaction of its "oral erotic" desires through the medium of the pacifier or the thumb; later substitutes may include chewing gum, pipe stems or the unlit cigar. Mixed with subsequent sexual activity, oral erotism is expressed in various behavior patterns ranging from kissing— acceptable in many societies—to various "oral perversions"—acceptable publicly in relatively few.

ORAL RECEPTIVITY AND AGGRESSIVITY.   Certain codicils to the theory of oral libido are of significance in the dynamisms of other symbolic acts and pattern formations. Abraham has pointed out that the earliest oral functions in the infant are passively receptive and incorporative in nature; i.e., the nutrient goodness of the universe is *introjected* and made, in fantasy, part of the individual. From such symbolic roots may spring the *oral incorporative* dreams of the insecure adolescent, the irregular episodes of abstemious loss of appetite (anorexia) and compensatory engorgements (bulimia) of the melancholic, or the delusion of "having swallowed the world," frequently found in the regressed schizophrenic; from such basic symbolisms, too, may arise the mystic rites of the eating of the beneficent god common to many religions. Mixed with these symbol formations, however, is a later or *aggressive* stage of oral erotism which develops in the infant when his earlier incorporative satisfactions become frustrated by weaning, food-training and other deprivations. To such traumata the infant reacts with a type of more preemptive and destructive oral seeking, seen during weaning in active biting of the nipple, or later in various verbal or gestural patterns such as "biting sarcasm" or gnashing the teeth during frustrated rage. Conflicts between passive oral longings and fear-engendering aggressive desires also appear during melancholic reactions in "functional" gastric disorders and in *anorexia nervosa*; indeed, in the latter neurosis, the self-starvation and protracted vomiting to deny the destructive symbolism of eating may become so severe as to endanger the life of the patient (cf. Case 39 and Appendix 3).

ANAL EROTISM.   In the early months of life the human infant becomes concerned with another body function which gives repeated "pleasure" through recurrent physiologic relief, namely, the evacuation of the bowels and bladder.* It is a common pediatric observation that infants have no aversion for the products of these evacuations; on the contrary, playing with the feces and other scatophilic manifestations are normal. This period of narcissistic "treasuring" of the body products is known as the *anal retentive* phase of development, although, of course,

* For descriptions of "anal erotic" interests and activities among children in various cultural settings cf. Malinowski (1927), Hamilton (1929), Terman (1938) and Landis et al. (1940).

it has no certain time of onset, and its course and expression in any one child are greatly influenced by constitutional factors, parental attitudes and contingent experiences. In later life, "anal erotism" may remain as a hidden component in many "normal" personal and cultural patterns such as the quasi-masturbatory seclusiveness of the excretory act, or the enthusiastically advertised preoccupation about "regular bowel movements" being essential to health. Correspondingly, "functional bowel distress" is one of the most common psychosomatic disorders, whereas more overt reversion to anal pleasures leads to various sexual perversions.

ANAL AGGRESSION.   Somewhat later in the infant's life he faces the necessity of making his first serious social adaptation—that of controlling his bowel movements until the proper place and time for evacuation. To the complacent parent this training appears to be but a part of the "natural development"* of the child, but to the latter it may be a time of frustrations, disillusionments, and libidinal inhibitions and reorientations as sweeping and as difficult as any other he may, with far greater resources, be called on to make in later life. For to the dim awareness of the toddler the situation may appear to be this: he is no longer the autonomous ruler to whom the whole universe had heretofore been obeisant; on the contrary, his parents, whom he had previously counted upon to satisfy almost every want, now, perhaps quite suddenly and inexplicably, turn into firm taskmasters who insist that he conform to the conveniences and demands of others. Even under the best of circumstances this readjustment on the part of the child is a stressful one; however, should bowel-training and other discipline be started too early or be too harsh and abrupt, the impairment of the child's capacities for adequate adaptation may be serious. In the latter case, hidden resentment or frank hostility—first against the parents and later against parent-surrogates or society in general—may be engendered and unconsciously linked with bowel functions, excreta, and their symbolic equivalents. Common manifestations of such "anal aggressiveness" may be expressed in the infant and child by "mischievous" self-indulgence in dirt and filth, combined with destructive habits of soiling, breaking and scattering.†

Similar anal symbolism may pervade the "normal" habits of the adult: he may take sly delight in scatologic jokes and expressions, convince himself of the value of mud-baths or similar mysophilic pursuits, or take a special fetishistic pleasure in accumulating and hoarding money—"filthy lucre" symbolically equated with the alimentary products of his labor. But apart from the direct anal and urinary desecrations of their enemies common to children and savages, perhaps nowhere do the destructive connotations of excretion find more direct expression than in certain types of obsessive-compulsive neurosis, in which the patient may become so fear-

---

* Gesell (1941) has particularly emphasized the danger of attempting to establish patterns of behavior in children before adequate maturation of their capacities.

† Cf. Blanton (1917), Levy (1928) and Willoughby (1937). However, Susan Isaacs has also described voyeuristic, exhibitionistic and other "phallic" activities in children only two years old. Significantly, Halverson (1940) observed that genital erections in infants aged 3 to 20 weeks occur in apparent compensations for oral or anal frustrations.

ful of contamination by germs, dirt or his own metabolites that most of his waking life is spent in rituals of washing, sterilizing, cleaning and prophylaxis so that he might not—as he covertly wishes to do—defoul others and, in retribution, himself be destroyed.

GENITAL EROTISM.   Penile and clitoral erections in human infants are easily observed in the first months of life, and their detumescence on genital manipulation is accompanied by unmistakable relief of tension and restlessness—a fact usually denied by fond parents and utilized by pragmatic nursemaids. Masturbation with partial orgasm may begin in the first year of life and continue irregularly thereafter in both sexes.* However, it is probably not until the third or fourth year that the child becomes in any sense heterosexual, i.e., associates the pleasure of genital stimulation with fantasies of the opposite sex. Such fantasies are usually derived from observation of primary and secondary sexual differences in parents, siblings and other children, from witnessing coitus between the parents (the *primal scene*), and from diffusely exploratory heterosexual contacts—although, of course, in the child's mind, genital activities are as yet only rarely associated with concepts of impregnation or childbirth. Obviously, too, the specific persons about whom early sexual fantasies revolve can be only those with whom the child has actually experienced close physical contact: in the case of the boy, his mother or an older sister; in the case of the girl, homosexual erotism directed toward the mother and only later transferred heterosexually toward the father or some male surrogate (cf. Appendix 3). But the child has also observed that his mother, however much he may desire to possess her exclusively, really "belongs" to the father, who remains in the parental bed and retains the right to demand and obtain her sexual attentions.

Thus arises in children of both sexes the so-called *Oedipus complex*, named by Freud after Oedipus Rex, the Sophoclean hero who, though unaware of the nature of his deeds, slew his father and married his mother in order to establish his own kingdom.† But in the case of most children the parallel does not quite hold, since the all-powerful father not only stays very much alive, but also seems quite capable of swift, terrible and specific retribution symbolized in the possibility of depriving the child of its penis or clitoris—the organic nidus of its fantasies of potency and conquest. In the case of the boy, the specific content of this *castration fear* obviously has many determinants: the association of erotic wishes with his prominently erectile genital organ, threats of castration thoughtlessly made by "joking" elders or by parents horrified by the child's masturbation, or fear-inspiring observations of the genitalia of girls and women who, to the boy ignorant of differential anatomy, appear to have been actually castrated. Thus it is that in many children genitality may become charged with persistent *guilts* (unconsciously generalized apprehensions of deserved punishment) that color all the later patterns of personal and social behavior. For instance, masturbation,

---

* St. Augustine, in his "Confessions," remarked: "It is not to the babe's soul that we must attribute its innocence, but to the weakness of its limbs."

† In pre-Freudian medical terminology, *Oedipism* meant amaurosis, from Oedipus' expiatory act in blinding himself.

being originally associated by the child with "Oedipal" incest fantasies, is often feared as leading not only to loss of "manhood" or, less frequently, "womanhood," but also to more physical catastrophes such as "consumption," "insanity," and so on. Or, in his interpersonal contacts, the adult with a deeply ingrained *incest guilt* may develop a *character neurosis;* i.e., he may abjure heterosexual contacts, or lead a sex life frustrated by impotence or frigidity, or try to compensate by a loveless, restless promiscuity (*Don Juanism* in men or *nymphomania* in women), or become reactively aggressive toward either sex, or fly from heterosexuality altogether either into precarious homosexual relationships or into passive, asexual dependencies.

Post-oedipal development. THE LATENT PERIOD. In orthodox analytic theory it was thought that after the age of five or six years, erotic libidinal tensions abated and became relatively quiescent until puberty, at which time the maturation of the gonads reawakened the psychosexual life of the adult. However, many leading child analysts (e.g., Levy, Lorand) no longer regard the years between six and puberty as libidinally *latent* or inactive; indeed, even in the children of Western cultures* there is a good deal of sex curiosity and exploration. What is more characteristic of the period, however, is the progressive channelization of the child's interests and activities into educational and social pursuits outside the immediate family. During this process the child partially transfers his libidinal relationships—dependent, aggressive or erotic—from his parents and siblings to various substitutes or *surrogates*: governesses, teachers, playmates and others. Concurrently, by the processes of *displacement, symbolization, sublimation,* and so on (Chapter 4) he gradually turns from infantile interests to broader ideals and objectives. During this period, too, in reaction to his as yet uneasy emancipation from his infantile dependence on the family, the child may seek security in extra-familial groups, may form intense loyalties to his school, the neighborhood gang, his boy scout troop, etc., and thus mold his future social adaptations. These allegiances should not be underestimated; for example, Anna Freud reported that children of early school age evacuated from localities bombed during World War II felt more secure when kept in their accustomed school or neighborhood groups than if placed according to sibling or family relationships. Certainly, the primary school years are of great pedagogic and cultural importance, since in them are formed the ideologies and future social patterns of the individual—a fact long ago recognized by religious bodies, thoroughly exploited by dictatorial regimes from Sparta to modern times, and only recently accorded due importance by the practitioners and teachers of more democratic and humanitarian principles (cf. Appendix 4).

PUBERTY AND ADOLESCENCE. This, too, is a period of intensified adaptational stresses, when dependent, exploratory, erotic and other urges

---

* Malinowsky (1927) observed no "latency period" whatever in the sexually less inhibited culture of the Trobriand Islanders, and Mead, Bateson and others have reported similar findings elsewhere. Hamilton (1929) found as high an incidence of homosexual behavior between the ages of six and eleven years as occurred later in life, and later studies by Kinsey, Bowman and others confirmed this.

clash among themselves and add to the conflict between reawakened longings for the peace and security of childhood as opposed to tempting but anxiety-ridden drives to self-expression, emancipation and freedom. Concurrently, the adolescent is faced with many problems: renewed friction with "old-fashioned" parental or school discipline, the multiplied demands of scholastic, athletic or sexual competitions with their attendant frustrations, the growing necessity of choosing a career and other stresses that may appear jejune to adults, but grave and portentous to the youth. Adolescence, then, is characterized by many emotional hypersensitivities, deep concern about personal appearance, accomplishment and belongingness, impulsive and over-intense libidinal attachments and revulsions, exaggerated self-assertiveness or regressive timidity, and a tendency to intense, dereistic fantasies.

It is at this time, too, that defects in earlier training become especially manifest: the unwanted or excessively punished child cringes before a world presumed to be forever inimical; the adolescent who has been overprotected or overindulged by irresponsible parents is enraged because they can no longer fulfill his burgeoning demands; the youth who had been covertly encouraged to act out his parents' own repressed wishes for unrestrained sex or vicarious aggression (*parental-superego lacunae* of Johnson and Szurek) now finds that his delinquent conduct is punished by others. Under effective guidance such youngsters may relearn and adapt; alternatively, they may develop other behavioral aberrations such as a retreat into puerile cynicism, disruptive attempts at defiant emancipation from social codes, or a breakdown into various neurotic or psychotic (e.g., "dementia praecox") patterns. Indeed, early adolescence may be the most difficult, and often the most deeply unhappy time of life; certainly, it is the period that requires the clearest understanding and most skillful handling on the part of parents, teachers and physicians.

Personality development does not, of course, stop at adolescence, and there are later crises of stress and evolution: e.g., marriage, parenthood, the poignant reappraisals of late middle age, and the camouflaged retreats of senility. However, these periods and their behavioral vicissitudes had best be considered in the clinical context of the *Practice*.

The "structure" of the personality

In Freudian theory, the functions of the total personality are divided into three parts as follows:

The Id.* This is conceived to be a repository of the "instincts" or drives of the individual expressed as narcissistic, oral, anal and genital *libidinal tendencies,* which constitute the *primary processes* of behavior. These are below the limen of the direct awareness of the individual, hence they comprise a large portion of what Freud reified as *the Unconscious.* Opposed to the primal conations of the Id are the repressive forces of the

---

* The term "Id" was taken by Groddek from Nietzsche's philosophy of "das Es" and incorporated into psychoanalytic theory by Freud.

Ego (v.i.), which prevent inadmissible aggressive or erotic impulses from erupting into the awareness of the individual, pervading his behavior and so endangering his personal and social adjustments. In dreams this unconscious *censorship* and monitoring is relaxed, so that the undisciplined, unrealistic, unintegrated wishes of the Id, though still clothed in allegory and symbolism, appear in more easily recognizable forms. The atavistically sexual or aggressive primary processes of the Id are likewise discernible, though less easily so, in fantasies, in free associations, in the hostile or sexual "inadvertencies of speech and action" that constitute the *psychopathology of every-day life* and, of course, in neurotic and psychotic* symptom formation.

The Ego. This designates a portion of the personality that adapts to "reality" by exercising a two-fold function. On the one hand, the conscious Ego utilizes the information imparted by the senses, subjects such data to the discerning and integrative processes of the intellect, and so evaluates the milieu in terms of available sources and means of gratification as opposed to possible dangers of frustration or injury. On the other hand, another portion of the Ego, largely unconscious, is "directed inward" to oppose the forces of the Id by the use of various specific *secondary processes* or *defense mechanisms* (cf. Chapter 5). In effect, the Ego is the interpretive, adaptive and executive "part" of the personality, driven by the Id and conforming to the demands of the Super-ego as described below.

The Superego. In psychoanalytic parlance, the Superego denotes "a psychic apparatus" that directs the primal strivings of the Id, as modified by the Ego, into behavior that further conforms to the double standards of the *conscience* and of the *Ego-Ideal,* differentiated as follows:

The Conscience. In this capacity, the Superego is the repository of internalized prohibitions derived from the frustraneous, conflictful and traumatizing experiences of childhood, and thereby consists of multiple pervasive "don'ts" which can be paraphrased variously as "thou shalt not preempt and incorporate aggressively"; "thou shalt not soil and attack"; "thou shalt not desire incest," and so on. In the early training of the child, these prohibitions draw cogency from two main sources: fear of physical punishment from parents or parent-surrogates, or, far more serious to the helpless child, dread of loss of love should such parent-figures be displeased or injured by its actions. In this way, abnegation of dangerous and forbidden modes of behavior comes to be regarded as a matter of self-preservation and of ultimate hedonic gain, and thereby becomes fixed in the adaptive patterns of the child. These self-imposed *inhibitions,* if later threatened by temptation or transgressed even in fantasy, evoke *anxiety,* or, if flouted in action, occasion conscious apprehensions of varying intensity. Thus, the "conscience" derives its regulative powers from unconscious but persistent fears of punishment or deprivation—the ultimate source of all "guilt." Classic analytic theory holds that by the age

---

* Brosin in particular equates the primal drives, fantasies, and actions of the psychotic with the primitive expressions of the "primary process."

of from four to six years the child has already run the gamut of narcissistic, incorporative, aggressive and erotic urges and their limens of retributions, hence his conscience is patterned relatively early in life and subsequent modifications become progressively more difficult.*

CULTURAL INFLUENCES.   Horney, Sullivan, Kardiner, Fromm, and others have pointed out that, since the conscience is formed largely in accordance with parental, environmental and educational norms, the behavioral standards of adult individuals will vary widely from culture to culture. Thus a child raised along harsh authoritarian principles would be praised and rewarded even during his early formative years for behavior patterns that might be regarded elsewhere as ruthless, aggressive and cruel, whereas he would be punished only for "transgressions against the family name" (or gang, party, church, state, etc.). Such a child grown to adulthood might feel "guilty" over ideologic disloyalty or military cowardice, but he would see no "wrong" in lying, stealing, or even murdering for the supposed good of his group.† Fortunately, most children raised in democratic traditions adopt and live by humanitarian principles; however, a child strongly inculcated with antisocial attitudes by the precept and example of his parents might react to subsequent legal punishment by becoming more wary, but this would create little *internal* conflict or reorientation of values and objectives. Currently, an adult who sincerely insists on his good intentions but exhibits unconsciously determined compulsive, repetitive and largely symbolic failures in social adaptation is termed a *sociopathic personality;* one who more deliberately plans preemptive and destructive antisocial acts is considered a *criminal;* finally, if the antisocial behavior became manifestly bizarre, dereistic and delusional, his *criminal psychopathy* (Cf. the *Practice,* Chapter 10) is treated with varying mixtures of mystification and revenge.

THE "EGO-IDEAL."   This function of the Superego parallels and supplements the conscience, but controls behavior less by fear of consequences than by directing it toward internalized goals and standards. During the course of his social development the child derives such standards from various persons important in his environment whom he thereafter strives to emulate. Analysis generally shows that the child does this not for idealistic reasons but in a wishful attempt to attain the fancied advantages and prerogatives of the exemplar with whom he tries to *identify.* For instance, a little girl playing with dolls is, in her own fancy,

---

* Margaret Mead (1935) has reported that in some cultures (as among the Arapesh), late weaning and the encouragement of almost every form of oral satisfaction in children may establish feelings of infantile security which persist into adult life, and so contribute to the formation of a stable, content and relatively noncompetitive society. However, Gesell's dictum (1942) is here pertinent: "It is very apparent that the human infant assimilates the cultural milieu only by gradual degrees; that he has vast immunities to acculturation; that his nervous system sets metes and bounds to what the societal group would do for him; indeed, determines what is done. The culture is adapted to him, primarily; he adapts when he is ready."

† The very word "mores" is the plural of the Latin *mos,* meaning social custom, devoid of implications of normality or morality. Peters (1933) puts it trenchantly: "There is perhaps not a single vice in the code of our own society that some other group has not considered a virtue—murder, theft, dishonesty, torture, suicide, adultery and the rest." Cf. also Westermarck, and Sumner and Keller.

herself a "mother" with all her perquisites and privileges; just as in later life she will dress and gesture like the class belle or a popular actress so that she, too, may be a claimant to adoration and influence. Similarly, male youngsters cherish the trappings of glorified adulthood: cowboy range rider, "Superman" or space explorer suits, miniature weapons, toy automobiles, or other appurtenances with which they can, in fancy, equate themselves with their powerful, feared and envied elders. More specific identifications with the traits of parents, teachers or group leaders, or, later, artists, conquerors or, for that matter, rebels or criminals may permanently mold the Ego-ideal and so direct behavior into social or antisocial, successful or unsuccessful and thereby "normal" or "neurotic" channels.

References

Adler, A.: The Practice and Theory of Individual Psychology.
Alexander, F.: Psychoanalysis and Psychotherapy.
Beres, D.: The Contribution of Psychoanalysis to the Biography of the Artist.
Brenner, C.: An Elementary Textbook of Psychoanalysis.
Fenichel, O.: Outline of Clinical Psychoanalysis.
Freud, Anna: Psychoanalysis of the Child.
Freud, S.: General Introduction to Psychoanalysis.
Freud, S.: The Interpretation of Dreams.
Freud, S.: The Problem of Anxiety.
Freud, S.: Three Contributions to the Theory of Sex. 4th ed.
Freud, S.: New Introductory Lectures on Psychoanalysis.
Freud, S.: The Interpretation of Dreams. Rev. ed.
Freud, S.: Outline of Psychoanalysis.
Gesell, A.: The First Five Years of Life.
Gesell, A., Thompson, H., and Amatruda, C.: Infant Behavior, Its Genesis and Growth.
Horncy, Karen: The Neurotic Personality of Our Time.
Hunt, J. McV.: Personality and the Behavior Disorders (Chapters 20, 21, 22, 23 and 26).
Kardiner, A.: Psychoanalysis and Psychology.
Lewin, B., and Ross, Helen: Psychoanalytic Education in the U.S.
Mullahy, P.: Oedipus, Myth and Complex.
Munroe, Ruth: Schools of Psychoanalytic Thought.
Murchison, C.: Handbook of Child Psychology.
Piers, G., and Singer, M. B.: Shame and Guilt.
Prescott, D. A.: Emotion and the Educational Process.
Pumpian-Mindlin, E. (Ed.): Psychoanalysis as Science.
Thompson, Clara: Psychoanalysis: Evolution and Development.

Chapter 4

The dynamics of adaptation

IN PSYCHOANALYTIC theory the methods by which work-
able compromises are reached among the ruthless impulses of the Id, the
realistic orientations and resources of the Ego, and the cultural cautions
and directives of the conscience and Superego are known as *Ego defense
mechanisms.** We shall examine these by first reviewing the nature of
anxiety, and then citing clinical examples to illustrate various "normal"
and "abnormal" methods of mitigating the conflicts signaled by this
warning.

Anxiety

This is a feeling of diffuse, unformulated uneasiness and apprehension
reflected in a characteristic configuration of visceral, vasomotor and skeletal disturbances, and manifested symptomatically in an *anxiety syndrome*
characterized by tachycardia ("heart pounding"), dyspnea ("catching of
the breath"), flushing, splanchnic paresthesias ("butterflies in the stomach"), light-headedness ("dizziness" or "faintness"), muscular tremors or
tensions ("nervousness") and, in severe degrees, incontinence, vertigo or
syncope. Anxiety differs from *fear* in that the former is not referable to
specific objects or events (e.g., fire, drowning) but rather to an unreasoning dread of unresolved and threatening situations that symbolize unconscious conflicts. For example, a claustrophobic patient who as a child
had been repeatedly punished by confinement in a sub-basement may
suffer intense anxiety if forced to enter any constricted space, yet be
unable to explain his reaction on the basis of any realistic fear of direct
physical injury. Anxiety, then, stems from repressed fear, and its adaptive
function is to warn of a *symbolic* danger to be avoided. A more detailed
clinical example may help to clarify the point:

Case 1.   Anxiety-cathected claustrophobia

A sixteen-year-old boy was brought to the Clinics with the complaint
(among many others here irrelevant) that he was frightened of the dark and
of being left alone in constricted quarters. Specific investigation of this par-

---

* Anna Freud's choice of this designation reflects her father's *Sturm und Drang*
metapsychology in which the individual is pictured not as a functioning part of a
society which he himself fashions, but as being continuously in conflict with an alien
and hostile social order—ergo, "aggressions," "defenses," "containments," "narcissistic
retreats" and other warlike terminology.

ticular symptom in his past history revealed that, as a child, the patient had been alternately pampered and neglected by his parents, and had become highly dependent and demanding, yet jealous and insecure in his relationships with them. When he was five, they took him on an automobile trip and one night all three were forced to share a single hotel room. That night, for the first time, the child witnessed intercourse between his parents. He was greatly excited and frightened by this "primal scene," in which he fancied that his parents, oblivious to his needs, were engaged in some sort of horrifying struggle that he was helpless to control. He cried, was punished and then banished to a cot where he lay in silent terror for the rest of the night. The next day his contrite parents calmed his fears and redoubled their indulgences (thus adding a *secondary gain* to the patient's reactions) and within a week all parties concerned had ostensibly forgotten the incident. However, a significant displacement remained: the child began to suffer severe anxiety when left alone, or when taken into closets, darkened theatres, or other places symbolic of his traumatic experience. Despite this somewhat dramatic aftermath, at the time of therapy it was only with great difficulty that either the parents or the patient could recollect the incident described or recognize its symptomatic significance.

Here anxiety was a subjective warning against a situation previously interpreted as near-catastrophic, and was all the more intense because the symbolic nature of the threat was excluded (*repressed*) from awareness (*consciousness*) or ready recall (*pre-consciousness*). These qualities distinguish anxiety psychologically from the basic fears from which it is derived, whereas in all other respects, including symptomatic expression*, the two are closely allied.

Suppression

By this is meant the deliberate exclusion from awareness of dangerous antisocial impulses and the rejection of their accompanying fantasies. This phenomenon is often cited as a demonstration of "free will" and the "triumph of reason" and is thought to have transcendent ethical and theological implications. As we have seen, however, the "decision" as to the expression, deviation or suppression of inner drives actually depends on a dynamic balance of physiologic urgencies, latent anxieties, learned choices and perceived opportunities, many aspects of which do not enter into "conscious" or "reasoned" deliberation at all. A second case example will illustrate the point.

Case 2. Conscious and unconscious factors in suppression

An only son was subjected to a premature and tyrannical educational regimen by his father who, himself a frustrated and unsuccessful schoolteacher, wanted his child to become a "genius" and thus rescue the prestige of the

---

* All attempts at physiologic differentiation between fear and anxiety have been unsuccessful to date, including recent postulates by Almadjian that norepinephrine is excreted in response to external threat (fear) and epinephrine in reaction to "internal" danger (anxiety). Cf. Grinker, Persky, Havens, et al.

family. The boy, though intelligent and mathematically gifted, rebelled against all learning, but was pushed into advanced work by his relentless father. By this time, the youth hated all teachers and their teachings, and became almost unbearably sensitive to discipline by them. One day in a flash of resentment against a fancied slur in class (which he mistakenly thought was perceived by everyone) the boy felt a nearly overwhelming urge to strike his teacher and to stalk out of the classroom. However, he "reconsidered" the situation, supressed his pride and anger and decided to stay; later, in fact, he apologized to the astonished instructor who had remained completely innocent throughout the patient's inner struggle. But the boy was never aware of how deeply the "sensible" decision he thought he "deliberately" reached had really been influenced by many unconscious factors: the identification of every teacher, however kindly, with the tyrannical father; the equation of even mild aggression with unthinkable patricide, and the necessity he felt to placate the father-teacher by an apology for the impulse of sudden hostility he had experienced.

The mechanism of suppression, then, is not dynamically explained by referring it to "reason" or "will"; instead, "self-control" is itself but the adaptive resultant of experientially determined but unconsciously prescribed patterns of behavior.

Repression

In psychoanalytic terminology, the term *repression* applies to the inhibition of dangerous impulses or conflicts so that they are neither presented consciously as urgent reality problems, nor apprehended within range of recall (pre-consciously) as insoluble tensions provocative of anxiety. Instead, the troublesome urges and impulses are returned to the "unconscious"* where, unfortunately, they continue to exert pressure unless diverted into other defense mechanisms as described below.

Thus, a person rarely "permits himself" to become aware of frankly erotic or aggressive urges in his everyday social relationships, since to do so more often would invite rejection and thereby eventually be disruptive to his security and equanimity. Nevertheless, if these impulses, though ordinarily amenable to repression, are strengthened under special circumstances (e.g., erotic arousal through dancing with a seductive but sexually forbidden partner, or mounting hostility in an ostensibly polite intellectual contest with a deeply hated rival), raw and dangerous impulses may threaten to break through. This is signaled first by general tension, and next by increasing anxiety which, though not consciously formulated in relation to its source, can be relieved only by increased repression, a solution of the conflict, or a hurried escape from the threatening situation. However, repression has its psychobiologic limitations: for instance, a person can deliberately subjugate and temporarily "forget" (repress) a physiologic need to empty the bladder when social circumstances dictate urinary continence, but eventually the desire will obtrude on awareness and outweigh all contrary considerations.

* The term "subconscious" is not used in psychoanalytic psychology. For a review of various other concepts of the "unconscious," see J. G. Miller (1942).

Range of repression. Repression may be seen in many of the minor aberrations of daily living: we "forget" unpleasant occurrences, unwanted information or the names of people we don't like—phenomena which Freud described as the *psychopathology of everyday life*. Similarly, analytic theory holds that the loss of infantile and childhood memories is due less to temporal fading or overlay by later experiences than to defensive repression of the poignant frustrations and disillusionments of early life. Thus, many apparently "forgotten" occurrences in childhood may be recollected if their accompanying anxiety is temporarily or permanently relieved by nepenthic,* or narcotic drugs, hypnosis, the permissiveness of "free associations," or merely the reassuring receptiveness of a sympathetic listener. Conversely, severe motivational stresses may again require repressions of such sweeping thoroughness and intensity that entire configurations of behavior may be obliterated in space or time. Examples of such reactions may be seen in the functional amnesias, in which large segments of experience are repressed while more acceptable patterns are retained in a dissociated "fugue state." Morton Prince regarded patients showing such phenomena as *split* or *multiple personalities*, since their behavior in one state seemed to differ so completely from that in another; however, it is probable that each "personality" merely represented a more or less independently integrated set of behavior patterns that, for predominantly unconscious reasons, best suited the patient for the duration of the fugue. An illustration of this type of reaction is the following:

Case 3. Repression: fugue state

Bernice L——, a forty-two-year-old housewife, was brought to the hospital by her family who stated that the patient had disappeared from her home four years previously, and had recently been identified and returned from R——, a small town over a thousand miles away. On rejoining her parents, husband and children she had at first appeared highly perturbed, anxious and indecisive. Soon, however, she had begun to insist that she really had never seen them before, that her name was not Bernice L——, but Rose P——, and that it was all a case of mistaken identity; further, she threatened that if she were not returned to her home in R—— immediately, she would sue all concerned for conspiracy and illegal detainment. Under treatment the patient slowly formed an adequate working rapport with the psychiatrist, consented to various ancillary anamnestic procedures such as Amytal interviews and hypnosis, and eventually dissipated her amnesias sufficiently to furnish the following history:

Bernice was raised by fanatically religious parents, who despite their evangelical church work and moralistic pretenses, accused each other of infidelity so frequently that the patient often questioned her own legitimacy. Instead of divorcing each other, the parents had vented their mutual hostility upon the patient in a tyrannically prohibitive upbringing. In the troubled loneliness of her early years, Bernice became deeply attached to her older sister and together they found some security and comfort; unfortunately, the sister died when the patient was seventeen and left her depressed and inconsolable. At her parents' edict, Bernice then entered the University of A——

---

* Greek *ne penthos*—no sorrow.

and studied assiduously to prepare herself for the life of a "Missionary Sister." During her second semester at the University, she was assigned to room with an attractive, warm-hearted and gifted girl, Rose P——, who tactfully guided the patient to new interests, introduced her to various friendships and encouraged her to develop her neglected talent as a pianist. Bernice became as devoted to her companion as she had formerly been to her sister, and was for a time relatively happy. In her junior year, however, Rose P—— became engaged to a young dentist, and the couple would frequently take the patient with them to act as a chaperone on week-end trips. Predictably, the patient fell "madly in love" with Rose P——'s fiancé, and spent days of doubt and remorse over her incompatible allegiances and jealousies. The young man, however, paid little attention to his fiancee's shy and awkward roommate, married Rose P—— and took her to live with him in Canada. The patient reacted with a severe depression and left the university because she "did not deserve to be a Sister in God"; however, at her family's insistence, she returned, took her degree, and entered a final preparatory school to qualify her for a foreign assignment.

On completion of these studies, and in further expiation for what she now called her previous "sin of jealous coveting," she entered into a loveless marriage with a man designated by her parents as a "worthy partner in her work," and spent six unhappy years in missionary outposts in Burma and China. The couple, with their two children, then returned to the United States and settled in the parsonage of a small midwest town. Bernice's life as a minister's wife, however, grew less and less bearable as her husband became increasingly preoccupied with the affairs of his church, and as the many prohibitions of the village (e.g., against movies and plays, most recreations, politically liberal opinions and even secular music) began to stifle her with greater weight from year to year. During this time the patient became increasingly prone to quiet, hazily glorifying reminiscences about the only relatively happy period she had known—her first two years in college with her friend, Rose P——; these years, in her day-dreaming, gradually came to represent all possible contentment. When the patient was thirty-seven years of age, the sickness and death of her younger, musically talented and favorite child culminated her frustrations and disappointments. The next day the patient disappeared from home without explanation or trace, and her whereabouts, despite frantic search, remained unknown to her family for the next four years.

Under therapy, the patient recollected that, after a dimly remembered journey by a devious route, she finally reached R——, the college town of her youth. She insisted that she had lost all conscious knowledge of her true identity and previous life, except that she thought her name was Rose P——. Under this name she had begun to earn a living playing and teaching the piano, and was so rapidly successful that within two years she was the assistant director of the local conservatory of music. Intuitively, she chose friends who would not be curious about her past, which to her remained a "mysterious blank," and eventually established a new social identity which removed the need for introspections and ruminations. Thus Bernice lived for four years as Rose P—— until the almost inevitable happened; she was recognized by a girlhood acquaintance who had known both her and Rose P—— in their college years. The patient at first sincerely and vigorously denied this identification, resisted her removal to Chicago where her husband was now a prominent minister, and failed to acknowledge either him or her family until her psychiatric treatment (cf. Chapter 14 and the *Practice*, Part IV) penetrated her amnesia. Fortunately, her husband proved sympathetic and co-operative, and the patient eventually readjusted to a fuller life with a more understanding as well as devoted spouse under happily changed circumstances.

Comment. This case history illustrates many dynamisms, but outstanding is the patient's use of repression as a means of escaping a mode of living that was no longer tolerable. Denied was her unwanted existence as Mrs. Bernice L——, the unhappy wife, and substituted was an indentification with an intensely desired way of life personified by Rose P——, the loved and successful sister surrogate. Without conscious recognition of either the fact or the dynamics of this wishful transfiguration, the patient had therefore changed her identity and for four years followed the dictates of desires and fantasies long repressed but insistently recurrent. However, the "new" personality was not really novel, but consisted rather in certain unconsciously selected, isolated and recombined patterns of the old. Significant, for instance, is the fact that despite proposals from acceptable men, in her identity as the spinster, Rose P——, she neither married again nor permitted herself any form of direct sex expression, since bigamy or unfaithfulness, conscious or not, would have been untenable. Nevertheless, when she was returned to her family, her fears of punishment for her desertion of them again induced severe anxiety and renewed denials, and the transition back to being Bernice L—— became stable only when new and predominantly satisfactory readjustments were attained.

Repressed impulses, however, only rarely cause as drastic and sweeping a revision of personality adaptations as occurred in the fugue state illustrated above; instead, if sufficient outlets are available, they are ordinarily channeled into patterns of behavior more acceptable to the current social group and thereby more advantageous to the individual. Thus, had Bernice L—— found a new sister-substitute in her parish who, perhaps even in the guise of close fellowship in the church, could have satisfied her needs for dependent alliances, or had she been allowed expression of her esthetic longings in music or art, or had she been permitted to find vicarious gratifications in the anticipated success of her pretty and talented daughter, a complete amnestic break with her mundane, inhibited, small-town existence might not have become necessary. Such modes of adaptation, however liminal, are generally accepted and keep many of our otherwise inexplicable social customs and institutions going.

Reactions of repression with partial substitution. Other clinical examples of such combinations of expression, displacement and sublimation (v.i.) may be briefly cited as follows:

Case 4. Reaction formation and substitution

The neglected, childless wife of a wealthy alcoholic could satisfy neither her marital nor maternal longings and, in compensatory over-reaction, became openly antisocial and misanthropic. However, she professed a great love for animals, provided a home for strays, kept numerous dogs, cats, parrots and canaries (which not infrequently maimed or killed each other) and organized militant antivivisection movements. Finally so fanatic and irrational did she become in the latter activity that defensive legal action and adverse publicity finally induced her family to persuade her to seek psychiatric help.*

Other general examples of displacement are these:

A man in many modern cultures can no longer safely kill a personal rival in an open duel, but he can, with social approval, eliminate him almost as effectively in economic, athletic or sexual competition.

Direct exhibitionism or voyeurism is frowned upon—except at art galleries, beach resorts and Danse Moderne recitals.

A "gentleman" from certain sections of this country was formerly required to be ready at any moment to "die in defense of the honor of any woman"—provided, of course, that she were of a specific color and class. At the same time, he was rather expected to find traditional outlets for his "masculinity"—and for his covert contempt of womanhood—by having a succession of mistresses irrespective of their race, antecedents or marital status.

In these examples and many others readily available, repression of inadmissible aggressive or erotic drives is combined with the displaced satisfaction of these same impulses in ways that are, frankly or covertly, socially acceptable.

Reaction formation

When antisocial impulses, because of their strength and persistence, cannot be deviated completely into acceptable substitutive channels, some degree of balance may sometimes be achieved by directly contrary action. This dynamism is called *reaction formation* and may be readily seen in everyday behavior as well as in neurotic aberrations. Thus, we are precise and excessively polite toward a person we must respect but don't like—often enough so, indeed, to make him uncomfortable. Or, the

---

* The following are verbatim excerpts from an interesting and self-diagnostic letter received from another (anonymous) antivivisectionist possibly faced with similar problems:

"I read [a magazine article] . . . on your work on alcoholism [cf. Exp. 16] . . . I am surprised that anyone who is as well educated as you must be to hold the position that you do would stoop to such a depth as to torture helpless little cats in the pursuit of a cure for alcoholics. . . . A drunkard does not want to be cured—a drunkard is just a weakminded idiot who belongs in the gutter and should be left there. Instead of torturing helpless little cats why not torture the drunks or better still exert your would-be noble effort toward getting a bill passed to *exterminate* the drunks. They are not any good to anyone or themselves and are just a drain on the public, having to pull them off the street, jail them, then they have to be fed while there and it's against the law to feed them arsenic so there they are. . . . If people are such weaklings the world is better off without them. . . . My greatest wish is that you have brought home to you a torture that will be a thousand fold greater than what you have, and are doing to the little animals. . . . If you are an example of what a noted psychiatrist should be I'm glad I am just an ordinary human being without letters after my name. I'd rather be just myself with a clear conscience, *knowing I have not hurt any living creature,* and can sleep without seeing frightened, terrified dying cats—because I know they must die after you have finished with them. No punishment is too great for you and I hope I live to read about your mangled body and long suffering before you finally die—and I'll laugh long and loud."

frustrated spinster who covets the children of others over-reacts against her preemptive wishes by being "unable to bear" children around her. Other examples of social reaction formation are the following:

Case 5. Sublimated reaction formation

A ruthless financier who had worked his way up from poverty loudly professed his social cynicism and his callousness to the fate of the improvident "rabble of suckers"; nevertheless, to ease his own anxieties, he felt impelled to give large sums of money anonymously to various charitable organizations, libraries, art institutes, etc.

In another case, the reaction formation was even more specific: A man who had made millions by exploiting the domiciliary and occupational needs of Negroes in a large city endowed a foundation dedicated to research on the supposedly obscure causes of inter-racial resentments and unrest.

Case 6. Antisocial reaction formation

An intelligent, attractive girl who had been brought up in circumstances of frustrating sexual temptation by an irresponsible, negligent and eventually parasitic father later in life became a prostitute with the following (relatively common) pattern: she displaced her filial ambivalence to a dependent, seemingly "masochistic" but actually preemptive and exploiting relationship with an underworld procurer, and expressed her hostility to all other men in her complete indifference to how many others she frustrated, robbed, infected or blackmailed.

Sublimation

In the two illustrations cited under Case 5 it is apparent that certain of the reaction formations described, though they sprang from deviated anxiety, nevertheless served various socially useful purposes such as the endowment of charitable and research institutes and the encouragement of art. Freud called such defense mechanisms *sublimation,* in poetic reference to the process whereby a crass solid may be converted, under proper conditions, into an ethereally pervasive essence. This analogy, like many another psychoanalytic comparison, is somewhat strained; however, the fact that ostensibly altruistic activities spring from essentially selfish motivations makes them no whit less socially useful.

For example, many professional workers like to think—and some of them insist—that they became nurses, doctors, ministers, social workers, etc., because of an altruistic ache to help suffering humanity, although a few admit that desires for economic security and social prestige played some role. However, on franker and deeper introspection, and certainly under objective analysis, both levels of motivation can usually be traced to comparatively primitive needs; e.g., "security" resolves itself into adequate food, warmth and shelter, and "social prestige" protects, implements and enhances these basic satisfactions plus, of course, providing better opportunities for mating and procreation.

Special configurations of unconscious drives may also be sublimated in more specific directions; anatomic inquisitiveness and a desire for quasi-thaumaturgic powers to heal by the effective laying on of hands may combine in the unconscious motivations of a surgeon, just as, perhaps, a closely allied type of curiosity and quest for omnipotence may actuate a psychiatrist. Motivational analyses such as these do not in any way impugn the skill, intent or indispensable usefulness of any profession. Nor need all the various more complex motivations such as ethnic or religious loyalties or the struggle for status or economic advancement always be traced to their elements; for sociologic purposes, such group-oriented conations become sufficiently integrated to be regarded as unitary "social forces." Nevertheless, in the analysis of aberrant behavior, it is essential that ineffective cultural or esthetic sublimations be traced more deeply to their dynamic sources in individual behavior.

"Denial of reality" and fantasy formation

Subjectively, every person is prone to deny the unwanted aspects of experience and to reconstruct the world in his fancy as he would like it to be. In dreams and reveries, everyone escapes from the usual fetters of time and space, and reconstitutes the universe according to his own imagery. For that matter, it is a traditional epistemologic problem whether "realistic" thinking itself is more than a feeble attempt—needfully reassuring in our ignorance—to erect various conceptual systems about an unknowable cosmos and then defend these as "self-evident truths" against persons who imagine differently. And since thinking, like all other activity, is motivated by the needs of the individual, in one sense his "facts"* are what he wishes them to be. This concept, whatever its metaphysical validity, has an important operational value in the analysis of behavior, as the following sections will indicate.

Denial of death and attendant fantasies

The most predictable of all biologic "facts" is the inevitability of death, and yet this "certainty" is one which evokes the most urgent set of protean denials. At first sight, this statement appears easily refutable, since almost everyone professes to be quite resigned to the thought of death, and may even essay to describe—although with a macabre humor subtly indicative of the deepest anxiety†—the physical aspects of his own bodily decay. Nevertheless, despite this conscious acquiescence and beneath the ready acceptance of the certainty of death for everyone else, no one can really conceive of his own dissolution into complete and absolute nullity. Cessation of physical being can be conceded, but then there is still cherished the ineffable fantasy that a more subtle part of his personal existence such as the "spirit," the "soul," or some other essence, remains inde-

---

* Latin *factum*, a thing done (as in factory), or *facet*, an aspect (part looked at). As a simple "psychologic" demonstration of the conative influence on the "perception of facts," Sanford (1936) found that fasting subjects "identified" a progressively larger proportion of gastronomic objects (e.g., food, dishes) in vague pictures given them for description.

† Cf. Freud's *Collected Papers*, and Ernst Kris on the role of wit and humor as a "thin ledge above an abyss of anxiety."

structible and immortal.* As a result, conscious or unconscious beliefs in "life after death" are ubiquitous, whether or not such beliefs are incorporated into primitive or elaborate metaphysical and religious systems. So it is that those individuals proudest of their hard-headed "objectivity" —as, for example many a famous physical scientist†—become increasingly preoccupied with "spiritual affairs" as old age approaches. Moreover, such men will, again quite unconsciously, indulge in what Freud has called *rationalization*; i.e., they will try to "prove," by arguments full of wishful fantasy, various corollaries of immortality such as the transmigration of souls, the possibility of "communicating with the departed" or even the "scientifically demonstrable" existence of a benificent Deity who can grant eternal life.

This analysis of the unconscious dynamisms of faith and of various religious beliefs will be extended in Chapter 14, but let it be stated immediately that such discussions can in no way detract from the verities of any religious system—nor, on the other hand, do they either confirm or deny the existence of a universal Order or of a Supreme Being. A psychiatrist, as a scientist, must recognize the limitations of human knowledge, but he is then free to adhere, as does the author, to any moral and theologic system he considers beyond, and sublimely independent of, the mundane experiences and comprehensions of man. His faith, however, must be kept distinct from his science until the day when both may be fused into truly transcendent knowledge.

References‡

Abrahamsen, D.: Crime and the Human Mind.
Baynes, H. G.: The Mythology of the Soul.
Freud, Anna: The Ego and Mechanisms of Defense.
Freud, S.: Beyond the Pleasure Principle.
Freud, S.: The Problem of Anxiety.
Freud, S.: The Psychopathology of Everyday Life.
Miller, J. G.: Unconsciousness.
Money-Kyrle, R.: Superstition and Society.
Murray, H. A.: Explorations in Personality.
Nicole, J. E.: Psychopathology.
Smith, H. W.: Man and His Gods.
Zilboorg, G.: Mind, Medicine and Man (Chapter 8).

* Hopes for a vicarious physical immortality lie behind the ancient practices of embalming and mummification, whereas a desire for continued influence after death occasions contingent wills and bequests. A famous combination of both was employed by Jeremy Bentham who, at his death in 1832, left his fortune to the University of London on the condition that his clothed skeleton continue to sit at all meetings of the executive council of the University. Similar desires for "survival through life-work" prompts much building, art and writing, whereas strivings toward actual germ-plasm immortality through posterity play a role in marriage and child-bearing. Witness the hasty wartime marriages and compulsive fatherhood of many service men who, consciously or not, feared they might never personally return to their homes and wives, and wished to leave a living representative behind.

† Pythagoras, James Jeans, Oliver Lodge, et al.

‡ Cf. also References to Chapter 2.

Chapter 5

Neurotigenic dynamisms

ANY OF THE "normal" modes of response thus far considered may, of course, be exaggerated to the point of definitely aberrant behavior, as in reactions of overwhelming anxiety or panic, paralyzing repressions and inhibitions, frenetic attempts to escape into restless, joyless pleasure-seeking, excessive use of drugs, political extremisms or escapist fanaticisms (e.g. dietary and calisthenic fads, or the misapplications of yoga, Zen or other esoteric cults). However, anxiety is, within limits, a biologically useful warning, and without suppression, regression, rationalization, sublimation and comforting fantasies in thought and action, satisfactory interpersonal relationships would hardly be possible. But we must now consider a group of dynamisms that shade more directly into the socially non-adaptive or "abnormal" and are thus of particular psychopathologic significance.

Phobias

A *phobia* is a persistent fear of a class of objects or situations which in "reality" (i.e., according to most casual observers) present no actual danger to the subject. As exemplified in Case 1, phobias are derived from traumatic experiences, often but not always during childhood, and differ from fears only in their tendencies toward symbolic generalization. For instance, dread of a rampant tiger is easily understandable, but not so readily accepted are the reactions of a patient who exhibits anxiety within a mile of a well-protected zoo, cannot bear the presence of a kitten, and experiences discomfort when any member of the genus *Felis* is shown on a motion picture screen. No "casual observer" could know that such an aelurophobic patient may have killed the family pet in a tantrum of childhood jealousy, and may have then been told by his shocked and exasperated parents that poor dead pussy would forever haunt and remind him what an unlovable creature he was. The phobia, then, would have little to do with the patient's various attempts to explain (rationalize) his fears on the grounds that big and little cats were, after all, mean and dangerous creatures, that he was "allergic" to them, that they "carried disease" and so on, since his trepidations would stem from an unconsciously symbolic threat of rejection and punishment for his persistently destructive rivalries and hostilities. The following is a case history in point:

Case 7. Phobic reactions

Anne A——, eighteen years old, was brought to the psychiatric out-patient clinic by her family, who stated that they were greatly concerned over the patient's irrational fear of small pets: dogs, cats and even canaries. So marked was the patient's apprehensiveness in this regard that, to guard against the possibility that such an animal might somehow enter the house at night, she insisted on locking all the doors and windows in the house and those of her own and her parents' bedrooms, while leaving an intercommunicating door between the two rooms open. Psychiatric examination revealed many other obsessions, compulsions and neurotic symptoms, but the origin of the animal phobia was of particular interest and may be recounted briefly as follows:

The patient had been a particularly indulged child until about the age of four, but had then been almost completely displaced in her parents' affections when her mother gave birth to a long-anticipated son. The patient at first showed frank jealousy of her infant brother, but when this merely increased what she sensed to be her parents' rejection of her, she became an apparently devoted sister except for one significant displacement; she was persistently destructive of her brother's clothes and other belongings, and particularly so of such of his toys as were mechanically animated. The parents, distressed by the patient's behavior, but blind to its motivations, sought to change it by giving her a puppy in order, as they remembered it, "to show Anne how cute and lovable any little pet could be." Anne professed delight and seemed to cherish the pet; once, however, in her parents' absence, she so mistreated it that they later found it dead. Her punishment, now reinforced by an intuitive recognition by the parents of the unconscious intent of the patient's act, was made unusually severe. The patient's overt hostilities and destructiveness diminished, but unfortunately she developed various other neurotic patterns, prominent among which were a recurrent anxiety syndrome and a persistent fear of being alone with small animals of any description. Now thoroughly alarmed, the parents again began to shower attentions on the patient but, regrettably, mainly on the rationalized basis that she was a "sick, nervous child" who needed frequent medical and pediatric consultations. As may have been expected, this merely fixated the patient's phobias and other neurotic reactions until, after many years of well-meaning parental and medical mismanagement, she was referred for psychiatric therapy.

Comment. Obviously, this patient's persistent phobia of small animals had little relation to fear of physical injury by them, but served quite other and deeply unconscious functions. On the one hand it protected her from temptations to express aggressions originally directed against her brother, and on the other it signified a reunion with her parents, as unconsciously symbolized by the open door between their bedrooms and by the precautions against outside intruders. The secondary gain of her phobic state was also symbolic; i.e., it secured renewed attention and protective indulgence from her parents or from various surrogates such as nurses and doctors.

Thus, many phobias are defensive maneuvers that protect the neurotic patient from situations in which his own repressed aggressive or erotic impulses might become dangerous; and at the same time the behavior patterns induced by his phobias may bring him substitutive and regressive satisfactions. Other examples of this may be cited briefly.

Case 8.   Street phobia

An unhappily married woman developed a fear of being alone in the street or in crowded places. Analysis of her previously unconscious motivations and fantasies showed that such fears arose because of repressed temptation to erotic exhibitionism and promiscuity; significantly, she experienced much less anxiety in either situation when she was accompanied by a member of her own family, since under such conditions her self-control was supplemented and reinforced, and her feelings of regressive dependence were strengthened.

Case 9.   Phobic-compulsive behavior

A male patient complained that he experienced marked anxiety and stuttered almost unintelligibly whenever he had to give an impromptu verbal report of his work to his supervisor or to a meeting of coworkers; conversely, no matter how well he had memorized his remarks, he experienced much less difficulty if he could read them from a previously prepared manuscript. Investigation showed that he worked under conditions of intense rivalry and distrust, that spontaneous verbal exchanges with his colleagues entailed the more or less conscious danger that the patient might let slip expressions of contempt or anger, and that under such circumstances his speech became compulsively (v.i.) stilted, hesitant and inhibited to the point of stuttering. In contrast, he could read safely from a manuscript if the latter were meticulously prepared and carefully censored beforehand.

The son of a forceful business executive (cf. Case 36) was so afraid of tall buildings, which to him were unconsciously symbolic of his father's threatening power and authority, that he could not visit the center of the city—including the physician's office—unless led by the hand by a protective father-surrogate such as a close relative or a male nurse.

Obsessions and compulsions

Obsessions are urgent ideas or impulses that remain in consciousness despite their recognized irrationality and ostensibly unwelcome obtrusiveness. They thus differ from phobias in that they are less charged with anxiety and do not necessarily evoke specific avoidance behavior; they are also distinguished from delusions in being consciously rejected or resisted by the patient. "Normal" obsessions may range in persistence and disruptiveness from the tenacity of a haunting melody that may become wearisome, through the persistent concern of the unhappy wife who debates with herself throughout a day of resented shopping whether she is *entirely* sure that she had turned off the oven at home, to the *idée fixe* of a well-known physician who has spent thirty years of his spare time and a great deal of money in amateur geologic research trying to prove that the moon was thrown off from the Indian rather than the Pacific Ocean. Obsessions, then, are reaction formations in thought to repressed fears or wishes, and their counterparts in external behavior are *compulsions,* likewise designed to channel the dangerous impulses into typically stereotyped and ritualized patterns. Conversely, if the performance of such substitutive acts is difficult or impossible, the obsessive-compulsive defense is robbed of its effectiveness and the anxiety aroused by the forbidden urges is experienced directly.

Puberty and adolescence, as has been indicated, are times of greatly increased motivational stress and conflict, and it is during these periods that displaced and obsessively intellectualized ruminations about the nature of life and the universe are prone to occur and, when excessive, to develop into dereistic and schizoid tendencies. Exaggerated self-regulatory behavior is also so common at this age that it is regarded as normal: e.g., excessive orderliness alternating with almost coprophilic disarray, displaced eroticisms in literature, music and dance countered by strict conformity to local norms of dress, comportment and speech (gang uniforms, signals and secret language) and even a certain stereotypy in prescribed modes of familial and social rebellion. In general, obsessive-compulsive behavior during adolescence may be regarded as expressing inner conflicts among regressive longings and emerging social orientations and responsibilities; fortunately, in most cases the external manifestations of the struggle disappear as the tensions abate and more practical compromises are evolved. Nevertheless, residual compulsive acts subtly permeate all subsequent behavior and may determine a host of minor "habit patterns" ranging from which side of the face a man shaves first in the morning to the type of erotic satisfactions or philosophic convictions he obsessively seeks or compulsively avoids. Beyond this, obsessive-compulsive patterns may become so pervasive and deviant that they constitute a disabling neurosis, usually symptomatic of repressed but severe and precariously compromised hostilities continuously evoked or exacerbated in the patient's environment. A few clinical examples may be illustrative.

Case 10. Counter-aggressive compulsions

A successful executive who, for various reasons, unconsciously hated the responsibilities of marriage and fatherhood was troubled many times a day with the idea that his two children by his divorced wife were somehow ill or in danger, although he knew them to be safe in a well-run private school to which he himself took them every morning. As a result, he felt impelled to interrupt his office routine thrice daily to make personal calls to the school authorities. After several months the principal began to question the sincerity of the patient's fatherly solicitude and thus intensified his obsessive-compulsive rituals by bringing the issue more nearly into the open. The same patient could not return home at night unless he brought a small present to his second wife and each of his children, although, significantly, it was almost always something they did not want.

Case 11. "Ablutomania"

A thirty-year-old woman developed such severe washing rituals that she was compelled to spend practically her entire day scrubbing her hands, the dishes, the rugs, the basement steps, the toilet bowl and almost every other object about the house. Her history revealed an insecure childhood spent in poverty and squalor, to which she had reacted with ambivalence toward her ignorant foreign-born parents and a defensive overemphasis on "culture and cleanliness." She contracted a loveless marriage at eighteen mainly "to get myself a decent home" and for more than a decade her husband, an insensitive, easy-going individual, tolerated her sexual frigidity and her frequently annoying overmeticulousness in running their home and in disciplining their only son. A year before her hospital admission, however, two circumstances seriously disturbed her precarious marital adjustments: her husband secured a job as foreman in a steel plant and moved their home to the noisy, smoky vicinity of the factory, and her son began to emancipate himself from her preemptive discipline and to cultivate extrafamilial contacts in the new neighborhood. The patient almost immediately wished to move back to their former isolated home in the suburbs, and rationalized her desires by stating that "no one could live in all this smoke and dirt." The husband and son, however, both refused to surrender their respective advantages in the new environment, whereupon the patient began a series of washing compulsions which became more elaborate and prolonged until she had time for little else. When analyzed, these rituals were seen to subserve at least two purposes: They were at the same time a counter-phobic denial of, and a symbolic return to, the dreaded yet safe squalor of her childhood, and they also served as concealed avenues of "anal-erotic" aggressions against her faithless son and husband, whose lives were made miserable but without possibility of recourse against the patient's pathetic illness.* Needless to say, the patient could not recognize either of these motivations; all she knew, before therapy slowly established partial insight and better adaptations, was that she "had to keep washing" or else suffer inexplicable but scarcely bearable fears that somehow her husband, her child or she herself "might get sick and die if I left a speck of dirt—and it would be all my fault."

Finally, it must be noted that compulsive rituals and other stereotypies may also serve as defenses against "catastrophic reactions" in patients with cerebral or other physical defects that impair their capacity for a more eclectic and resilient adaptability to stress (cf. K. Goldstein, 1942). A handicapped person often feels that he can compensate for his defect only by carefully organized and methodical behavior; so also, there is little left for the waning aged but the reminiscent and protective shells of old habits.

Displacement

As has been indicated, phobias, obsessions and compulsions, like sublimation, symptom formations and other defense mechanisms (v.i.), partially meliorate the threat of forbidden impulses by channeling them into less dangerous thoughts or activities. This process of partial substitution is known generally as *displacement* and serves many adaptive purposes in everyday behavior: A man wishing to emphasize a controversial point pounds his fist into his palm instead of his opponent; a courtier kisses his lady's hand to denote a larger ardor. Exploratory, aggressive or other displacements are also evident in the values placed on symbolic objects (*fetishes*): e.g., the numismatic enthusiasms of the would-be traveler, the prized gun collection of the desk-bound colonel or the cherished

---

* Jackson, Haley, et al. call this form of family maneuver a *ploy*, a term adapted from S. Potter's semi-serious book on "How to Win Without Actually Cheating." Bateson terms it a double-bind; if the victims tolerate the patient's behavior, it is perpetuated by being profitable; if they protest or rebel, they are at best sadly lacking in understanding and at worst viciously cruel to an innocent sufferer—hence deserving of even more punishment.

lock of hair sent by the popular crooner to his "dearest fan."* *Sexual fetishisms* with pregenital cathexes to erotogenic zones such as the mouth, breasts or pudendum may channelize various *sexual perversions* such as irrumation, cunnilingus or fellatio. *Sexual inversions* are of similarly complex psychologic origin, since in many cases the homosexual partner is a symbolic love object sought not only for displaced erotic gratification, but as a mother-, father- or sibling-surrogate. Displacement (a term preferable in the instances cited to "equivalence" or "substitution," since the symbolic equation never exactly balances) is, then, a process common to many adaptations and is, indeed, fundamental to the genesis of all conscious and unconscious symbolisms (cf. Chapter 14 and Appendix 1).

Psychosomatic symptom formation†

All motivations, as the term indicates, are inferred from visceral and skeletal bodily movements, but when these are uncomfortable for the patient, family or physician, they are somewhat redundantly referred to as "psychosomatic disorders." From the standpoint of the directness of physiologic expression, these symptomatic disturbances may be classified as follows:

Physiologic accompaniments of overt repressed affective states. Since, as we have seen, the common dynamic source of the neuroses is anxiety, the direct physiologic manifestations of this state are found with great frequency in patients who are unable to repress their anxiety or resolve it effectively by various "defense mechanisms." Such individuals develop a recurrent *anxiety syndrome* so typical that a history of their complaints is itself almost diagnostic. As noted in Chapter 3, this syndrome consists of palpitation, disturbed respiration, global sensations in the chest or throat, flushing, sweating and tremulous weakness accompanied subjectively by a diffuse, unformulated but intense and obsessive apprehensiveness. The language patients use to describe such symptoms varies, but it is generally apparent to them that they suffer these reactions in relation to emotional stresses, and that the symptoms are alleviated when these stresses are relieved. Moreover, it is usually not difficult to ascertain that anxiety occurs when the patient's repressions are threatened (as during sexual temptations) or when his phobias, compulsions or other defensive rituals are transgressed (as when a claustrophobic is inescapably confined). Clinical examples may be cited as follows:

Case 12. Anxiety syndrome, erotogenic

A twenty-eight-year-old married woman whose husband had entered the Army eight months previously applied for the treatment of "heart trouble"

* Much fetishism is traditionally accepted as "normal." Thus, in 1840, Jenny Lind was so popular that a New York promoter made a small fortune by letting people kiss a glove she had worn during a concert tour. The standard rate was twenty-five cents for the outside of the glove and fifty cents for the inside.

† The psychosomatic accompaniments of psychotic deviations of affect will be discussed in Chapter 6.

because of attacks of heart-pounding, faintness, giddiness and trembling. These attacks, she stated, were generally worse at her menstrual periods. Physical examination revealed no evidence of cardiac disease, nor did special investigations confirm a previous physician's expressed suspicions of "ovarian trouble or possible thyroid toxicity." However, the psychiatric history showed that while the symptoms had no relationship to exertion or other physical stresses, they very definitely depended on the following situational factors:

After her husband's departure, the patient had resumed her former work as the private secretary of a minor industrial executive, with whom she had had occasional sexual relations before her marriage. Her employer attempted to renew their liaison, but out of loyalty to her husband (and also because of jealousy over her employer's other affairs) the patient had resisted; nevertheless, being sexually passionate and deprived, she was erotically aroused by his advances, and sometimes responded to them just short of intercourse. The patient first experienced her anxiety symptoms in connection with such episodes, but later they began to occur when she was not conscious of so direct a relationship, e.g., on her way to work, at USO dances or while witnessing war movies that intensified her reactive guilt. The exacerbation of her anxiety during menstruation was similarly related to heightened erotic cravings during this period, and was also manifested by frankly sexual dreams and fantasies.

Case 13. Anxiety, compulsive

A boy of sixteen, troubled by open conflicts with his fanatically religious father and currently much concerned by his "secret sin of masturbation," had developed a number of compulsive rituals which had become annoying to his family. Among these was a peculiar insistence on repeating grace not once, but three times before every meal. The father, enraged by what appeared to be a travesty of the usual family custom, had begun to force the boy to eat without his preliminary prayers. The patient had attempted to comply, but found himself unable to do so because of trembling, palpitation, "all-gone feeling in the stomach," sweating and, more particularly, a "lump in the throat" that made swallowing impossible. These symptoms abated only slowly if he was ordered from the table, but disappeared promptly if he were permitted to go through his ritual and then discard his first bite of food. Investigation indicated that the three prayers were intoned to expiate guilt not only for his masturbation, but also for "bad thoughts about mother and father"; so also, he felt compelled to renounce his first mouthful of food before he "deserved to be given more." He was sorry that his family "had to suffer so for my sake—but they will go to heaven and they say I won't—so we'll be even." When permitted his rituals, he felt little anxiety; when they were proscribed, the symptoms described above inevitably recurred.

Reactive states other than anxiety may, of course, also find expression in "psychosomatic" symptoms, e.g., symbolic yearning for affection in "heartburn" (v.i.), inhibited erotic tumescences in nosebleeds, blushing, evanescent "hives," etc. On the other hand, the somatic resonances of rage may be so repressed that the patient feels only an "icy calmness" reflected in clenched jaws, rigid posture, prickly skin from pilo-erection and generalized muscular tensions which later leave him limp and exhausted.

Subacute and symbolic bodily dysfunctions—"organ neuroses." Neurotic dysfunctions of bodily organs are not always as direct an expression of relatively elementary and transient emotional states as those just described; nevertheless, repressed conflicts rarely signalled by overt anxiety may produce chronic organic disturbances that impair the well-being of the patient more seriously. Thus, an intense and unrequited "hunger" for love and security in a person with unconscious feelings of inadequacy and social isolation may be expressed characterologically in a restless, possessive ambitiousness; at the same time, the incorporative cravings that constitute the physiologic counterpart of the symbolic "oral" needs (cf. Chapter 3) might find bodily expression in gastric hypermotility and hyperacidity and so predispose to the formation of a peptic ulcer. Again, a chronically frustrated individual may show his latent rage through "the language of the body" in persistent vascular hypertension or, at a more primitive "anal" level, in chronic diarrhea.

Psychoanalytic investigations of other psychosomatic syndromes inexplicable on purely physical grounds have suggested corresponding relationships between symptoms and attitudes, such as those between asthma or urticaria and "frustrated crying," or anorexia nervosa and "rejection of oral incest" (cf. Appendix 3). Such "psychosomatic formulas," however, should not be considered as in any sense specific, and should never be divorced from the complexly interrelated dynamisms of the total behavior of the individual (cf. the *Practice*, Chapter 12). An additional consideration is that chronic "psychosomatic" disturbances in the functions of organs may eventually result in pathologic alterations in the organs themselves, after which the illness is no longer dependent upon the original "psychologic" precipitating factors and, indeed, may demand independent medical and surgical care. For example, "functional" gastric hyperacidity, as we have seen, may *favor* the formation of a peptic ulcer but does not inevitably produce one unless certain other organic conditions (e.g., unwise diet, excessive acid and pepsinogen levels, delayed gastric emptying) are fulfilled. Again, long-continued "emotional" hypertension in an adverse metabolic setting may lead to, *and then be perpetuated by,* vascular sclerosis and renal disease; similarly, oft-repeated states of severe anxiety may initiate hyperthyroid and other endocrine disturbances which then become independently pathogenic and so complete a vicious cycle. Whether physical alterations follow psychosomatic dysfunction is dependent, then, not only on the severity and chronicity of the latter, but also on many intercurrent physiologic and pathogenic factors that may become of urgent medical rather than purely "psychodynamic" concern. It is for such reasons that the psychiatrist and psychoanalyst, as physicians, must maintain a vigilant medical orientation and a diagnostic acumen sufficient to differentiate reversible functional aberrations in their neurotic patients from the presence and dangers of established tissue changes.

"Conversion" symptoms. In contrast to the sympathetic and organic disturbances just described, "conversion" symptoms primarily affect the *sensorimotor* functions of the body. The term *conversion* was first used by Freud to indicate that such symptoms express an altered (converted) form of sexual energy, but the term is now employed more generally to denote all sensorimotor disabilities that serve as symbolic resolutions of unconscious motivational conflicts. In some cases, moreover, this resolution may be so effective that the patient, instead of experiencing anxiety, may regard his "illness" with relative equanimity (*la belle indifférence* of Janet). Conversion symptoms may effect any motor or sensory function, as the following discussion will indicate.

HYSTERICAL MOTOR DISTURBANCES. The term "hysteria" (Greek *hysteros*=uterus), along with "melancholia" (black bile), "frenzy" (*phrenos*=brain) and a few others, is one of the oldest etymologic relics in psychiatry, since in Hippocratic medicine it was used to designate illnesses thought to be caused by the wanderings of the uterus to the throat (globus hystericus) or elsewhere. Charcot and Janet labelled as *hysteria major* those dramatic sensory or motor dysfunctions which could be cured by "suggestion," and in lay usage "hysteria" still signifies a tantrum of rage, fear, or other extreme excitement. In technical usage, however, the term denotes an involuntary disturbance of sensorimotor functions expressive of neurotic conflicts related to the unconscious needs of the patient. Hysterical disturbances may be generalized or limited, and expressed in increased or diminished activity as illustrated by the following case examples:

Case 14.   Hysterical hyperkinesia with epilepsy

A seventeen-year-old girl, the only daughter in a laborer's family, was referred for the treatment of "major epilepsy." Typical grand mal attacks (cf. the *Practice,* Chapter 14) with unconsciousness were observed on two occasions; however, during a psychiatric interview, a rather atypical "seizure" occurred: the patient became opisthotonic as usual, but the succeeding clonic movements were vaguely masturbatory and in the semi-stupor that followed the patient tore her clothes and became almost frankly exhibitionistic. She regained her composure in a few minutes and denied any memory of the attack, but in subsequent psychiatric interviews, the following history was reconstructed.

The patient had become subject to true epileptic seizures at about the age of eleven, and was soon able to predict by certain well-defined premonitory feelings (prodromata) the days when she would have her attacks. On such days she remained home from school in the care of an older brother who, because of his mental retardation (I.Q. about 65), could neither attend school nor hold a job. Masturbatory sex play between them had occurred since she was eight and had stopped short only of intercourse. When the patient's own erotic urges increased after her menarche she had begun to stay home in deliberate, though partially apprehensive, anticipation of such relationships, but actual intercourse had always been prevented by the onset of muscular movements resembling those of her true epileptic seizures. An hysterical "attack" of this type was precipitated by an initial discussion of these episodes in the psychiatric interview, and apparently represented an outburst of mixed guilt and erotism deviated into frustraneous skeletal motor channels. The "seizure" was easily stopped by reassurance and suggestion, and left no postdromata or true amnesia. Under further therapy directed toward giving the patient partial insight, furnishing more normal outlets of her erotic urges (athletics, dancing, etc.) and removal of the feeble-minded brother from the home, the patient's pseudoepileptic hysterical seizures disappeared and her true epileptic attacks also became less intense and frequent.

Case 15. Hysterical paralysis

A thirty-eight-year-old mechanic was referred by his employer, a local steel company, for a persistent weakness of the neck not explicable on a physical or neurologic basis.

The history revealed that the patient, a Scandinavian émigré, had had the equivalent of only six grades of schooling, and had begun to work for his present employers as a common laborer soon after his arrival in this country at the age of sixteen. He was steady and reliable, but showed no special abilities; accordingly, he never progressed beyond assignments to manual labor and, in the depression of 1930, was laid off. Unable to find another job, he retired to a small cottage in the north woods and supported himself by gardening, fishing and trapping as his parents had done in Lapland. In 1942, however, he was summoned back to the war-expanded plant and, because of his previous experience, he was given a supervisory job actually beyond his intellectual and administrative capacities. He tried to hide his inefficiency by hard work over long hours, but he felt harrassed, inadequate and increasingly tense and confused. This also served to make him "accident-prone" by repeatedly getting him into actual physical danger. One day, while he was particularly resentful of his situation, he escaped having his head crushed only by the presence of mind of a fellow employee who jerked him away from a falling cable. The patient suffered a slightly sprained neck, for which, unfortunately, the local doctor prescribed an impressive-looking metal and leather supporting collar and a week's rest from work. At the end of this period the collar was removed, and recheck physical, neurologic and x-ray examinations showed completely normal findings; however, the patient insisted that the collar be replaced. This was done for another two-week period, during which it was noted that the patient rarely rested even his chin on its padded supports; yet when the collar was again removed, the patient could not hold his head erect. Moreover, he began to complain that he suffered from general fatigue, "nervousness," muscular weakness and sexual impotence. At the time of his referral two months later the patient was still receiving full disability compensation from his employers, was wearing his collar (although it was laced loosely with elastic and gave no cervical support) and was being cared for by his wife like a helpless child.

Psychiatric interviews by the ordinary techniques revealed few significant data other than the above, but the patient's rather naive dreams and his direct associations when given 0.30 cc. of Sodium Amytal intravenously showed clearly that his "paralysis" signified a surrender of masculine potency and self-sufficiency, and that the collar symbolized "support"—literally, care and protection—by parent-surrogates in the form of his employers, his physicians and his wife. The patient, therefore, unconsciously clung to his weakness and dependence as his way of acquiring greater security in what he deemed to be a frustrating and dangerous world. The techniques of treatment were attuned to these reactions. At the instance of the therapist, tactful but firm and well-coordinated pressures by the wife, company physician and insurance company removed the secondary gains (v.i.) of his illness, and his employer's offer of a more suitable job at no loss in pay mitigated his occupatoinal conflicts and mobilized a desire to return to the manual work, status and companions that had formerly been his sources of prestige and safety. In this more favorable setting, simple insight combined with a few face-saving doses of placebo and neck massage produced a rapid and lasting recovery.

HYSTERICAL SENSORY DISTURBANCES. DIMINUTION OF SENSORY FUNCTION. This is well illustrated in the following case:

Case 16.   Hysterical amaurosis: homosexuality

A twenty-four-year-old girl was brought for therapy with the statement that she "had been blinded by a sudden flash of light" two days previously. Careful examinations revealed no abnormalities of the eyes or nervous system, yet the patient insisted that she could barely distinguish light from darkness; in fact, she stumbled painfully over furniture when permitted to walk unguarded and was seen to do so even when she thought herself unobserved. The history revealed that for the preceding six years the patient had been the active homosexual partner of an older woman with whom she lived, and that during the past year she had become intensely jealous of another girl who, she thought, was replacing her in her roommate's affections. Two days before her admission she had followed her roommate to this girl's house and had seen them enter her rival's car in a darkened garage. When the lights of the car were flashed on and they began to drive away, she had stumbled into the path of the automobile, had been knocked over, and had narrowly escaped being seriously injured. When picked up off the street she stated that her vision was gone, and she had to be helped back to their home by her frightened and thoroughly contrite roommate. Characteristically, the patient professed little concern over her serious disability, and was loathe to leave her home to enter the hospital. Hypnosis after preparatory therapy and a reconciliation with her roommate readily restored her sight, but the patient continued to regard her recovery as a miraculous "cure" of what she preferred to consider a purely organic ocular injury. Obviously, insight into the reality-denying and symbolically self-castrative nature of her hysterical blindness (in her dreams and fantasies her eyes seemed symbolically equated with testicles) was too disturbing to be admitted to consciousness.

FURTHER CONSIDERATIONS IN CONVERSION NEUROSES.   HYPERCEPTIVITY.   Hyperacusis and other sensory hyperesthesias commonly occur in phobic and anxiety states; for instance, a mysophobe will be troubled by the appearance or smell of a minute contamination hardly discernible to anyone else; or a mother who is reacting with guilt and anxiety to the death of a child will hear the cooing of a neighbor's baby two apartments away. Similarly, a soldier exhausted by weeks of exposure to front-line blast and fire under conditions of extreme emotional conflict may escape an acute "combat neurosis" but may show startle reactions to the unexpected buzz of a fly or the flame of a match for months or years after his battle experiences.

OVERDETERMINATION.   The examples cited above illustrate comparatively simple sensorimotor disturbances traceable with relative directness to the unique conflicts of each patient, yet several factors played a role in determining the specific nature of the neurotic reactions. Thus, in the "blind" girl (Case 16) the hysterical amaurosis served both to reject the traumatic visual experiences and to deny the patient's frustrated masculine identification; similarly, in the epileptic girl (Case 14) the hysterical seizures not only expressed her deviated incestuous urges but also rendered the patient "comatose" and, therefore, in effect not "responsible" for a possible seduction. This confluence of the unconsciously adaptive functions of any symptoms is called *overdetermination,* and constitutes a process whereby a single neurotic pattern may become a complex compromise formation among many concurrent unconscious needs.

A thorough anlysis of even a single symptom, therefore, often entails an almost complete understanding of the multiple motivations and adaptive patterns of the patient; fortunately, however, in most instances (e.g., Case 15) the leading determinants of the symptom are sufficiently apparent to make fairly accurate evaluation possible.

PRIMARY AND SECONDARY GAIN. In an analysis of overdetermination, however, it is usually illuminating to make a distinction between the primary dynamic (*paranosic*) determinants of a neurotic disorder and the secondary (*epinosic*) advantages that a patient may later derive. For instance, it might be tempting to say that the laborer with the paralyzed neck (Case 15) developed or retained his disability simply to secure financial compensation from his employers—and, indeed, such secondary social gains often render a neurotic disorder all the more tenacious, and must be removed or counteracted during effective treatment. However, his financial compensation for the accident was actually much less than his normal earning power, and in addition he had to forego many personal and social satisfactions because of his disabilities. Further, there were no evidences of conscious malingering directed toward monetary gain; the patient sincerely believed his neck to be organically paralyzed, and gladly offered to mortgage his belongings if necessary to pay for treatment that would restore his capacity for work. Again, the girl with the epileptiform hysterical attacks (Case 14) derived no gain from her symptoms other than their unconsciously determined auto-erotic functions; on the contrary, she lived in conscious dread of commitment to an epileptic colony.

HYPOCHONDRIASIS. This is a term, often misused nosologically, which denotes a tendency to excessive and prolonged concern over bodily processes and dysfunctions. This can occur in both organic and "functional" illnesses, although, of course, in the former case it represents a defensive preoccupation with the body when its well-being is actually threatened by disease. When these narcissistic introspections reach the point of exclusion of all other interests, the "hypochondriac" process may, indeed, transcend the limits of neurosis and become psychotic in the sense of autistic isolation, delusional preoccupations and schizoid retreat (v.i.).

"Self-punitive" and "masochistic" aspects of neurotic symptoms. It has often been stated that the symptoms of conversion and organ-neuroses are "self-punitive" in the sense that they constitute self-imposed suffering in expiation for guilty unconscious wishes. Examples such as the following are sometimes cited to support this interpretation:

Case 17. Migraine with anxiety

A twenty-two-year-old girl, Mary M——, applied for the treatment of a severe migraine syndrome which began with prodromata of tension and restlessness and progressed to an excruciating hemicrania with anorexia, vomiting and visual disturbances. These symptoms usually lasted about twenty-four hours and were followed by fatigue and lassitude for another two days.

Physical, neurologic and laboratory findings were normal, and no allergic or other organic cause could be found for her migraine. The psychiatric history, however, revealed the following:

The patient was a foundling and had been adopted at the age of four by a well-to-do couple, Mr. and Mrs. M——. These foster parents had a son of their own eight years old, but Mr. M., despairing of his wife's fecundity and desiring a daughter, had taken the initiative in the adoption despite his wife's reluctance. Throughout her early years the patient was greatly indulged by her foster father and protected from the jealousy of his wife and son; unfortunately, when the patient was sixteen, Mr. M. died and left the patient exposed to their repressed but accumulated hostilities. Because of her early experience in the orphanage and her later protected upbringing, the patient was unable to emancipate herself from her passive dependency on her foster family; instead, she convinced herself that she was "greatly devoted" to them. Mrs. M. in turn, for the sake of appearances—and also because she was directed to do so in her husband's will—continued to provide for the patient's material wants, but in many subtle ways made her ambivalence toward the patient evident. One of her favorite methods was to have "a nervous headache" which demanded personal attendance and nursing from the patient, especially when the latter was otherwise occupied or wished to be elsewhere. A year after Mr. M's. death, moreover, the patient's foster brother married and brought his bride to live with the family, where she was treated with flagrant favoritism by Mrs. M.

It was under these circumstances that the patient's migrainous headaches began to occur. Each "attack" at first followed definite episodes of frustration and suppressed rage against the other members of the household; later, however, the precipitating circumstances became more remotely displaced and symbolic. The specific temporal relations of each attack were usually as follows: after a series of subtle slights or deprivations the patient would begin to feel a nameless anxiety accompanied by rapid pulse, cold sweat, constricted breathing, sensations of choking and, occasionally, urinary urgency, diarrhea, vertigo and faintness. After a period of minutes to hours the anxiety syndrome would either pass away, or else, if her preceding irritations had been sufficiently great, would be succeeded by an oppressive feeling of tense restlessness on a subjective substrate of chill, diffuse, undifferentiated anger. These symptoms were a reliable signal that within a short time her headache and visual disturbances would grow so severe that the patient herself would have to remain in a quiet darkened room, isolated from her family and almost immobile for from several hours to two days. Significantly, the headaches cleared when she was away at college or on vacation, but invariably reappeared when she returned home.

Comment. It might with some relevance be said that through her illness Miss M.—— was "punishing herself" to expiate hatred of her foster mother who, after all, had helped rescue her from an orphanage and was still supporting her; in this one sense, her illness might be considered "masochistic" (v.i.). But from a dynamic standpoint it is almost equally obvious that her anxiety signalled the threatened emergence of these inadmissable aggressions, and that her migraine concealed her anger and protected her from the consequences of frankly hostile or preemptive behavior. Less apparent but equally determinative were other symbolic functions of her headaches: her identification in illness with Mrs. M. as head of the household, notice of her own needs for special care and attention, and temporary isolation from her foster family in times of excessive stress while nevertheless continuing her general dependence upon them.

Course. Significantly, her migrainous attacks did not recur during her hospitalization, but all types of extramural treatment including diets, ocular refractions and various courses of medication and allergic desensitizations were only temporarily effective as long as she was at home. Nevertheless her headaches cleared completely two years later when her foster mother also died and, according to the terms of the father's will, left the patient free and financially independent.

Another brief example of an ostensibly self-punitive hysterical reaction is the following:

Case 18. Hysterical monoplegia

A fourteen-year-old boy was brought by his parents for a complete paralysis and anesthesia of the right arm which, they stated, had been precipitated by a "nervous breakdown due to overwork" at a military school. Examination revealed no organic lesion; indeed, the anesthesia and muscle weakness followed no neurologic pattern, and movements of the arm could readily be elicited by making them inadvertently necessary for balance, retaining his falling trousers, etc. The boy himself was relatively unperturbed by his disability, and it took little more than a cursory investigation to reveal its functional nature. In short, it appeared that for some time he had been developing severe guilt over manual masturbation, and that his fears of the consequences of "self-abuse" had greatly increased after the headmaster in a somber and portentous lecture had warned his charges that such "vicious habits" could cause "loss of manhood, paralysis of the body and incurable insanity." The boy reacted with severe anxiety which, significantly, cleared almost completely when his arm "became paralyzed." Explanations, reassurances, manipulation and authoritative suggestion quickly restored normal function to the arm within twenty-four hours and the boy was discharged symptom-free.

Comment. Significantly, this case also seems to illustrate the self-punitive aspects of neurotic disabilities, since the boy suffered a self-imposed monoplegia in apparent expiation for masturbatory guilts. And yet here again psychiatric investigation revealed that the specific paralysis of the right arm had many covert determinants: he "cast out the member that hath offended" him and thus made his arm (instead of his total "self") the symbolic whippingboy; he chose, from all the possible "evil consequences" of his masturbation only the partial "paralysis" of an arm in preference to the threatened "loss of manhood" or "insanity"; moreover, his specific illness not only made it impossible for him to indulge in the usual techniques of auto-erotism, but it took him out of school away from the threatening headmaster, restored him to his sympathetic parents and had a number of similarly regressive and compensatory overdeterminations. His neurosis, then, represented not a "need for self-punishment" but an advantageous choice of a lesser set of evils, some of which also brought him definite though unconsciously determined gains. Little wonder that the boy's "illness" had served to dissipate his anxiety, and that he showed less concern over his symptoms than over separation from his parents at the time of his hospital admission. This case likewise illustrates the overdetermination of even a seemingly simple "psychosomatic" dysfunction by a multiplicity of factors, each of which must be given proper weight in therapy.

MASOCHISM. Contrary to the formulation given above as to the economic functions of neurotic symptoms, it has often been contended that "true" masochism represents a primary tendency to suffer pain for its own sake, or, at least, that masochism is "sadistic aggressivity turned inward." These concepts spring from the theory proposed by Freud in *Beyond the Pleasure Principle* to the effect that the "life instincts" (*Eros*) are opposed throughout all nature by a biologically evolved "repetition compulsion" which dooms all organisms to recurrent and inevitable suffering, senescence and death (*Thanatos*).

As is likely to be the case with all theories that propose such strikingly dramatic dichotomies, the concept of the "death instinct" gained wide initial interest (Alexander, 1927) and is still advocated by a few "classical" writers (e.g., Menninger, Sterba). However, for the most part the question of the so-called ero-thanatic conflict has been relegated to the historical phase of analytic dialectics, and both sadism and masochism are now approached more dynamically as secondary aspects of more complex adaptive patterns. This may be illustrated by the following case history:

Case 19.   "Masochistic character"

A woman of forty-two was brought to the emergency ward after she had attempted suicide by swallowing an ounce of tincture of iodine. The social service history as secured from various informants left a somewhat confused impression. On the one hand, the facts indicated that the patient had been living in pitiable circumstances. She was the wife of a drunkard who had deserted her several months previously. Unable to secure outside employment because of various organic illnesses she had been reduced to knitting gloves and sweaters at home to support herself and her three children. She had lived in squalor and privation, but had stoically refused help from neighbors or charitable organizations. And yet this pathetic account was somewhat altered by further data. For instance, the patient had also refused medical care that would have greatly improved her health. Again, her present marriage was the third of a series, and it seemed more than a coincidence that all three of her husbands had been irresponsible, improvident and abusive. Finally, the patient, despite her refusal of material help, had made so obvious a spectacle of her suffering and "martyrdom" that her neighbors had almost unanimously agreed that she "just gloried in misery," and her social worker had concluded that she was a "masochist." In all instances the outcome was the same: everyone had eventually ceased trying to help her.

Physical and laboratory examinations in the hospital confirmed the presence of mild arteriosclerosis, general malnutrition with anemia, and moderate but uncontrolled diabetes with pruritus and dependent edema. More significantly, however, the psychiatric history revealed the following:

The patient's father had been an illiterate, sadistic backwoods farmer who kept his family in isolation and physical subjection and who terrorized them by excesses of cruelty during his drunken rages. However, even in this fear-torn household there was a scale of relative security, ranging from the mother down to the younger and more helpless children. In this hierarchy the patient envied her mother, the only one able to resist her father's abuse or ever to elicit from him even a transient sign of physical affection. Warped by this unconscious but deeply embedded identification with her mother and, indeed, hardly acquainted with any other conception of marriage, she had passively "let herself be married off" at the age of sixteen to a neighboring farmer of her father's choosing. This man soon lost his farm and moved to Chicago where, after four years of neglecting or abusing the patient, he deserted her and their two children. The patient supported herself for two years, and then married again—this time deliberately selecting an irresponsible drunkard for the announced purpose of "reforming him." The sequence of poverty, abuse and desertion was repeated, and the patient three years later again found herself divorced and now with a third child on her hands. And yet within a short time she was again married, again to an alcoholic, and was again mistreated and deserted. By this time she had become known to various social agencies who, after a third suicidal gesture on her part, abandoned their well-meaning attempts to help her directly and arranged for her admission to a psychiatric hospital.

Here the patient, with a characteristic air of resigned but valiant martyrdom, insisted on telling her troubles and sufferings in interminable detail to all who would listen until she was avoided by patients and nursing staff alike. Moreover, although she professed profound gratitude for everyone's care and kindness, she actually cooperated very poorly in regulating her diabetic diet and medication or in conforming with ward routine. Similarly, she welcomed —indeed, demanded—frequent interviews with the physicians and social workers, yet progressed not an iota in acquiring any insight into her own responsibility for many of her difficulties, or any realistic reorientation as to future plans for work, care of her children, or better social adaptations. Finally, her behavior became so annoying to other patients that she had to be discharged, to return for renewed and equally futile attempts at extramural guidance and social service care.

Comment. This case, then, is an example of a type of "masochistic character" that ranges from the everyday brand of minor trouble-seeker to the familiar "professional martyr" who somehow arranges to suffer needlessly, usually for causes that appear to others idle or vain. Yet even in extreme instances masochism need not be accepted as an intrinsically integrated and unanalyzable pattern. On the contrary, repeated seeking of painful experiences may indicate not an actual "joy in pain"—a semantic and dynamically meaningless paradox—but rather a compulsive urge (a) to reexplore danger in order to dispel anxiety or (b) to attain symbolic goals which in the deeper evaluations of the patient justify concomitant sufferings. With such unconscious attitudes, each new travail becomes a means to an end, with the result that suffering eventually appears to be sought for its own sake. Thus, the patient cited above was sensitized in her early life to drunken abuse by her father, and, therefore, when she was old enough to do so, kept marrying drunkards under a compulsive necessity to relive, master and so dispel the fears of her childhood.* Such reexplorations were overdetermined by unconscious identifications with her mother who had withstood a similar ordeal, and by even more deeply repressed incestuous longings for physical contacts —erotic or otherwise—with father-surrogates. Deeply buried, too, were fantasies (revealed in the patient's dreams) that by drinking iodine in a suicidal gesture, she also rejoined her father, who, quite literally, had always seemed to be "drinking himself to death," but actually was still hale and reprobate at the age of sixty.

---

* Perhaps the simplest example of this type of defense against anxiety is the tendency to keep touching an aching tooth or wound in order to *explore the tolerable limits of the discomfort* and thus reassert mastery over it. However, once such retestings begin to evoke unbearable pain, anxiety is reevoked and the direct testing normally stops for the time being. On the other hand, the severity of a pain-percept itself is highly contingent on expectancy, and can be readily influenced by induced changes in attitude (Wolff and Goodell, 1943; Beecher, 1959).

EXPERIMENTAL MASOCHISM. This formulation of the long-term unconscious hedonic economy of masochism may be further demonstrated by the production of apparently masochistic behavior in animals, as illustrated by a typical experiment:

EXPERIMENT 1. Experimental masochism

> Normally, cats show reactions of intense fear to sudden blasts of air (cf. Exp. 9, p. 134), yet a cat can be trained to administer airblasts to itself with seeming avidity by the following procedure. The animal is first taught to feed from a box at a bell signal, and is then trained to depress a simple pedestal switch that sounds the bell and automatically makes the food reward available. When the feeding pattern has become well established the animal is exposed to progressively stronger currents of air when it operates the switch, at a rate of increase not sufficient to impair the feeding. The air blast can then be given simultaneously with loud noises, dazzling lights, rancid odors or other deterrents and the combined stimuli can reach high intensity; nevertheless, because they are now part of the signal complex leading to feeding, the experimental animal is not disturbed by them. On the contrary, when the food itself is not forthcoming, it frequently works the switch to elicit them as intermediate goals. At this point an observer unacquainted with the dynamic evolution of the animal's adaptive patterns would conclude that it must be "masochistic," since it "deliberately" seeks experiences that are avoided as painful by "normal" members of its species. In similar experiments a cat or dog can be trained to "seek" and apparently "enjoy" even severe electric shocks provided, of course, that the latter represent —or had at one time represented—part of a sign-gestalt for food, water, release from restraint, sex gratification, or some other biologic reward.

NORMAL MASOCHISM. At a less deviantly symbolic level, voluntary self-abnegation and even temporary suffering are everyday means to the eventual achievement of desired satisfactions. In general, most people find no "inherent joy" in hard work, privation and "selfless" service to others, yet they undertake their daily chores with a relative cheerfulness derived not out of direct love of "duty," but in anticipation of future recompense either here on earth or at least in a wishfully anticipated hereafter. Such expectancies may often be traced to the experiences of childhood, when unpleasant tasks were set by the parents and accomplished by the child for the essential rewards of their approbation and love.

SEXUAL MASOCHISM. It may be noted that the term "masochism" was itself derived from the name of an Austrian writer, Leopold v. Sacher-Masoch (1836–1895), whose fictional characters occasionally extolled the erotic ecstacy of pain. It was in this restricted sense that Freud originally used the term to mean sexual gratification from "suffering pain, ill-treatment and humiliation . . . during sexual intercourse." Later, however, the signification of the term spread to include those who mutilated their sexual organs (e.g., Siberian Skopts), other seekers of expiatory physical affliction or injury (e.g., religious flagellants), and finally those who also seemed to enjoy pure travail of body and spirit for its own sake. The term is, of course, still applicable in its original sense to patients who cannot reach orgasm in intercourse without professed physical "suffering" of some sort, or who displace their orgastic pleasure into various abusive and humiliating acts they demand from their sex partners. Detailed accounts of such erotic rituals, however, usually reveal, first, that the erotogenic pains sought by non-psychotic patients are very rarely such as to entail serious trauma and, second, that the "abuse" demanded from the partner must remain in the nature of pretense and play-acting, else the entire mummery is spoiled and orgasm not attained. Moreover, further analysis of such symbolic behavior nearly always indicates that the masochistic element in the erotic sequence is derived from repressed memories of sexual pleasure having been obtained in early life only at the cost of some humiliation or suffering (e.g., initially painful masturbation or defloration) with the result that the unconscious association of sex and pain persisted and was expressed in later erotic patterns.

PSYCHOTIC MASOCHISM.   Nevertheless, some of the deeper symbolisms and fantasy-formations of a masochistic patient may be bizarre in the extreme, and may lead to behavior prejudicial not only to the patient's ultimate well-being (cf. Case 19) but to life itself. This is a particular danger in the psychotic patient in whom impairment of reality function (including the image of his own body)* and disintegration of adaptive control may lead to horrifyingly self-destructive behavior with little or no accompanying affect.

An example in point is that of a schizophrenic girl who, in a gesture probably symbolic of self-castrative renunciation of the world, plucked out one of her eyes while being interviewed—then, in the flurry of first-aid that followed, calmly plucked out the other.

SADISM.   This term is derived from the name of the Marquis de Sade (1740–1814), who practiced sexual perversions of such fantastic cruelty on his victims (including children) that he was finally committed as insane. Freud, in his *New Introductory Lectures* (1933), interpreted sadism as "the destructive instinct directed outwards, thereby acquiring the character of aggressiveness" and, as we have seen, this explanation of the phenomenon in terms of a postulated "death instinct" is still adhered to in some psychoanalytic quarters. Like masochism, however, sexual or other sadism may be analyzed more dynamically as aggressivity or cruelty not necessarily employed for its own sake or as an expression of primary instincts, but as a behavior pattern of the organism determined directly or symbolically by its previous adaptations to deprivation, frustration or displacement in a group hierarchy.†

"Conscious" vs. "unconscious" determinants of neuroses.   Finally, as has been implied throughout this chapter, there need be no overconcern as to which patterns of reaction are "consciously" determined and therefore classifiable as "malingering," and which "unconscious" and thereby "neurotic." Symptoms of all origins are frequently overdramatized

---

* Cf. Schilder and Bender.

† Further demonstrations of such mechanisms by animal experiment and case history will be found in Part Two of this volume.

—including the pose of uncomplaining nobility—for social gain, whereas even a deliberate malingerer is, by psychodynamic definition, immaturely demanding and dependent, neurotically devious and eventually self-defeating. In fact no adaptation, whether "normal," "neurotic" or "psychotic," is ever completely "conscious," "pre-conscious" or "unconscious"; rather, in Adolf Meyer's terms, all are *more or less consciously* (i.e., purposefully and deliberately) evolved.* Apart from the verbal necessities of description and teaching, behavior must be dealt with as a configuration of transactions which, however complex, are thoroughly integrated in space, time and sequence rather than as a compendium of independent processes artificially separated into "libidinal phases," "levels of consciousness," "defense mechanisms," "organic vs. functional components," etc. As a prosaic example: A person does not ordinarily "desire" to catch a cold, but when he is suffering from coryzal discomforts that exceed his individually determined and situationally variable tolerance, he may demand care, sympathy, attention and relief from responsibilities to a degree not altogether justified by the "actual" severity of his physical illness. Should these regressive satisfactions be found available and highly satisfying, he might prolong his "illness" for a variable period, yet it would hardly be justifiable to contend that the secondary gains in themselves "caused" the original infection. On the other hand, should his invalidism, dependence and regression be exacerbated by unfavorable combinations of internal proclivities and external circumstances, the mild aberrations precipitated by a cold could develop into persistent neurosis or, under intolerable combinations of stress, end in psychotic reactions such as those described in the next chapter.

References†

Dunbar, H.: Psychosomatic Diagnosis.
English, O. S., and Pearson, G. H. J.: Common Neuroses of Children and Adults.
Freud, S.: The Economic Problem in Masochism.
Fromm, E.: Escape from Freedom.
Laughlin, H.: The Neuroses in Clinical Practice.
Menninger, K.: Love Against Hate.
Reik, T.: Masochism in Modern Man.
Rickman, J.: The Development of the Psychoanalytic Theory of the Psychoses.
Waterman, S.: The Story of Superstition.
Weiss, E., and English, O. S.: Psychosomatic Medicine. 3rd ed.

* Under military conditions of group isolation, oppressive ennui and inescapable stresses such as are found in remote outposts, nearly all euphemistic distinctions between "conscious" and "unconscious" determinants of "neuroses," "malingering," "character disorders" and even "psychoses" may vanish. (Cf. Lt. Commander A. R. MacLean: The Aleutian Paradox. Also, section on Isolation, Chapter 6).

† Cf. References to Chapters 3 and 4.

Chapter 6

Psychotic dynamisms

It may safely be estimated that the forms of neurotic reaction reviewed above constitute well over nine-tenths of all psychiatric problems, and are therefore of the greatest medico-sociologic importance. But there remains to be considered a class of more severe and often less tractable disorders of behavior which, until the turn of the century, were considered the sole field of psychiatry and which still seriously affect about one person in fifteen throughout the world. These are the *psychoses,* currently subdivided (cf. the *Practice,* Appendix 1) into *involutional, affective* (manic-depressive), *schizophrenic* and *paranoid* reactions, and differentiated by one or more of the following criteria:

1. In the *functional psychoses* listed above, there occurs:

a. Loss of contact with, or marked distortions of, generally accepted concepts of time, place and person (*sensorial* aberrations) or of causality (thinking disorders) which may become manifest as sensory misperceptions (*illusions*), vividly projected imagery (*hallucinations*) and unrealistic convictions (*delusions*).

b. Overintensity, fixity or inappropriateness of situational or interpersonal responses (*distortions of affect*): e.g., restless hyperactivity with pseudo-euphoric ebullience (*mania*), persistent feelings of hopeless futility (*depression, melancholia*), irrationally systematized and exaggerated reactions of resentment, fear, anger or grandiosity (*paranoia*), emotional blunting (as in *hebephrenia*), or bizarre *dissociations* (*schizophrenia*) between situation and response sometimes leading to explosive outbursts (*catatonic excitements*).

c. Excessive and persistent reversion to childhood patterns (*regression*) no longer appropriate to adult life: e.g., pseudoinfantile passivities, destructive aggressions and uninhibited or perverse eroticisms.

d. *Concurrent personality disintegration,* with release of repetitive, dissociated part-patterns (*echopraxia, stereotypies, autisms*).

2. In the *acute brain disorders,* severe but reversible derangements of apperceptive, interpretive and manipulative (intellectual) capacities, often with confusion and/or disruptive panic, as in the *toxic deliria,* or finally,

3. In the *chronic brain disorders,* the permanent impairment (deterioration) or loss (*dementia*) of intellectual capacities as in the various forms of organic cerebral disease.

Further discussion of the differential diagnosis and therapy of the psychoses will be presented later in this volume and in the *Practice;* here, however, we shall consider briefly, first, various biologic and pharmacologic factors, and, second, current dynamic concepts as to the causation and phenomenology of these disorders.

Organic factors

Freud, despite his preoccupation with the effects of early childhood experiences on all later behavior, remained convinced throughout his life that both the neuroses and psychoses were essentially metabolic (probably hormonal) disorders, and predicted that their ultimate therapy would be specifically pharmacologic.* Many clinicians today find this to be almost their only point of agreement with Freud, and continue to search for a genetic-somatic cause of the psychoses that would furnish a rational basis for treatment. As noted, no such etiology has as yet been confirmed, but combinations of metabolic, pharmacologic and psychologic stress (biodynamically considered, the three forms merge) can certainly induce "organic" psychosis (*acute and chronic brain disorders*) and markedly influence the so-called functional psychoses (*manic-depressive, schizophrenic* and *paranoiac reactions*) as follows:

Physiologic stresses

It has long been known that acute want of oxygen, prolonged hunger or thirst, extremes of temperature, excessive fatigue and other physiologic deprivations or insults can produce serious disturbances of consciousness, thought and action which may assume psychotic proportions. Recent studies on the effects of one such form of stress deserve special consideration.

Sleep deprivation. The intense weariness, distress and confusion and the desperate seeking for relief during sleep deprivation—a torture that leaves only internal scars—has made this a favorite form of duress among medieval and modern inquisitors seeking false confessions ("brain washing") and religious or political indoctrination (cf. Glass, J. Frank). From the clinical standpoint, L. J. West and others have demonstrated that interference with conditioned sleep cycles (Kleitman) by enforced wakefulness for 72 hours or more causes most subjects to develop marked hypersuggestibility, sensorial aberrations, affective or schizoid distortions, and an increased susceptibility to psychotogenic drugs (Bliss et al.). However, the delirious nature of the induced effects and their rapid amelioration after rest and sleep suggest that physiologic

---

* Freud attributed what were formerly known as "neurasthenic" symptoms to the supposedly debilitating effects of masturbation or ejaculatio praecox, and distinguished these *actual neuroses* from (a) the *psychoneuroses* which were in part experientially as well as organically determined and (b) the *narcissistic neuroses* (psychoses) unreachable by analysis because of the self-isolation (narcissism) of the patient.

In his *Outline of Psychoanalysis* (published post mortem in 1949), he wrote: "The future may teach us how to exercise a direct influence by means of particular chemical substances upon the amounts of energy and their distribution in the apparatus of the mind. . . . But for the moment we have nothing better at our disposal than the technique of psychoanalysis, and for that reason, in spite of limitations, it is not to be despised."

stresses, like their pharmacologic counterparts, described below, can induce only the toxic-exhaustive forms of behavior disorder.

Pharmacologic influences

Since neolithic times, man has apparently known the intoxicant effects of various brews and fermentations (wines and beers in pre-Biblical Egypt and Chaldea) and various plant extracts (opium poppy in the ancient East; cocaine in pre-Columbian South America, peyotl in Aztec Mexico). Indeed, man has always avidly sought such substances as media of temporary or permanent escape from harsh realities into a haze of forgetfulness, fantasy and disinhibition during extremes of which his behavior would be termed "psychotic." Recently, however, specific chemical compounds* have been found which, when administered in amounts as minute as 25 micrograms, can cause states of disorientation, depersonalization, affective distortion and hallucinatory and delusional behavior lasting from several hours to several days. These drugs have been termed *psychotogenic* by those who believe that they produce "model psychoses" and thus indicate that all psychoses are of chemical origin. However, the validity of these inferences is thrown into question by many considerations, among them (a) that as many as half of the volunteers presumed to be normal controls for such studies were later found to have been psychiatrically disturbed to begin with (Pollin and Perlin); (b) that almost any substance, including common psychiatric medications such as the amphetamines (Connell), barbiturates (Isbell), isoniazid (Jackson) and various ataractics (Diekel and Dixon), may, when taken in even slight excess, cause "psychotic" reactions; (c) that metabolically harmless *placebos* such as milk sugar, when given under conducive circumstances, can also induce aberrant and bizarre behavior (v. Beecher, Lasagna, S. Wolf and Gildea's control studies on "taraxein"); and (d) that psychotic patients themselves show no constant differential effects to any known "psychotogenic" drugs, and rapidly develop a tolerance to them.

In view of these and other methodologic considerations it must be inferred that although various substances, some in minute quantities, can cause temporary deliria or perhaps even chronic deteriorative psychoses through toxicosis or permanent cerebral damage, this effect is only ancillary to the etiology, psychopathology or therapy of the psychotic states.

Psychologic stress

The preceding chapters of this book have developed the fundamental relationships between psychologic stress and neurotic or psychotic responses in some detail, but certain more technical aspects remain to be reconsidered in the present connection.

Apperceptive. Walter and Ulett have shown that "psychic driving" induced by so simple a stimulus as a light flickering at a rate that

---

* E.g., lysergic acid diethylamide (LSD-25), (cf. H. Solomon, Bercel, et al.), mescaline (Klüver, Huxley), bufotenine (Fabing), dimethyltryptamine (Evarts), and the atropine-like substances JB-318 and JB-329 (Abood).

happens to coincide with and reinforce the electrical beating of the cerebral cortex (8 to 12 per second alpha rhythm) may induce states of tension and disorientation or, in especially sensitive subjects, convulsions followed by aphasia and automatism (fugue states). In a broader application of the disrupting effects of communication overdrive, J. G. Miller (cf. Chapter 3) has pointed out that modern life is becoming so complex that the items of information which the human brain must receive, interpret, sort, classify and respond to appropriately may have begun to exceed its capacities as either a digital or analogic computer, with resultant "nervous breakdowns" in an almost literal parallelism to those in an overloaded cybernetic* system.

Isolation. But what is perhaps of even greater theoretical and clinical interest is the fact that a marked diminution of contacts with the external environment can also cause serious disorders of function. Jacques Loeb believed that all life avidly seeks for stimulus and reaction (e.g., plant roots "seek" water; flowers, the sun), and called these seekings *tropisms*. Animals search for progressively greater varieties of experience: a rat will spontaneously run alternative routes through a maze (Heron) and a cat or monkey will prefer exploration to food or sex (Butler). Most humans abhor "boredom," however safe—a circumstance that motivates much travel or research and, conversely, makes solitary confinement,† even apart from the factor of social rejection ("being sent to Coventry"), among the most dreaded of punishments for child or adult. Persons too long deprived of living company even in adventures of their own choosing experience what Admiral Byrd, during his Antarctic vigil, called a "terror of loneliness"—a state that often necessitates an elaboration of ritual and a vividness of imagery which may reach the intensity of relentless obsessions and wishful hallucinations. Captain Joshua Slocum, thrice incapacitated while sailing single-handed around the world, each time was convinced that he saw and heard a lusty, cheerful bo's'n steer his little yawl *Spray* safely through gales and dangerous seas while he lay helpless below. So also, John the Baptist, Joan of Arc, Charles Lindbergh and countless other isolates, from deserted children to lost spelunkers, have rejoiced in times of stress in mortal or spiritual rescuers who were as "real" as man's eternal yearning for succor.

These observations have recently been experimentally confirmed by the work of Hebb, Lilly, P. Solomon and others, who deprived normal subjects of customary sensory stimuli by suspension in a warm bath, by keeping them in a continuously darkened room, and by earplugs or other modes of masking sounds, and noted that within six hours to three days, many subjects became intensely anxious, showed disorders of perception, memory and self-image, and developed various somatic disturbances and cerebral hallucinations that persisted for hours or days after release. Any variations in technique that admitted a greater access of diverting stimuli mitigated these effects (Vernon), and the responses were also greatly

---

* Greek *kybernos* = governor.
† Christopher Burney thus summed up his vivid experiences "in solitary": "Variety is not the spice of life; it is the very stuff of it."

influenced by the various meanings the same situation had for different subjects*; nevertheless, sensory deprivations or, more generally, feelings of personal isolation may be exceedingly important factors in a wide range of clinical phenomena. Among these may be cited the accident-causing illusions of a weary truck driver too long on a monotonous run; the "break-off point" at which a pilot of a supersonic plane suspended seemingly silent, motionless and alone in the endless stratosphere experiences a panic of "disconnectedness with the world"; the observation that 7 per cent of patients blindfolded and "at complete rest" after cataract operations suffer psychotic episodes (Ziskind); the fact that consigning disturbed alcoholics to a "quiet darkened recovery room" for complete rest favors the onset of delirium tremens (Lemere); or the possibility that persons socially isolated from childhood because of real or fancied disappointments or rejections may develop schizoid disturbances of thought, affect and reality-interpretation.

With these additional data as background, we may proceed to consider the various forms of psychoses under their usual classifications of manic-depressive, paranoiac and schizophrenic reactions, and once again trace each of these from its origins in "normal" behavior to its clinical extremes of intensity, persistence and social incompatibility.

Deviations of affect

Certain swings of mood (e.g., morning "blues," premenstrual dysphorias) are possibly correlated with hormonal (Benedek), other physiologic (K. Brown) or even climatic (Peterson†) rhythms; however, there are nearly always subtle psychologic admixtures—e.g., monthly "cycles" of increased social activity in unmarried women who sublimate periodically increased sexual tension. The clinically important dysthymias shading from borderline through neurotic to psychotic may be reviewed as follows.

Hyperthymic reactions. EUPHORIA. At first sight, true euphoria would seem to be rather desirable, since the term is generally taken to connote a persistent cheerfulness, a heightened feeling of well-being and an unabashed or even obtrusive optimism. Although this state should be distinguished from the quiet, undemonstrative equanimity (literally, "balanced spirits") and happiness of the truly contented individual, it is obvious that mild euphoria is hardly likely to be regarded by the patient as a condition requiring psychiatric treatment. Much more often seen by the psychiatrist, then, is the pseudo-euphoric who subtly senses that his mimetic ebullience and forced gaiety would quickly vanish should he

---

* For example, E. Z. Levy et al. noted that suspicious or resentful military volunteers were much more disturbed by even a simple blindfold than were others who resigned themselves to the isolation experiment as part of inexplicable and unavoidable Army routine. Similarly, control subjects withstood much longer periods without adverse effects if the duration of the experiment was agreed upon in advance rather than set by arbitrary action or as an indefinite challenge.

† Peterson's data and conclusions have been severely criticized on statistical and heuristic grounds (Wilson et al.)

stop compulsively trying to be "cheerful" and face his problems directly. In most cases it is not difficult to discern the tensions underlying the frenetic hyperactivity of such individuals who, in restless flight from their anxieties, occupy every moment with work, theaters, athletics, sexual affairs, travel and countless other crowded activities—all performed with professed gusto but actually with thin enjoyment and little satisfaction. This often holds true for the exaggerated euphoria and hyperactivity that characterize *hypomanic* states severe enough to require institutionalization. The following case is an instance of this:

Case 20. Hypomania

A wealthy executive forty-eight years of age was brought to the hospital by a business associate who stated that the patient "had been running himself so ragged with too much work and too much play" that his friends had insisted that he come to the hospital for a "check-up and a rest-cure." Further questioning revealed that for the preceding four months the patient had been working intensely but erratically, making quick business decisions that sometimes produced brilliant results, but as often proved unsound and unprofitable. Moreover, his social behavior had become impulsive and unpredictable; for instance, he had twice abruptly adjourned business conferences in the midst of serious work with a sudden invitation to everyone present "to quit, have a drink, and come play golf at my club." On the first occasion a few present had good-naturedly accepted, but while he was driving them to the golf course the patient suddenly expanded his invitation to include a complete week-end for everyone at his country home 200 miles away, and had been with difficulty dissuaded from heading there immediately. In his executive capacities he continued, with similar impetuosity, to arrange unnecessary trips and conferences and to propose extravagant promotional schemes; similarly, in his entertainments for the firm's customers, his restlessness, unnecessary lavishness, excessive drinking and forced gaiety had been increasingly embarrassing to his friends. These insisted, however, that the patient had previously been a sober, stable and rather undemonstrative individual.

In the hospital the patient's behavior was characteristically pseudo-manic. He dressed in flashy pajamas and loud bathrobes, and was otherwise immodest and careless about his personal appearance. He neglected his meals and rest hours, and was highly irregular, impulsive and distractible in his adaptations to ward routine. Without apparent intent to be annoying or disturbing he sang, whistled, told pointless off-color stories, visited indiscriminately and flirted crudely with the nurses and female patients. Superficially, he appeared to be in high spirits, and yet one day when he was being gently chided over some particularly irresponsible act he suddenly slumped in a chair, covered his face with his hands, began sobbing, and cried, "For Pete's sake, doc, let me be. Can't you see that I've just *got* to act happy?" This reversal of mood was transient and his seeming buoyancy returned in a few moments; nevertheless, during a Sodium Amytal interview his defensive euphoria again dropped away and he burst into frank sobbing as he clung to the physician's arm. He then confided that during the preceding year he had begun to suspect, with some reason, that his young second wife whom he "loved to distraction" had tired of their marriage and had been unfaithful to him. He had accused her of this, and she had replied, almost indifferently, with an offer of divorce. His pride had been greatly wounded, but to salvage it, avoid the scandal of a second divorce and keep her as long as possible, they had agreed that she take an extended European tour and postpone her decision until her return. During her absence he had been obsessively torn by suspense, jealousy and anger, could no longer take an interest in his work and had lost sleep, strength and weight. He consulted his family physician for the latter symptoms but the doctor, after finding little physically wrong with him, had simply advised him "to forget your business troubles [sic], play a bit more golf, get about more and enjoy yourself." He had followed this advice with compulsive intensity, but with the abreactive exaggeration that had eventually led to his admission to the hospital.

Needless to say, this account by the patient as to the reasons for his disturbances of mood and behavior was far from complete, but served to initiate further confidences in later interviews. Thus, the patient confessed that during the past several years he had begun to feel that his place near the head of a business concern was being threatened by younger, more energetic and better-trained men, in competition with whom he himself had thought it necessary to become ultra-"progressive" in his executive tasks. In private life, too, he had become afraid of being considered "just a nice old has-been" and had therefore begun to indulge in drinking, athletics, and exhibitionistic stag-party venery which he didn't really enjoy. But perhaps his greatest defense against his obsessive fears of obsolescence had been his second marriage to a young, pretty and popular girl whom he had, by offering her a life of wealth and ease, won away from more youthful admirers. The patient unconsciously prized his wife as a symbol of his own renewed youth; but, unfortunately, in his anxiety to prove his sexual competence, he had frequently been impotent with her, and had then made their marriage almost intolerable by his reactive rages and jealousies. As a result she had very probably become unfaithful and was currently spending more of his money in Europe in anticipation of an eventual divorce.

Under a regimen of rest, sedation, physiotherapy and a gradual working-through of his emotional difficulties preparatory to extramural readjustments in his business, social and marital affairs, the patient's hypomanic tension abated and he regained relative equanimity with attendant improvement in behavior.

Mania. In "true" mania overwhelming tensions may be expressed in extreme distractibility, a continuous flow of ideation and speech with rapidly changing context, a furor of exhibitionistic and other uninhibited activity and a highly labile emotional tone. In most cases these reactions abate spontaneously after several weeks or months, but in some instances the patient's behavior may become chronically disorganized, to produce the "délire chronique" of Charcot or the "chronic mania" of Schott.

Hypothymic reactions. Depressions or melancholic fixations of mood, unlike pseudo-euphoric states, are more directly allied with anxiety and more overtly charged with suffering, and yet they too can be shown to have certain adaptive functions. Thus, at the physiologic level the usual accompaniments of a depression are: insomnia, anorexia, constipation and motor tension sometimes accompanied by restlessness or agitation—symptoms that might be expected to occur in an individual watchfully mobilized against what seems to him to be a hostile and threatening world. Other depressive symptoms also have their symbolically defensive overdeterminations: impotence or amenorrhea unconsciously signifies a surrender of adult genitality; petulant helplessness, passivity and dependency connote a regression to infantile emotional orientations; and fixed hypochondriasis is only a thinly veiled reversion to narcissistic and auto-erotic concern with the patient's own body. The ideational content of the depressive, too, is symbolically significant; exaggerated self-accusations (e.g., "I am the greatest sinner that ever lived, and all the world knows it") seem to express ideas of extreme guilt and unworthiness, yet at the same time reveal the patient's tendencies toward perversely paranoid and delusional self-aggrandizement. Again, while the retarded and depressed patient is evidently far from comfortable in his reactions, his behavior often enough seems almost deliberately though subtly aggressive toward those (usually members of his family) against whom he has deep but repressed hostilities. Finally, at even deeper unconscious levels primitive "oral incorporative" and "introjective" symbolisms may occur; thus, the melancholic who fears he "has lost everything" may develop schizoid delusions that he "has swallowed the world," or, conversely, that through suicide he can, by destroying only his condemned and unwanted physical being, either regress spiritually to a womb-like Nirvana or be reborn cleansed of sin and guilt (cf. Appendix 4). Such fantasies are, of course, difficult to elicit even in psychotic patients, but variants of them are illustrated by the following case:

Case 21. Melancholia

An intelligent, but physically rather unattractive Catholic schoolteacher married secretly at the age of thirty-eight and a year later became pregnant. Her husband, an improvident, middle-aged ne'er-do-well, did not like the prospect of the patient losing her position if her marriage were discovered. He therefore strongly urged her to have an abortion; when she refused, he deserted her. This left the patient no alternative but to violate her religious scruples and attempt to abort herself, not only to keep her job and social position but to remove all memories of her unhappy marital experiences. But her crude attempts failed, so that the patient was forced to reveal the date and fate of her marriage to her family. On their advice—tinged with considerable covert condemnation—she obtained a leave of absence from her job and reversed her conscious attitude toward her pregnancy; in fact, she began to plan with ominously overcompensatory zeal for every detail of the immediate and remote future of her child, on whom she intended to focus her "every remaining interest in life." She was delivered normally at term but, again tragically, the child was congenitally deformed and died within a few hours. The patient almost immediately entered into a deep melancholic state in which she refused to eat, slept fitfully or not at all, lost twenty pounds of weight in as many days and needed mechanical restraint to prevent suicidal attempts. This acute phase gradually passed, but for months of institutionalization thereafter she had to be nursed, washed, dressed, spoon fed and cared for as though she herself were a child. During this period she seemed to have lost all her former intellectual and social interests: she could not be induced to read, listen to news or music, or engage in occupational or group activities. After visits by her family she was particularly querulous and demanding; at other times she sat rocking to and fro chanting to herself in an almost inaudible, repetitious sing-song in which the following content could sometimes be distinguished: She accused herself of having committed "the Unforgivable Sin" the nature of which she never further specified. The Catholic Church and all its clerical hierarchy had been informed of this. Indeed, the Holy Trinity Themselves had condemned her to eternal perdition, and this was a universal catastrophe, because she herself had become "Mrs. Pope Pius XIV" and even now her womb was "pregnant with a Holy Child" which had to be guarded and protected eternally. These bizarre and self-excoriative fantasies were charged with an intensity of affect difficult to describe but immediately sensed as deeply melancholic by nearly every observer. And yet, despite her apparent suffering, the patient concentrated into her melancholia a wealth of defenses that seemed economically essential if her anxiety was to be made bearable at all. On the one hand the patient condemned herself as a lost soul, automatically excommunicated from the Church because of her "unforgivable sin"—her attempt to murder an unborn child, but, at the same time, she compensated for this guilt by the grandiose and subtly self-preserving fantasy that the entire Church was concerned with her particular conduct. Further, her punishment would be supervised by the Heavenly Court itself Who, in view of her exalted position as the "wife" of a future pontiff, might eventually condone her transgressions and grant them absolution. Similarly, while she confessed her previous wishes for the death of her unwanted baby, she overcompensated for these by a delusion of possessing a deathless child forever reincorporated into her womb. Finally, in her external behavior she made herself actually a helpless being who required all the care and protection of a newborn infant in the midst of a loving and forgiving foster family.

Comment. In this case, then, it may be seen that even frankly psychotic behavior patterns, whether depressive or schizoid, are not, as is sometimes inferred, merely shapeless fragments from a personality shattered by some hypothetical "mental disease"; on the contrary, the psychosis itself is an integrated syndrome which, however socially deviant, is adaptively operative at all "levels" from the physiologic to the most abstrusely symbolic.

Regression. By regression is meant the readoption, under circumstances of deprivation, frustration or conflict, of behavior patterns associated with earlier and more satisfactory experiences. Normally, this may mean a strategic retreat from current stresses into previous modes of thought and conduct, followed by a redirection of energies into new experiences and explorations until, by trial and error, more satisfactory adaptations are found. As a borderline example, a man who is dissatisfied with a contentious and unsuccessful marriage and who longs for his premarital freedom, might act as though he were again a bachelor by not supporting his wife, keeping his own hours, having extramarital affairs, and so on; nevertheless, whatever our moral judgments, the man could be said to show *regressive character traits* only if, after divorce and remarriage to a more deserving woman, he continued such patterns and showed no tendency to resume mature habits of responsibility and self-discipline.

NEUROTIC REGRESSIONS. These usually denote a reversion to much earlier (i.e., childlike or infantile) patterns of conduct rather than a retrial of other relatively mature ones. Obviously, there are no really sharp demarcations among the various dynamic "stages" of "normal," neurotic or psychotic regression, since not even in the psychoses (cf. App. 4) is there a literal reenactment of early patterns totally unmodified by resi-

Plate I

A seventeen-year-old girl (A) was brought to a psychiatric clinic by her mother with the complaint that for the preceding five months her behavior had become increasingly irrational and destructive. The history revealed that after the patient was about four years old her parents had begun to quarrel violently, making her early environment extremely contentious and unstable. At about this age she first developed various neurotic traits: nail-biting, temper-tantrums, enuresis and numerous phobias. When the patient was seven the mother refused further sexual relations with the father and left the marital bed, but the patient continued to sleep with the father until she was thirteen. At this time the mother suspected that the patient was being incestuously seduced, obtained legal custody of the girl and moved away with her to a separate home. The patient resented this, quarreled frequently with her mother, became a disciplinary problem at home and at school and acquired a police record for various delinquencies. Three years later, at the patient's insistence, she and her mother paid an unexpected visit to the father, and found him living with another girl in questionable circumstances. In a violent scene, the mother denounced the father for unfaithfulness and, again contrary to the patient's wishes, took her home. There the patient refused to attend school and rapidly became sullen, withdrawn and non-communicative. During her mother's absence at work she would keep the house in disorder, destroy clothes her mother had made for her, and throw her mother's effects out of the window. During one of these forays she discovered a photograph of herself at the age of five (B), which, incidentally, was so poorly lighted and faded that, for one detail, it did not show her eyebrows. Using this as a pattern, she shaved off her own eyebrows, cut her hair to the same baby bob, and began to affect the facial expression and sitting posture of the pictured child (C). When brought to the hospital her general behavior was correspondingly childish; she was untidy and enuretic, giggled incessantly or spoke in simple monosyllabic sentences, spent most of her time on the floor playing with blocks, or paper dolls, and had to be fed, cleaned and supervised as though she were an infant. In effect, she appeared to have regressed to a relatively desirable period in life antedating disruptive jealousies and other conflicts; moreover, she acted out this regression in unconsciously determined but strikingly symbolic patterns of eliminating the mother as a rival and regaining the father she had lost in her childhood.

Plate I. **The symbolisms of regression.***

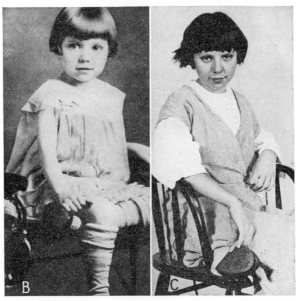

* Thanks are due to Dr. John Romano, Professor of Psychiatry, University of Rochester, and to Dr. Richard Renneker for providing the photographs and data for Plate I.

dues of later experience. Every person tends, consciously or not, to re-adopt puerile patterns when faced with severe disappointment, disease or other serious threat to his well-being. Certainly, every physician, attorney and minister soon becomes familiar with the fact that those who come to him physically, socially or spiritually in trouble approach him with the same plaintive dependence with which a child unloads its burdens on a trusted parent. Regressive ambivalences, as we have seen, become particularly evident in the process of psychoanalysis and may then have the specific content of the mixed loves and hatreds which the patient previously felt toward his parents and which are now "trans-ferred" to the analyst. However, equally frank manifestations of regression may be observed outside the analytic process if the emotional stresses become sufficiently great. The war furnished many examples which could be typified as follows:

Case 22.   Acute regression, combat neurosis

A soldier, normally well-disciplined and self-reliant but subjected overlong to physical exhaustion and the unremitting hell of combat and carnage in the ever-present shadow of death, eventually reached his limit of tolerance and thereafter showed a gradual dissolution of adult habit patterns and an ac-celerating return to childlike and then infantile behavior. First, his intellectual interests and activities became dulled and his affective reactions progressively more labile and primitive; concurrently he began to neglect habits of personal hygiene, even to the point of careless evacuation and soiling. Next he became preoccupied with hazy dreaming of the comforts and security of his own home; finally, in sudden desperate denial of all mature considerations of pres-tige, duty, discipline or even physical danger, he abandoned his weapons, cried out against all about him and fell to the earth sobbing piteously and inconsolably for his mother. During this extreme reaction threats of further discipline or even death were useless; the soldier had to be evacuated as a psychiatric casualty, permitted for the time being to cling emotionally to a kindly therapist as a parent-surrogate, and thereafter treated by every means at hand to restore his self-confidence, his group loyalties and his normal de-fenses against anxiety to prevent his regression becoming fixed at the level of phobic, helpless passivity.

In military psychiatry, reactions such as these are relatively frequent and their accompanying regression may take a rapid course from pre-monitory to acute stages; fortunately, however (cf. Part Two), prompt and skillful treatment may reverse the process. In civilian neuroses (ex-cept those occurring after catastrophes) regressive behavior is less extreme, but more chronic and more subtly intertwined with other neu-rotic defenses. Moreover, the secondary regressive gains of the neuroses (such as relief from onerous responsibilities, repression or deviation of aggression and the attainment of protective familial or other care) are less easily controlled than in military practice, and therefore make the treatment of chronic civilian neuroses usually more complex and difficult.

PSYCHOTIC REGRESSION.   This term is used when the regressive processes have become deeply fixated, bizarrely symbolic, highly disrup-tive to the social functions of the patient and almost completely unap-proachable by ordinary therapeutic means. Examples of such extreme stages of regression may be seen by the thousands in the back wards of mental hospitals: patients who, whatever the original diagnosis of their psychosis, have "deteriorated" into infantile habits such as thumb-sucking, soiling, inability to clothe and feed themselves, polymorphous auto-erotic activities and almost neonate helplessness* (cf. Plate I).

Schizophrenic dynamisms

Finally, there is open to the personality under extreme stress an *ultima Thule* of reactions that are usually grouped under the term *schizophrenia*. As will be seen, these may forestall complete disintegration, but, to use a tactical analogy, they are accompanied by the shattering of so many previous defenses, the loss of so many useful forces or so great a retreat and containment that, from the standpoint of reality control, the conflict may often be regarded as having been almost irretrievably lost. Specifically, these final schizophrenic maneuvers may be considered from a dynamic and developmental standpoint under the following headings.

Withdrawal from "external contacts." As we have seen, very serious adaptational traumata may occur in the first few years of childhood (Chapter 3) and may be exacerbated by the physiologic and social stresses of puberty. It is possible, therefore, for a child to begin to withdraw from a world he interprets as frustrating and hostile at an early age, and to show an accentuation of this withdrawal into circumscribed narcissistic isolation in fantasy and action during the increased stresses of adolescence—a syndrome that led to the Kraepelinian term "dementia praecox." In early life, this introversive retreat may take the form of a lack of interest in, or the loss of previous contacts with, parents, siblings, playmates, school, hobbies, sports and other socializing activities; later, the generalized constriction and "autistic" withdrawal, especially in those intellectually endowed, may be signalized by an ominously exclusive pre-occupation with one narrow field of interest which prejudices a progressive, rounded development of the social personality. This may first appear as a marked ambivalence in interpersonal relationships so that the patient is by turn uneasily affectionate or tensely aloof; later he may show strained, explosive deviations of affect and progressive "interpersonal distancing." Concurrently, there may be an insidious or rapid dissolution of learned social customs and amenities, e.g., in habits of sleep, diet, study, dress and cleanliness. Libidinous expressions are apt to show corresponding aberrations: tumultuous, headlong infatuations, dreamy over-idealism, or guilt-ridden asceticism leading eventually to a distortion of all social transactions. During various stages of this process those with whom the schizophrenic comes in contact begin to sense his suspicious isolation and remoteness, and their own unconsciously defensive reactions serve to accelerate his withdrawal. Unfortunately, by the time psychiatric aid is sought there may have been established so great a breach in all interpersonal relationships that a therapeutic transference and rapport can be gained, if at all, only with the greatest skill and patience.

---

* As will be seen in subsequent clinical discussions, however, this "deteriorative" process does not imply organic cerebral degeneration.

Blunting and distortion of affect. It is, nevertheless, impossible for a person to exist completely walled off from all external impressions, and some of these must necessarily penetrate even the most deeply fortified self-isolation. To ameliorate the anxiety accompanying such apperceptions the schizophrenic may either deny their personal significance, or invest them with a distorted or less painful affective charge. The first process produces what is usually described as "emotional shallowness" or "emptiness," whereas the second characterizes the schisms "between thought content and affective tone" that give schizophrenia ("split mind") its graphic name.* These phenomena, like the peculiarly impenetrable resistance of the schizophrenic to attempts at interpersonal communication, are much more easily learned by clinical experience than from didactic description, but the following example may serve to illustrate some of the typical patterns.

Case 23. Schizophrenic distortion of affect

A fifteen-year-old girl was brought into the hospital by her parents, who stated that she had been sent home from a preparatory school with the recommendation from the school physician that the patient consult a psychiatrist for "a serious nervous breakdown." The patient was at first non-communicative, and since the parents had not been observant and were now defensive, the history of the patient's illness was obtained only in fragmentary form. However, as finally assembled from all available sources, including the patient's former physicians and schoolmates, the anamnesis was substantially as follows:

The patient's father was a successful lawyer whose political and other connections kept him in a continuous round of travel about the country. The patient's mother had artistic pretensions and, since she was wealthy in her own right, she continued to be preoccupied with the organization of clubs, exhibitions, artists' benefits, and other such activities. The marriage of the patient's parents had been a socially convenient, almost loveless affair, but since they each led a fairly full life they needed each other little and had few clashes of interests. There had therefore been few overt quarrels between them; on the contrary they both liked to think of their marriage as a model of modern "compatibility" between two "emancipated" people. Unfortunately for the patient, this superficiality of her parents' marital relationships and the diversity of their outside interests frustrated her needs for security and warmth in her early formative years; nor were her longings in this respect satisfied by a succession of children's maids, governesses and nursery schools. Similarly, the child was raised with the best of medical advice, but despite regulated diets and multiple immunizations, she fed poorly, was inactive and remained sickly and underweight. Moreover, she became what the parents called a "delicate and very sensitive child," subject to night-terrors, episodes of morose stubbornness, and impulsive attachments or aversions. A particularly illuminating instance of the nature of these reactions occurred on her seventh birthday. The parents had given her an elaborate children's party with many presents, including a set of expensive sleeping dolls, and had also promised her that they themselves would "now stay home with her for a long time." The

---

* Proposed by Bleuler, who correctly pointed out that, since schizophrenic reactions neither led to inevitable dementia nor necessarily occurred only at puberty, the Kraepelinian term *dementia praecox* was an inaccurate generic designation for all such processes.

next day, however, they each again departed on separate trips, with only the explanation that they had made the promise "so as not to spoil the party." On their return about a week later they found that the patient had destroyed all of her dolls, forcibly taken a ragged one from a neighbor child, and insisted on keeping this doll with her wherever she went. Soon thereafter the patient developed enuresis and an accentuation of her night terrors, which were now no longer mitigated by the increasingly impatient reassurances of her parents or nurses. Various medical and dietary treatments for these symptoms were tried without marked success, until a physician advised "a change of scene for the child." The patient was therefore sent to live with her paternal grandparents—a kindly though somewhat senile couple who, ignoring the parents' advice, "spoiled" the child and permitted her various indulgences, including permission to sleep with them. The enuresis and night terrors abated after several months, but the child developed peculiar dietary habits and continued to have moods of abstraction during which she would chant ditties of nonsense syllables while repeating apparently meaningless gestures and poses. After nine months' stay with her grandmother, she was returned to her own home because of a circumstance that her family tried to keep completely secret: the grandfather, after several outbursts of violence, had had to be committed to an institution for paresis. The family, worried that the patient may have "caught syphilis" from her grandfather, arranged for her to have another series of physical examinations. It was during these that the first definitely psychotic disturbances were noted; the child showed abject terror at the approach of the physician, and when forced to undergo the examination, entered into a semi-stupor in which she seemed not to hear, could not be made to speak, and would partially retain any posture in which she was placed. Somewhat later, the family gathered various bits of information that indicated that the child's repetitive miming and her terror of the physical examination dated from various sexual abuses to which she had been subjected by the grandfather. In any case, the patient's pavor nocturnus and spells of immobility, mutism and unapproachability became more frequent and alarming. A non-medical "child expert" and various physicians were again consulted, but no diagnosis was reached other than that the child possibly had a disorder of the thymus gland which, it was hoped, she would eventually "outgrow."

Since the patient could not be sent to either a public or private school because her behavior might elicit comment and gossip unfavorable to the family, a private governess was obtained for her. Fortunately, this individual was a warm, maternal woman who took a genuine liking to the child, and the latter in turn began to reciprocate her affection. After some months the patient began to take an interest in her studies and to learn quite rapidly. During the next three years, moreover, she also acquired increasing spontaneity, interest and ease in her interpersonal relationships although, again to guard against scandal, her extrafamilial contacts were guarded and kept at a minimum. A setback occurred at the time of her menarche, when it was discovered that she had been so frightened by the onset of her periods that she had worn rags and washed her own underclothes for months without daring to tell even her tutor. Nevertheless, in view of her seeming improvement, when she was fifteen the parents decided to send her to a private seminary for girls. The patient showed neither enthusiasm nor overt resistance to the plan, and accompanied the family docilely to the school. However, "matriculation" (in the symbolic sense of establishing an emancipatory relationship to an "alma mater") was completely unsuccessful: she developed no interests in her teachers, her work, her associates or in the school activities, and when she was pressed to fulfill even the minimal requirements, her behavior again deteriorated rapidly. As reported by the principal she became increasingly awkward and shy, frequently sat vacant and unheeding in her classroom, began to mark her books and papers with strange designs, and became subject to sudden outbursts of peculiarly unemotional weeping or laughter with no apparent provocation. One cold night she was discovered wandering about the campus in her nightgown and, when questioned, told an almost incoherent, strangely unconcerned story of how her roommates had burned the dormitory down because God Himself had told them the housemother was wicked. The patient was returned home and soon afterwards admitted to the hospital.

On the observation ward her behavior was quite evidently abnormal. She waved her hands, blinked her eyes and tossed her head in bizarre repetitive gestures interrupted by periods of blank immobility. She would not wash her face or body because "they might wash away," but would comb her hair for hours if permitted to do so. She refused to speak to any of the nurses, whom she identified as "delegates from the school," and would talk to the psychiatrist only after he removed his spectacles so that he "could not look right through" her. She was perfectly oriented for time and place, yet she stated with little apparent concern that the hospital call system was broadcasting her thoughts in Morse code "to all nurses," and that she was certain to be "brexed" (a neologism apparently compounded of "bruised," "raped" and "sexed") unless the "FBI lawyers," who were then mobilizing, were summoned to her rescue by the "Queen Mother." In any case, the psychiatrist, too, was "a good lawyer" and would help her—in fact, he must do so, since she had deliberately touched the marriage ring which he wore. The latter fantasy appeared again and again, and was often accompanied by a brief series of tearless, empty, tic-like sobs.

Unfortunately, the patient's parents, horrified and humiliated by "insanity appearing for the first time in our family," showed their hostilities toward the child even more clearly by demanding that we give her "modern shock therapy" immediately. They remained adamant in refusing to listen to explanations that, at this stage, drastic treatment would in all probability permanently harm the patient, and after a week removed her from the hospital.

Comment. This case illustrates a number of schizophrenic dynamisms—among them "concretization" of fantasy and spread of symbolism (e.g., the psychiatrist's ring, which allied her with her "lawyer" father), *projections* of her own impulses onto others ("the girls—not I— wished to burn the dormitory down"), defensive ego-aggrandizement in the face of deep anxieties (I am the object of concern to the "FBI" and the "Queen Mother") and, finally, an almost impenetrable narcissistic isolation from realistic interpersonal contacts. But perhaps the most outstanding feature was the defensive numbing of the patient's affective reactions: fear, rage and laughter were displaced or dissociated from their real or fantastic context, and lost their poignancy in a shallow travesty of true affect.

Thinking disturbances in schizophrenia. The example cited may also serve as an introduction to the distortions of thought processes common in schizophrenic reactions. These may be considered dynamically under the following headings:

REORGANIZATION OF "CATEGORIES." As we have seen, every individual, "abnormal" or not, has his own set of experientially contingent "categories" of time, space, systematization, sequence and "causality"; in fact, it is an age-old metapsychologic question whether the rubrics used by any two persons exactly agree, or whether any set can be shown to correspond with a postulated "reality." In addition, the subjective categories of an individual vary widely with changes in his psychobiologic status: for example, his distinctions and groupings of phenomena will be changed by accumulating experience; his "reasoning" process will depend on prejudices modified by the circumstances and mood of the current moment; his time "drags" when he is alertly anxious and "flies" when he is contentedly occupied; a tiny dental cavity ordinarily imperceptible to his tongue seems to grow to enormous proportions when the tooth begins to ache, and all concepts and their relationships are greatly altered by toxicity or the neurologic deficits and reorganizations resulting from a cerebral lesion (cf. Goldstein, Brickner et al.). But the schizophrenic, unable to abide even the usual approximations by social agreement as to time, space and causality, reorganizes his world into startlingly different categories of his own. Beginning, perhaps, with distortions of his own body image and vital tempo (Schilder) he changes his conceptions of time, space and logical order, and either reconstitutes their relationships or frees himself of their confines altogether.* This process may be seen on specific "tests" (cf. the *Practice,* Chapter 6); for instance, the schizophrenic will make highly unusual images out of the white spaces or minute details of the Rohrschach ink-blots, instead of seeing the large black figures "obvious" to everyone else. Similarly, when asked to arrange wooden blocks by color, size or weight in the Vigotsky test, a schizophrenic may group them instead by fantastic criteria of his own, e.g., blocks which are "good soldiers" as distinguished from "wicked" ones (Hanfmann and Kasanin). Nor need even the dimensions of "normal" orientation such as those of space, time, quality or value remain discrete in the thinking of the schizophrenic; on the contrary, these are mutually transmutable in his solipsistic universe, into which further experience can enter with difficulty, and only when clothed with markedly deviated symbolization and significance. Such schizophrenic aberrations of ideation and "reified" fantasy are then reflected in the striking symptoms that characterize the clinical course of the psychosis.

SENSORIAL DISTURBANCES. Since the schizophrenic, remote from external "reality" and unmindful of social consequences, acts in accordance with his distorted affect and ideation, his behavior appears to others to be characterized by *illusions, hallucinations* and *delusions.* These may be considered from a dynamic standpoint as follows:

ILLUSIONS. These are perceptual "misidentifications" of the sensory field, and as such they may range from the everyday and accepted "normal," to the grossly deviant phenomena seen in toxic or schizophrenic states. Gestalt psychology has demonstrated that we "normally" perceive stimuli as we become accustomed to categorize them: we "close" gaps

---

* The Gestalt concept of "intuitive" recognition of presumed universal space-time "configurations" (ah-ah *Erlebnis* or "insight") nowhere shows its inadequacy as a dynamic theory of learning more clearly than in the fantasy life and behavior of the schizophrenic (cf. Wertheimer).

to produce comfortably "whole" figures; we prefer to reconstruct known geometric patterns when an infinity of choice is possible (e.g., a penny is seen as "round" from any angle); we "recognize" indeterminate pictures of persons and scenes, and so on; in other words, we organize our sensory perceptions according to certain experientially predetermined "sets." Here again, however, biodynamic factors play a prominent role. For instance, in the "hypnagogic" state between sleeping and waking illusions are easily produced and given momentary credence: the room may appear inverted with the body suspended in mid-air; objects may seem to breathe or move in capricious fancy; time stands still, or is accelerated, or reversed. Should orientation, organization and other corrective "judgments" be concurrently impaired by drugs or toxins, such illusions may become continuous and exceedingly fantastic: e.g., the wall-paper design becomes filled with talking faces, or the chandelier a dangling gallows. Finally, with an extension of such apperceptual deviations channelized by wishful and dereistically symbolic thinking, the schizophrenic may "recognize" his dead mother's voice in the clatter of the hospital food-cart, or "see" his wife in the smoke outside the window, or "feel the radio waves sent out by the Masons" in the prickle of his bed-clothes.

HALLUCINATIONS.   These are percepts formed without any readily apparent "external" sensory stimuli. In dreams, such fantasies are partially freed from the sensorial and repressive inhibitions that control waking consciousness, and the universe is hallucinated in wishfully determined symbols; in fact, for a short period after waking, "actual" reality may seem for a time the stranger of the two. In the psychoses this socially required reorientation to an inimical reality is rejected—a circumstance that led Bleuler to characterize schizophrenia strikingly as a "waking dream" in which elemental wishes break through into hallucinatory and delusional behavior with only a thin veneer of displacements, condensations, projections and other defensive symbol-associations. A brief illustration may suffice:

Case 24. Schizophrenic hallucinations

A twenty-three-year-old woman with a markedly schizoid personality, paranoid tendencies and precarious "reality" adjustments was informed by her husband that he was soon to be drafted into the army. She reacted with feelings of deep insecurity and fantasies of regression to former sexual, familial and other relationships. Two days later she asked him if it was not possible that his selection had been "arranged" by a girlhood paramour of hers who had "fixed" it so that he could in this manner have the patient for himself. The husband, busy with his army induction, dismissed this as just a bit more bizarre than her usually queer ideas, and departed on schedule. Soon, however, the patient began to detect a peculiar taste in her food and noted that she was continually aroused sexually; this confirmed her suspicions that her paramour was drugging her food so as to seduce her. One morning a week later, after an erotic dream, she awoke to "see" this man "leering" into her window, and concluded that he had also hypnotized her while she slept. She upbraided him and he disappeared, only to return that afternoon. This time she called the police, who found no evidence of an intruder; however, at her demand, they issued a warrant for his arrest. Fortunately, it was found that the accused had moved to another city several weeks before his alleged attempts at poisoning and seduction. The Red Cross was called in, communicated with the husband at his army camp, arranged for a psychiatric examination of the woman and supervised her commitment to a private sanatorium.

This case illustrates a function which may in other circumstances be hidden by a more highly displaced and distorted symbolism: namely, that hallucinations are often projected pictorializations of narcissistic, aggressive or erotic conflicts. Since no one of the opposed wishes involved can be completely fulfilled without violating one or more of the others, hallucinations, like nightmares, may contain a large element of frustration and anxiety derived from the unconscious conflict they express. When the integrative capacities of the individual are further impaired by drugs, disease or cerebral injuries, the hallucinations assume the characteristically kaleidoscopic, disorganized, fear-ridden forms seen in hyperpyrexia, delirium tremens and other toxic states.

DELUSIONS. These are systems of concepts and beliefs which, though considered irrational by the cultural group to which the individual belongs, are nevertheless necessary to his psychic economy and therefore immune to argument and reason. Delusions may, indeed, be differentiated from the closely related phenomena of prejudices, superstitions and religious fanaticisms only by this criterion of relative rejection in culture and time; i.e., the accepted philosophy of one society is pagan fanaticism to another, and our own common beliefs of today will be the residual superstitions of the ignorant tomorrow. An example of a system of beliefs that would be considered psychotic by most people, yet was once accepted as self-evident fact, will be cited in relation to the cultural determinants of delusions (cf. p. 81).

In the unconscious dynamics of the individual, delusions, like other sensorial aberrations, subserve a number of inter-related *projective economic functions:* for instance, delusions attribute to other persons one's own inadmissible desires or ideas (*projective identification*); they blame others for "causing" one's own conduct (*delusions of influence*); they explain irrational behavior on spuriously "logical" grounds (*psychotic rationalizations*); they overcompensate for feelings of isolation through fantasies of being the focus of widespread or universal interest and attention (*ideas of reference*); or they counteract inadequacies or inferiorities by a sense of power (*delusions of grandeur, omniscience and omnipotence*), which has its roots in the transcendent narcissism of infancy. In aberrantly adaptive ways, therefore, the schizophrenic reconstitutes his universe in accordance with repressed unconscious wishes and unattainable fantasies, which are then organized into delusional formations. Nevertheless, the break with cultural norms is rarely absolute even in crystallized schizophrenic reactions, as the following case will illustrate:

Case 25. Schizophrenic delusions

Wanda Viasczinska,* the daughter of intelligent and cultured Czech immigrants, came to this country at the age of eight and was raised in a mar-

---

* All names used in the case histories cited in this volume and in the *Practice* are, of course, fictitious.

ginal slum district° where her father, though an excellent artisan, eked out a
poor living in his metal-working shop. Her older brother, a handsome, energetic lad, was the parent's favorite and received whatever indulgences the
family could afford: e.g., he was supported through high school and into college while the patient had to work to contribute to her own and her family's
support. Wanda, too, was sent to a parochial and later a public high school
where, by dint of her facile intelligence and application, she made excellent
grades during the first two years. However, since her extracurricular time was
so completely occupied and also because her early training had made her shy,
hesitant and self-effacing, she cultivated few social activities and no friends.
Instead, her only interest lay in the secret writing of highly dramatic novelettes and plays. The favorite heroine in these productions was a poor but
talented and beautiful girl who, despite various buffetings of fate, finally won
fortune and acclaim for some artistic masterpiece. In a peculiarly ambivalent
reaction to her family, she became increasingly ashamed of her "un-American-
ized" parents and her poor home surroundings; conversely, she professed
great pride in her popular and successful brother, especially when, in 1941,
he became a volunteer Air Force cadet. But this pride, too, was a private
affair; after his departure from home she became all the more reserved and
solitary, and, when otherwise unoccupied, began to indulge in long and fanciful daydreams, usually as to how she would become a nurse, join her brother
in the American military forces, liberate Czechoslovakia from Germany, and
herself become a world-renowned heroine. The parents were not unobservant
of her progressive isolation and social desuetude, and finally insisted that she
stop working after school in order to have time for normal recreations and
social contacts. The patient compromised by devoting her free time to volunteer war activities, but again selected solitary tasks such as folding and ad-
dressing civilian defense circulars at home. Other peculiarities of behavior
appeared which indicated a developing delusional context; for instance, the
patient suddenly decided to change her Slavic surname of Viasczinska to the
Anglo-Saxon "Wallace," and thereafter became infuriated if anyone used her
original name. The patient went out on a few dates on her parents' insistence,
but compared her companions openly and unfavorably to her idealized
brother, violently resented their tentative sexual advances and soon dropped
further contacts in this direction. Her grades during the last year of high
school dropped rapidly as her work became disorganized and fragmentary,
but although a few of her teachers noted the patient's growing peculiarities,
she was lost in the mass-education "platoon system" of the school and given
no individual attention or guidance.

The break that precipitated her frank psychosis occurred under these circumstances; one day the family received word that the patient's brother, far
from making a success in the Air Force, had actually been responsible for a
serious accident, and had been dismissed from training because of recklessness
and incompetence. The patient's reaction to this news was definitely abnormal; she assured her parents that although the notice received was "possibly
a joke," it was more probably the Government's test of their loyalty and
patriotism. Two days later the patient suddenly announced during a recital
in class that her brother was now the leading air ace of the war, and supported this assertion by displaying a newspaper bearing a photograph and
description of a flyer who in no way resembled her brother. When these dis-
crepancies were pointed out to her by an astonished teacher she explained
them in a mysterious, disconnected manner on the basis of "military secrecy"

° Cf. Faris and Dunham for a discussion of the "ecology of schizophrenia."

and asserted further—but with little emotion—that Nazi spies who were in conflict with "American pilgrims" were after her at that moment not only because of her brother, but to prevent her "from writing a book that would give away my information to make Czechoslovakia greater than Germany." Since the patient's behavior was now obviously psychotic, she was hospitalized soon after this episode. By this time her ideation and speech, disjointed or frequently blocked at best, was rendered even more incoherent by occasional *neologisms*, such as "frisgrace," by which the patient apparently meant a combination of "fame" and "disgrace." She wrote long letters to her brother "in the Czechoslovak Air Force," but the manuscripts consisted of criss-cross undecipherable writing and were illustrated by unexplained symbolisms of intertwined forms. One other episode was significant: with great difficulty, the patient was one day induced to join a group in a simple game of throwing darts at little wooden dwarf-like figures. She played mechanically and desultorily until quite by accident she hit one of the male figurines, whereupon she suddenly recoiled, gestured wildly and then fell to the floor in seeming oblivion. Later she explained vaguely that by her act she had not only "knocked her brother from the skies" but had, in some universal manner, injured all fliers everywhere.

Comment. An analysis of these and other fantasies and reactions indicated that this patient's delusional system, bizarre and unorganized as it was, nevertheless had specific meanings and subserved definitely compensatory functions. Thus, she displaced her reactive hostility toward her parents onto a condemnation of their "foreign customs" and even their surname, yet indicated her regressive yearnings for reunion with them by her allegiance to Czechoslovakia, her identifications with their favored son, and her rejections of social or sexual emancipations from the home. The brother-symbol at the same time served other purposes: it supported her claims to security in this country (reflected also in her fanatic patriotism, her alliance with "American pilgrims," etc.); it signified her own displaced masculine wishes, and it expressed her overcompensatory desires to rise from rejection and obscurity to fame and power through a delusional idealization of her brother. Nevertheless, her jealousies could not be denied, and they shone through in her literally self-paralyzing guilt when she hit the wooden figure with her dart and so "knocked him from the skies." Moreover, however displaced and condensed these fantasies were, they still approached too closely to her deepest anxieties and therefore had to be robbed, in typical schizophrenic fashion, of continuity, organization and emotional tone, especially when they dealt with symbolically pressing events.

CULTURAL SCHIZOPHRENIA. In the middle ages it was widely believed that agents of the Devil in the form of incubi and succubi "possessed" and inhabited persons who had made unholy compacts to sell their souls in exchange for earthly power over the devout. An official treatise, called the Malleus Maleficarum, was issued during the Inquisition to aid in the detection of such persons, and in it were described in detail certain typical experiences and identifying marks (such as an area of anesthesia outlining a "devil's claw"), by which a suspected "witch" could be condemned. It is a matter of record that many thousands of persons, though obviously psychotic by present-day standards, partici-

Plate II.   An influencing machine.*

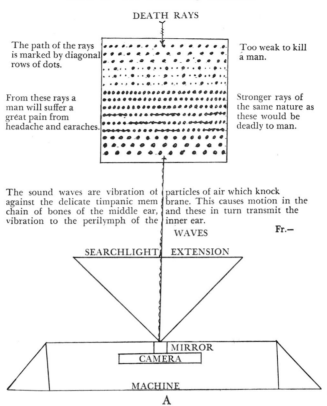

DEATH RAYS

The path of the rays is marked by diagonal rows of dots.

Too weak to kill a man.

From these rays a man will suffer a great pain from headache and earaches.

Stronger rays of the same nature as these would be deadly to man.

The sound waves are vibration of particles of air which knock against the delicate timpanic membrane. This causes motion in the chain of bones of the middle ear, and these in turn transmit the vibration to the perilymph of the inner ear.

WAVES   Fr.—

SEARCHLIGHT EXTENSION

MIRROR
CAMERA
MACHINE

A

A forty-year-old paranoiac drew these diagrams of a mysterious "machine" which, he claimed retrospectively, his "enemies" had been using since his birth to read and control his thoughts and feelings, govern his actions through "hip-not-ism" and "electronic waves," cause him to entertain evil sexual and other forbidden desires, and suffer trances, illnesses or, if they finally willed it, eventual death. The patient's persecutors were vaguely and variously identified as secret police, "astrologers," or supernatural cosmic agents possessed of an omnipotent influence called "Sumna Loqui" (the "highest word"?) but presumably jealous of his own great powers. These delusions evidently served a number of purposes: they replaced feelings of failure and deep inadequacy with fantasies of vicarious self-aggrandizement; they projected his erotic, homosexual and destructive impulses onto others and thus relieved him of responsibility for any counter-action he might take, and, less directly, they made it necessary for him to regress, in effect, to the custodial safety of a psychiatric hospital. The fixity of the patient's basic delusional formations is symbolized by the fact that, although the patient drew many diagrams of this machine, the ground plan of the construction was always the same and the objects it influenced varied within narrow limits (compare A and B).

* The author is indebted to Dr. Adrian H. VanderVeer for the material of Plate II. For a psychoanalytic discussion of the concept of an influencing machine cf. Tausk (1933).

Plate II. *Continued*

SOUND WAVES TO BE HEARD

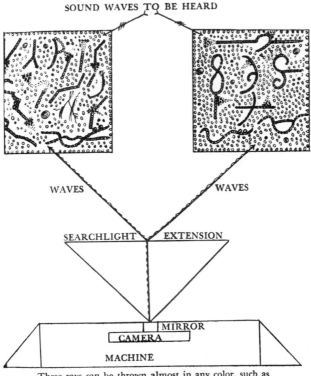

WAVES   WAVES

SEARCHLIGHT   EXTENSION

MIRROR

CAMERA

MACHINE

These rays can be thrown almost in any color, such as red, dark red, blue and silver.

B

pated so thoroughly in the beliefs of the time that they freely "confessed" hallucinated experiences with the Devil himself, almost gleefully pointed out the "marks" he had left on their bodies and claimed great powers as a result of these dealings. From the accounts of the various Inquisitors it appears that in many cases such delusions, although they made torture and death almost inevitable, yet had their functions; the victim was either convinced of his thaumaturgic powers and immune to the reality of his danger, or he was equally certain that his immolation was only an adventurous step to some other, more desirable non-earthly existence.

So also in later times psychotics have appropriated and distorted the popular beliefs of the day. For instance, in the early nineteenth century, after various misconceptions of "mesmerism" had been popularized, many persons believed themselves to be influenced by some known or unknown "hypnotist" who compelled them to act "against their will"— although it was usually demonstrable that what they were "compelled" to do really expressed their own inhibited and deviated desires (p. 149 f.). Later, and again running parallel with popular misconceptions of current physical science, psychotic individuals attributed their hallucinated sensations or experiences to "phlogiston," "magnetism" or "electricity." Today "radio waves," "radar" or even "atomic energy" is the mysterious all-penetrating tool of the nefarious "They," the eternally depersonalized persecutors of the psychotic (cf. Plate II). In this way, delusions, though they constitute a distortion of "reality," nevertheless reveal an indissoluble residue of the individual's experiences and culturally conditioned interpretations.

Disturbances in motor patterns.   Examples of psychotic motor patterns have already been cited in connection with Cases 20 to 25. Other disturbances particularly associated with schizophrenic reactions may take the following forms:

STEREOTYPY.   By this is meant a tendency to fixity (*posturing, attitudinizing*) or repetitiousness of behavior in thought (*autochtony*), word (*verbigeration*) or deed (*stereotypy*).* Dynamically, this concentration on one recurrent behavior pattern may serve to exclude other less acceptable ones, whereas the one selected may itself express certain obscure and deviated wishes, as condensed either into newly formed words (*neologisms*) or as symbolized by repetitive gestures and movements. The following is a clinical example.

Case 26.   Schizophrenic stereotypies

A Polish woman who had been in a state psychiatric hospital for two years did little all day but sit humped over a stool repeating the sound "Boligo!" and making a peculiar downward swoop with her right hand, followed by a waving, pushing motion of her palm. Her left arm, which was held motionless, showed a marked atrophy of disuse, whereas the musculature of her right shoulder and arm was hypertrophied from her apparently tireless exercise. The patient would struggle against any interference with her stereotyped motions; if they were forcibly restrained, she would go into a state of mute, semi-catatonic passivity, only to resume her chant and gestures upon release. One day a matronly attendant of Polish origin was assigned to duty in the ward, and, because of their ethnic kinship, began to take particular interest in the patient. The latter responded slowly and suspiciously, but after several weeks began to converse hesitantly in Polish with the newcomer. Through this relationship some history was obtained, in the light of which the patient's behavior could in part be interpreted. Briefly, the patient had emigrated from Poland at seventeen and had been given no opportunity to attend school or even learn more than a few words of English. Instead, she had been almost immediately apprenticed by her family to a middle-aged tailor, whom she was forced to marry two years later. He had mistreated her from the start and soon after marriage added beatings and various sexual abuses to their relationship. The patient appealed to her family, but their cultural attitude and religious convictions made correction of the situation impossible. The patient's repressed hostilities to her husband and children took various forms, among them an obsessive fear that her cooking might harm them; later this changed to a delusional conviction that she had already poisoned them and was therefore excommunicated from the Church. Unfortunately, she was committed to a state hospital where no one spoke her language or gave her any but the barest custodial care; under these circumstances, her habit patterns deteriorated rapidly into the peculiar stereotypies previously described. Symbolically, these consisted of a common Polish word of her childhood, "boli,"

---

* Cf. Schneider (1938) and Goldstein (1942) for a discussion of possible organic factors in such processes.

meaning "pain," combined with the English word "go." This wishful combination "pain, go!" was accompanied endlessly by the sweeping motion of a tailor working his needle (symbolically, her husband), terminated with the palm-outward, pushing gesture of avoidance and dismissal.

CATATONIA. This may be simply a generalized muscular immobility and lack of reaction to stimulation signifying narcissistic isolation and apathy, or it may be accompanied by the phenomenon of *flexibilitas cerea,* by which is meant a tendency of the catatonic to maintain, with seemingly indifferent passivity, any posture in which he is placed. Closely allied to this are the relatively rare phenomena of *echolalia* and *echopraxia,* in which the patient "echoes" the words or mimes the action of the examiner and so seems to make a distant mockery of interpersonal rapport and communication.

In contrast, a *negativistic* patient will resist all manipulation and, if force is used, may attempt to substitute the precisely converse motor pattern. As may be expected, such patients, between periods of relative quiet, are subject to *catatonic furors* characterized by rapidly changing hallucinations and delusions, wild excitement and violent hyperactivity that may be homicidally or suicidally dangerous.

Further implications of such dynamisms will be discussed in relation to the diagnosis and therapy of the psychoses in Chapter 14 of this volume and in Part IV of the *Practice.*

References

Arieti, S.: Interpretation of Schizophrenia.
Auerbach, A. (Ed.): Schizophrenia.
Bellak, L.: Dementia Praecox; Manic-Depressive Psychoses.
Bleuler, E.: Dementia Praecox: The Group of Schizophrenias.
Bleuler, E.: Textbook of Psychiatry (Sections on Manic-Depressive Psychoses and Schizophrenia).
Cameron, N.: The Functional Psychoses.
Davidson, H.: Forensic Psychiatry.
Fromm-Reichman, Frieda: Transference Problems in Schizophrenia.
Glueck, S. S.: Mental Disorders and the Criminal Law.
Hanfmann, E., and Kasanin, J.: Conceptual Thinking in Schizophrenia.
Hart, B.: The Psychology of Insanity.
Kraepelin, E.: Text-book of Psychiatry.
McDonald, J. M.: Psychiatry and the Criminal.

Part Two

Biodynamics

Chapter 7

Biodynamic correlates of
current theories of behavior

PART ONE of this book dealt with certain leading formulations of behavior that are implicit in current psychiatric thinking and practice. In this and succeeding chapters of Part Two we shall trace these concepts to their common source in the dynamics of biological functioning and then reconstruct a more comprehensive and integrative *biodynamic* theory of normal and abnormal behavior. We may begin this task with a brief historical and philosophic review.

Scientific development

In his *Cours de philosophie positive,* the French encyclopedist Auguste Comte traced the sciences then known through three evolutionary stages which may here be paraphrased as: first, the theological or mystical; second, the empiric or taxonomic; and third, the positive or dynamic. Applying a similar developmental analysis to the sciences of behavior, we have seen that primitive man, ignorant, overawed and anxiously groping for some explanation of the mysterious world about him, at first was inclined to attribute all phenomena, including his own conduct, to the unfathomable workings of supernatural forces—although, with characteristic egocentricity, he anthropomorphized these forces as gods or demons and naturally assumed that they were primarily concerned with the fate of their "highest creation"—man himself.* Much later, our scientific progenitors, as their observations increased in "objectivity," number and scope, began with a more becoming modesty to note that even if the ultimate origins of things could not be directly ascertained, the phenomena they witnessed could at least be described accurately, compared with each other, and then differentiated into convenient categories. Thus, the science of botany emerged from the legendary "natural history" of Pliny as the various plants were recognized and classified by "species differences" into a system that eventually attained Linnaean completeness. Similarly, in physics and chemistry, various early categories (e.g., the

---

* "It is we [and not any eternal verities] who determine sense-data by our interpretations, who impose structure, who regain from nature, which is infinitely varied, that which our minds have put into nature. We have found a strange footprint on the sands of the unknown. We have devised profound theories, one after another, to account for its origin. At last we have succeeded in reconstructing the creature that made the footprint. And lo! it is our own!"—Sir Arthur Eddington.

Ionic "earth, air, water and fire") were redefined until the known sub-stances in the physical world were identified, given their "proper" names and assigned to their "logical" physical, chemical or other domain. Only a few thinking men recognized then, as many do now, that these rubrics, however temporarily convenient, had no absolute existence or validity and often, indeed, retarded philosophic as well as scientific progress. For example, it is only recently that the ancient Democritean concept of the materialistic "atom," long cherished by physicists and chemists, has dissolved in the light of modern theories of nuclear dynamics and quan-tum mechanics. Instead, following Plato, our taxonomizing forefathers attributed an independent Form (more recently it is called *Existence** or *Being*) to the artificial categories they erected—a custom which, as we shall see, has cost the sciences of behavior particularly dear. Fortunately, scientific workers in other fields eventually found such metaphysical cir-cularities more diverting than helpful, and rediscovered that, after all, the phenomena in our universe of flux and interchange never really held still long enough to be permanently categorized by human fictions. In any case, all fields had to deal with events and their *relationships* rather than with static things—an operational concept that permitted the theory of any science to emerge into its third, or dynamic, phase of development. In this stage any seeming consistencies in the *sequences* of events could be formulated into mathematical "laws" (such as those of thermo-dynamics or of astrophysics) provided that two logically indispensable reservations were continually kept in mind: first, that these "laws" merely expressed current concepts and never represented mystical "forces," transcendent "forms" or "ultimate truths," and, second, that the "laws" themselves were never sacrosanct, but required continuous modification as additional events were observed and new relationships analyzed, how-ever greatly the new formulations differed from the old in range, com-plexity or form of expression.

This brief excursion into the philosophy of sciences has been included because, unfortunately, it has particular relevance to psychiatry—perhaps the most difficult, inclusive and complex of all sciences. For it must be admitted that the science of behavior has in many respects not altogether emerged from either the mystical or the taxonomic stages of its develop-ment, and as yet is only beginning to achieve a holistic and dynamic orientation. Thus, we still think as well as talk uneasily of being "stricken" by "mental disease" or of suffering hysterical "seizures" as though such reactions had quasi-demoniac implications of influence and possession. Or it takes only a glance through some psychiatric writings to see with what spurious neatness men are classified into "types," and with what obliging compliance their infinitely variable behavior patterns are sup-posed to differentiate themselves into convenient nosologic rubrics.

In Chapter 1 we discussed at some length the mystical and quasi-religious approaches to human behavior. Here let us review briefly the development of the second or taxonomic phase of behavior theory.

---

* Cf. Chapter 6. For a brilliant analysis of the inapplicability of Greek existentialism to modern science; also see Chapter V of Dewey's *Logic*. Whitehead, too, has deplored the "concretization of abstractions" as a fundamental error of logic.

"Typology" of behavior

We have seen that even as men speculated on the cryptic determinants of their actions, they also began to observe with greater care *how* their fellow-beings behaved and to distinguish one mode of behavior from another. The most penetrating observations in this respect were made not by our philosophers or psychologists but, as usual, by our poets and dramatists. Thus, Homer and Sophocles portrayed with consummate skill the varieties of human experience that also illumine the plays of Shakespeare, the novelettes of Voltaire, or the pages of Strindberg and Hemingway. Here were no automatons performing with mechanical precision according to some prescribed "type"; on the contrary, all *dramatis personnae*, real or fancied, were seen to be too richly complex for such hollow, predictable puppetry. And yet when self-professed savants began to investigate man's conduct, they neglected its dynamic subtleties and resonant depths in a vain search for a simple typology that would create, by force of edict if necessary, some semblance of order in their studies. This approach was first given a certain philosophic dignity by Theophrastus, Aristotle's successor at the Lyceum of Athens, and, as traceable through La Bruyere and the French characterologists to Allport and other more modern "trait" psychologists, still channels some phenomenologic and psychiatric thinking. A typical instance of such "character analysis" may be quoted from Theophrastus himself (who in his day also excelled in anatomical dissection):

Case 27. The Penurious Man—by Theophrastus

A Penurious Man is one who goes to a debtor to ask for his half-obol interest before the end of the month. At a dinner where expenses are shared, he counts the number of cups each person drinks, and he makes a smaller libation to Artemis than anyone. If someone has made a good bargain on his account and presents him with the bill he says it is too much. When his servant breaks a pot or a plate, he deducts the value from his food. If his wife drops a copper, he moves furniture, beds, chests and hunts in the curtains. If he has something to sell he puts such a price on it that the buyer has no profit. He forbids anyone to pick a fig in his garden, to walk on his land, to pick up an olive or a date. Every day he goes to see that the boundary marks of his property have not been moved. He will dun a debtor and exact compound interest. When he entertains the members of his deme, he is careful to serve very small pieces of meat to them. If he goes marketing, he returns without having bought anything. He forbids his wife to lend anything—neither salt nor lamp-wick nor cinnamon nor marjoram nor meals nor garlands nor cakes for sacrifices. "All these trifles," he says, "mount up in a year." To sum up, the coffers of the penurious man are moldy and the keys rust; they wear cloaks which hardly reach the thigh; a very little oil-bottle supplies them for anointing; they have hair cut short and do not put on their shoes until midday; and when they take their cloak to the fuller they urge him to use plenty of earth so that it will not be spotted so soon.

It is evident that in this interesting literary portrait Theophrastus skillfully elaborates the various expressions of a single "personality trait"—penuriousness—and, indeed, describes behavior patterns recognizable in certain guardians of academic and research purse-strings today. It is equally obvious, however, that in order to preserve this simple unidimensional approach, Theophrastus makes no attempt to canvass the total character of "the penurious man": his taste in music, his bravery in battle, his religious beliefs, his skill and delight in throwing a javelin, or his devotion to his country or his children. And if Theophrastus or his modern disciples were to postulate that special proclivities in these and other fields of human conduct are also to be subsumed under the headings of separate "traits," there still remain the highly important considerations as to the interrelationships of these patterns, their common or multiple dynamic sources, and the circumstances that influence their single or joint expression. In this connection, too, the subjective and social aspects of all "trait" evaluations make their troublesome appearance. For example, it is perhaps significant that none of Theophrastus' thirty classic sketches of various "types" of Athenian character is particularly complimentary to its subject; indeed, Theophrastus, despite his assumed scientific detachment, seems to have regarded his fellow citizens with a cynical, if not a pronouncedly jaundiced eye. And yet would not the man Theophrastus called "penurious" have been regarded by his grateful creditors or heirs as "foresighted" and "thrifty," or, quite conversely, denounced as "miserly" or "heartless" by disappointed aspirants for his benefactions? Moreover, scientific questions of even greater importance arise with regard to the origin, dynamisms and influenceability of the man's behavior. Why did the man become penurious in the first place? Was it "caused" by his genes, his liver, his complexes, or all three and much more? With a given etiologic configuration, under what circumstances is he likely to be more or less penurious? And, if his miserliness has become a burden to himself, his family or his society what, from a pragmatic standpoint, can be done to change him to a way of life more satisfactory to all concerned?

Questions such as these long ago probed the biases, inadequacies, and sterilities of the exclusively descriptive and classificatory approaches to the study of character, and made the development of a dynamic psychology of behavior scientifically necessary. However, before we describe this development, we must consider the application of the categorical method to abnormal behavior in the era of taxonomic psychiatry.

Taxonomic psychiatry

As we have seen, it was Hippocrates who classified human temperaments according to the "four humors" of the body: blood, yellow bile, black bile, and phlegm, and thus gave us the terms *sanguine, choleric, melancholic* and *phlegmatic* for a corresponding "typology" of character. It must be noted, however, that to Hippocrates these merely represented different behavioral *tendencies* which varied in intensity not only from individual to individual, but from time to time in the same individual. Certainly, in his clinical work Hippocrates adhered to relatively few such abstractions; instead, this greatest of ancient physicians recognized and dealt in comprehendingly human terms with the strivings, conflicts, and adaptations of his patients. Thus, it may be remembered that although Hippocrates attributed the symptoms of hysteria in a woman to "a dislocation of the humors," he nevertheless traced her disorder to concealed sexual conflicts, and actually prescribed "indulging the intentions of Nature and lighting the torch of Hymen." Interestingly, Soranus recognized the emotional complications that might arise from such treatment, and therefore criticized his preceptor with the words: "It is folly to think of curing one fury by another . . . good counsel and persuasion alone can effect a cure." In general, it was this type of empathic human insight, implemented by physical reconditioning, individual guidance and social rehabilitation, that constituted the astonishingly "modern" armamentarium for the treatment of what were apparently neurotic illnesses in the Aesclepiad sanatoria over two millennia ago (cf. the *Practice*, Chapter 21).

Unfortunately, this dynamic understanding and eclectic approach to behavior disorders faded with the heyday of Greek medicine and, except for flashes of intuitive insight from men such as Philo or Johannes Weier, most physicians reverted to mystical speculations about the various "diseases" of the "spirit" or "soul." After the Cynic, the Stoic, the Epicurean and other classic and medieval schools of medical philosophy, the science of behavior, when it did not revert to frank mysticism, remained at best in the descriptive and taxonomic phases of development well through the last century; indeed, it is still so regarded by many physicians today.

One other historical theme, however, requires mention; namely, the circumstances under which psychiatry came to be associated with medicine. When, in ancient and again in medieval times, behavior disorders were considered to be of spiritual origin, it was inevitable that they were relegated to the domain of priests and sorcerers who alone claimed to know the secrets of demoniac possession and the proper techniques of religious exorcism. Nevertheless, physicians never quite abandoned their right to diagnose and treat "diseases" of whatever nature, and pressed their claims with increasing courage and insistence after the Renaissance. But this reassociation of psychiatry with the field of medicine exerted a partly unfortunate influence on psychiatric thought, since behavior disorders came to be regarded as "mental diseases" despite the logical absurdity of applying the term "disease," defined as a metabolic disorder or tissue change, to the "mind," conceived as a metapsychologic abstraction. Nevertheless, in quasi-scientific imitation of their medical brethren in other fields, psychiatrists of the nineteenth century began "classifying" deviations of conduct not in terms of the infinite variety and combinations of hereditary, physiologic and experiential factors relevant to the individual case, but as different forms of a few basic "diseases" marshaled into inflexible nosologic systems. This had the salutary effect of stimulating more careful clinical observation of the individual patient; on the other hand, the preconception of fixed entities often impaired a discerning and comprehensive appraisal of the patients' behavior, since the psychiatrist, with Procrustean ruthlessness, cut off from consideration such phenomena as did not seem to fit the standardized cubicle of a prescribed "diagnosis." True, conscientious taxonomists throughout history, e.g., Zeno, Aretaeus, Paracelsus, Scott, Weier and, much more recently, Pinel, Kahlbaum, Kraepelin and Bleuler (cf. the *Practice,* Chapter 21) could not long blind themselves to the fact that every patient manifested *to a greater or less degree* an almost infinite variety of behavioral phenomena belonging to widely different "diagnoses" *; however, the usual reaction of most clinicians was, at best, merely to regard the patient as having a "multiple" or "mixed disease," or, at worst, to construct still other diagnostic entities (e.g., "schizothymia") to resolve the supposed nosologic paradox.

It must not be thought that this general account of the development of the taxonomic phase of psychiatry implies a denial of the usefulness of recording and cross-indexing clinical observations according to some standard nomenclature; on the contrary, the system now in use by the American Psychiatric Association (cf. the *Practice,* Appendix 2) has been found to be an indispensable adjunct to the classification and comparison of psychiatric records and observations, the gathering of vital statistics and other such laudable purposes. It must be evident, nevertheless, that mere description, while it culls various behavioral data for special examination, may at the same time wrench them completely out of their significant context, and that prematurely rigid classifications simply compound this error and lead even further afield from a more integrative understanding of "normal" behavior in its infinite transitions to the "abnormal." Moreover, a peremptory nosology has sometimes tempted its protagonists into the belief that once they have named and classified a behavior disorder they can dismiss the etiologic and clinical problems involved as nearly solved—a complacent and misleading attitude that has again impeded progress.

It was these inadequacies of purely descriptive and classificatory approaches that the various dynamic theories of behavior were designed to correct. We may, then, proceed to a brief review and critique of these theories—particularly behaviorism, psychoanalysis and psychobiology—as heuristic approaches currently most relevant to the biodynamic concepts to be discussed in the remainder of this volume.

Current dynamic theories of behavior

Reflexology and behaviorism

Concepts of behavioristic† theory. In his *Psychology from the Standpoint of a Behaviorist* (1919) John Watson, continuing in the traditions of psychologic associationism established by Hobbes, Berkeley and Hume, and taking the formulations of Sechenov and the work of Pavlov as his immediate paradigms, proposed that a new "objective

---

* With characteristic scientific honesty Linnaeus himself, in his middle years the epitome of biologic classifiers, eventually admitted the ubiquity of transitional forms.

† The adjective "behavioristic" is used in this book with specific reference to Watsonian behaviorism, and should be distinguished from "behavioral" which refers only to the phenomena of observed behavior.

psychology" be founded, based on the cardinal principle that the behavior of any individual is simply the aggregate of his inborn "unconditioned" patterns of reaction as modified only by a later accumulation of "conditioned reflexes." More specifically, Watson believed that the human infant seeks to experience elemental pleasures in simple physiologic satisfactions and, conversely, that the infant has only two innate aversions: those of falling and of loud noises. "External" stimuli directly or indirectly associated with pleasure become "positive" and are subsequently sought after; stimuli associated with displeasure become "negative" and are thereafter avoided. For instance, Watson reported that in his basic experiments he had exposed a baby to a rabbit and a clanging noise simultaneously, and so produced a generalized and persistent fear of animate and inanimate furry objects; conversely, when in later experiments by Jones (1924) and others, the animal gradually was "reassociated" with pleasant experiences such as feeding, the zoophobia disappeared and the rabbit became a "positive" object.* Watson therefore argued that by extending such reactions to the later experiences of each individual, all behavior could be reconstructed as a mechanistic expression of Pavlovian conditioning. In other words, the processes of generalization, extinction, inhibition and counter-conditioning were sufficient to explain human conduct without recourse to introspective artifacts and "epiphenomenologic" abstractions such as are usually called "instinct," "will," "consciousness" and so on.

Critique. The simplicity and seeming objectivity of this approach for a time entranced many psychologists, just as these qualities often attract the beginning student of today. Indeed, Watson's formulae served the very useful purpose of calling attention to the possibility that many of the hallowed shibboleths of introspective psychology were not really indispensable, inasmuch as an "objective" behavioral theory and research methodology could be constructed without them. Nevertheless, Watsonian behaviorism, in the elemental sense just outlined, failed to fulfill this promise in the following respects:†

1. It attempted to apply simple Pavlovian concepts of conditioning to the complexities and contingencies of human behavior, despite the fact that peripheralistic reflexology had already proved inadequate to explain the reactions of lower organisms with much simpler behavior patterns.

2. It attempted to atomize the environment of the individual into discrete "external stimuli" each of which was presumed to produce independent "conditioning," whereas Gestalt psychology had already demonstrated that the environment is perceived and reacted to in interpenetrating wholes (Wertheimer, Köhler).

3. The behavioristic theory of "elementary" satisfactions and aversions was inadequate, since it took into account neither the wide variety of

---

* Bregman (1934), Gauger, Sherman and others were unable to confirm these observations.

† For a more completely documented critique of Pavlovian and Watsonian concepts with reference to experimental evidence, cf. my *Behavior and Neurosis*, 1943, p. 110 ff. and p. 197 ff.

needs and desires present in early life, nor the spontaneous changes and elaborations that occur during the development and maturation of the individual (Gesell, Mittelman). Moreover, the behavioristic denial of the necessity of dealing with consciousness and subjectivity in behavior could not obscure the fact that, after all, these are perhaps the only incontrovertible data in psychology, and perhaps in all of science (McGill).

Because of these and other inadequacies, the formulations of Pavlov and Watson have been greatly extended, modified and supplemented by Guthrie, Tolman, Marquis, Skinner and others until, at least with regard to animal behavior, modern experimenters can offer a fairly specific and integrated set of concepts, capable in part of mathematical formulation (Hull),* and applicable to the laboratory investigation of "pure" stimulus-response and "equivalence" reactions (Klüver), goal-seeking (Warden), frustration (Hunt, Rosenzweig), and the simpler forms of "conditioned" conflict (Liddell, Gantt). Nevertheless, mechanistic behaviorism, however elaborate, has proved to be still too narrow an approach to the complexities of human conduct, and its popularity has steadily waned among educators, clinical psychologists, psychiatrists and others who must deal with the realities of life rather than with theoretical or arithmetical abstractions. Concurrently, there has been a compensatory interest in the more dynamic, comprehensive and clinically oriented metapsychology of Freud and the psychoanalytic schools. It may be well, therefore, to review here the heuristic and pragmatic contributions as well as the scientific shortcomings of classic psychoanalysis as a comprehensive approach to behavior.

Psychoanalytic theory

Various aspects of psychoanalytic theory have already been considered in Chapters 3 to 6, and its therapeutic applications will be further discussed in Chapter 13, in Appendix 4, and in Chapters 21 to 25 of the *Practice.* Here, then, we need only to reexamine briefly the conceptual framework of psychoanalysis as a background for a constructive critique.

Review of psychoanalytic concepts.   As we have seen, in Freudian theory the functions of the personality are divided analytically into those of the Id, Ego and Superego. *The Id* comprises all the "instincts" or "drives" and is developed from the solipsistic *narcissism* of the neonate. From this, various more specialized forms of "erotism" are differentiated as the *libido* of the growing infant becomes *cathected* onto organ-systems which successively play predominant roles in its development. Thus, *oral incorporation* and incisive prehension, derived from the corresponding passive pleasures and active demands of suckling, are later overlaid by

* Hull formulates behavior in equations with specific and quantitative symbols representing strength of motivations, their reinforcement, generalization and inhibition, the occurrence of "neural oscillations" in response patterns, etc. "Trial and error" and "conditioned" learning are thus expressed in a mathematical continuum of contingent stimuli acting on "unlearned response tendencies" to form "habit units." Hull notes, for instance, that "an increase in the drive alone will serve to reinstate the power of stimuli to evoke a reaction which has [apparently] been extinguished." For a review of Hull's concepts, cf. Leeper and N. Miller.

anal aggressiveness and *retention* as the infant, through bowel training, makes its initial adaptations to social requirements. At the age of from four to six, genitality develops in the form of urethral and *phallic* erotism, which, after a latent period, reappears at puberty and eventually forms the basis for extraverted interpersonal love. "Libidinal drives" of all levels of development remain potent throughout the life of the adult, but lie for the most part buried in his *Unconscious;* nevertheless, they emerge recognizably in the condensed symbolisms of dreams and fantasies, in the inadvertent behavioral expressions of daily living or in the defensively guarded and deviated symptoms of neuroses. To account for phenomena related to sadomasochism, senescence and death, Freud later postulated a dichotomy of the Id into *Eros*—comprising the constructive instincts of life and procreation—as opposed to *Thanatos,* which included unconscious but pervasive tendencies toward destruction and death.

The Ego in psychoanalytic theory is that portion of the personality which adapts Id tendencies to "external" reality (a) by exercising the resources of the *percept-Conscious* (sensorium), the *preconscious* (recallable direct and associated memories) and the *intelligence* (conscious reasoning) and (b) by directing behavior according to the dictates of the *Superego* (v.i.). The Ego is therefore oriented by sensations and perceptions, stores experience, is reflected in thought, and acts through somatic and motor functions. At the same time, the Ego dips deeply into the Unconscious for its contacts with the raw instincts of the Id on the one hand and the prohibitions and commands of the Superego on the other. In adapting to these, the Ego utilizes various *defense mechanisms* (Chapters 4 to 6), but under intense strain these may be breached or shattered, permitting uncontrolled Id impulses or excessively "self-punitive" Superego tendencies to be expressed in irrational, regressive and socially deviant (neurotic and psychotic) behavior.

The *Superego* is a largely unconscious repository of past experiences and "identifications" with parents and *parent-surrogates* (governesses, teachers, etc.) and thus patterns future interpersonal (transference) relationships. Through control of the Ego, the Superego channels the expression of Id impulses into activities that do not threaten the loss of love or invoke other reprisals. An Ego that has transgressed the limits of impulse or action despite the premonitory warnings of anxiety may be "punished by the Superego" through feelings of guilt and self-depreciation, as typically manifested in states of melancholia or in "self-destructive" behavior.

COMPLEXES. Residing in the Unconscious are also various "complexes" (e.g., the "Oedipus" or the "castration" complex*) each of which

---

* These are interrelated, i.e., the wish for sole possession of the mother, including the privilege of incestuous relations, is countered by the fear of retaliatory castration by the father. Sophocles, in *Oedipus Rex,* comments wisely:

> 'Tis best to live at random, as one can,
> But fear thou not that marriage with thy mother.
> Such things men oft have dreams of, but who cares
> The least about them lives happiest.

is invested with a separate configuration of affective and ideational content derived from infantile experience—a symbolic *cathexis* which determines or warps future attitudes, concepts and reactions in some particular sexual, social or other field of behavior. These complexes are formed by narcissistic, destructive or erotic Id impulses counterpoised against the repressive and inhibitive functions of the Ego acting in compliance with the demands of the Superego. To aid in repression, the Ego employs various *normal defense mechanisms,* e.g., displacement, substitution, condensation, sublimation, etc. If these relatively normal maneuvers fail, phobias, compulsions, symptom formations and other *neurotic defense mechanisms* are brought into play; when these, too, are breached, psychotic phenomena such as affective distortions, narcissistic regressions and dereistic projections are evoked (Appendix 2). Clinically, psychoanalytic therapy (cf. Chapter 14 and Appendix 4) employs the techniques of free association, dream interpretation and transference-analysis to bring these conflictful elements of the personality into consciousness and, thus, presumably under more direct Ego control. The therapeutic goal in the words of Freud is: "Where Id was, there shall Ego be."

Critique of psychoanalytic theory. As may be seen even from this very brief résumé, psychoanalytic theory attempts to penetrate beyond the phenomenology of behavior into its deeper sources and determinants. The theory correlates the instinctual evolution and early environment of the infant with the personality patterns and social adjustments of the adult; moreover, it accounts for clinically significant deviations ranging from the minor "psychopathology of everyday life" to the more severe aberrations that constitute neuroses and psychoses—and in doing so traces the origin and meaning of the seemingly fantastic and irrational as well as the "normal." Finally, it applies dynamic concepts to a technique of investigation and a rationale of therapy that in certain respects have proved more illuminating than any other single departure in psychology and psychiatry. The science of behavior, therefore, owes an eternal debt to Freud for having expedited its transition from the taxonomic to the dynamic phase of development and directed it toward a course of investigation and formulation by which man may learn to know much more about himself, his foibles and his paths to a more promising future.

And yet a task remains that is rendered no less difficult by the circumstance that the author is himself a fully trained and accredited psychoanalyst with many respected friends in the movement: that of integrating the unique vocabulary, concepts and dynamic formulae of psychoanalysis with other data and principles of biology and medicine. Unfortunately, this task is somewhat complicated by the historical development of psychoanalysis itself. Freud was an inspired but intensely individualistic worker who, when his theories were neglected or scorned by scientific circles, isolated his thinking all the more from other currents of biologic and psychologic progress, and so set an unfortunate precedent for those of his followers less capable of working in solitary grandeur. Moreover Freud, himself an honest and recurrently self-critical investigator, changed his concepts and formulae radically to fit new clinical observations made by himself or others as psychoanalysis developed, so that his later formulations, particularly on anxiety and on the "death instinct," contradict his initial ones and create confusion in the mind of the student. Again, in the early days of his teachings, Freud accepted many disciples (e.g., Ferenczi, Groddeck, Reich, Rank) whose contributions became identified with psychoanalytic theory, but whose writings consisted of intuitively penetrating insights inextricably combined with quasi-philosophic speculations and flights of uncontrolled fancy highly vulnerable to sober scientific criticism.

Finally, in addition to the classic approach there are today many schismatic "schools" of psychoanalysis, each of which claims that its special formulae represent the acme of modern progress toward understanding, supplementing, correcting or refuting Freud. Thus, the disciples of Carl Jung speak mystically of individual souls or "anima" participating in a "collective Unconscious"; Rank and his followers attribute all anxiety and its attendant evils to the irreversible "trauma of birth"; Adlerian "individual psychologists" dwell almost exclusively on the "inferiority complex" and its ubiquitous "overcompensations"; and the disciples of Sullivan and Karen Horney reemphasize the role of social and cultural factors. Contrary to the intransigent claims of a diminishing group of "orthodox" Freudians, then, psychoanalytic theory today is still far from an accepted body of dogma; on the contrary, much of it is so ambiguous or polemic as to render difficult specific criticisms and stable evaluations. However, if we regard the nuclear concepts outlined above as fairly representative, it can be shown that these, too, need extension, clarification and reformulation before they can be integrated into a comprehensive theory of behavior. Specific comments may be made under the following general headings:

LACK OF BIOLOGIC INTEGRATION. Despite Freud's professed intentions to the contrary, psychoanalytic theory, during the course of its development, lost touch at too many points not only with medicine but with the biologic sciences in general. As a result, some psychoanalysts have erected overelaborate superstructures of speculation based only on circularly interpreted "analytic observations," without placing their clinical data in a general biologic context or including observations that contradicted their premises. In effect, analysts have tended to assert theoretic absolutisms as dogmatic and yet as questionable as those they criticize in other systems. For example, in their conative formulations orthodox analysts retain a vague concept of "sexual libido" and then, contrary to almost self-evident considerations of biologic evolution, structure and function, further assume that all needs and their derived drives, desires, wishes, etc. are of similar "sexual" origin. Conversely, Freud first stated that all deviations of behavior would eventually be traced to hormonal or other specific physiologic causes, then postulated the existence of "self-destructive urges" contrary to nearly every tenet of biologic survival.

TAXONOMIC TENDENCIES. Psychoanalysis, despite its predominantly dynamic orientations, has in some respects persisted in earlier modes of mystic-categorical thinking. One example we have already discussed is the subdivision of the total personality into compartments called the "Id," "Ego," "Superego," "Ego-ideal," etc.; another instance is the classification of all mental processes as conscious, preconscious (Kubie) or unconscious with little recognition of the existence of an infinity of transitional stages and qualitative variations. Once these largely untenable distinctions were made, analytic theory then complicated the error by dealing with its "constructs" not only as if they had a real existence but almost as if they had an independent will and spirit of their own—once again exemplifying what Whitehead calls false concretization. Thus, many early analytic writings read like mythologic sagas of how the pristine Unconscious, buried in durance vile, "seduced" a "corruptible" Ego which was itself in rebellion against a "tyrannical" Superego, and so on (cf. Appendix 2)—as though such altercations, alliances or reconciliations actually occurred among intrapsychic *dramatis personae* each endowed with unique purposes, foibles, "wiles" and "dishonesties" of its own. Fortunately, there is a growing recognition among analysts that the dynamics of behavior are topologic and not topographic, functional rather than structural (*vide* defense "mechanisms" of the "Ego") and in all events involve complex total adaptations rather than localized conflicts among artificially isolated segments of a mythically tripartite "psyche."

PSYCHOANALYTIC DUALISM.   Despite these corrective tendencies, however, a large portion of psychoanalytic theory, as its name indicates, continues to be almost exclusively mentalistic in orientation and thus contravenes its own purposes by actually fostering a Cartesian dichotomy between "mind" and "body." True, the psychoanalytic evaluation of "mental" functions is for the most part dynamic, but in some of its aspects the theory subtly implies that "the mind" controls the body; i.e., that wishes, ideas, symbols and verbalizations *induce* specific behavior patterns instead of being themselves aspects of the total adaptations of the human organism. This insistence upon the priority of "mental" processes, "conscious" or not, over motor or organic expressions has contributed to a peculiar methodologic confusion in analytic technique which will be discussed further in Chapter 14.

PSYCHOANALYTIC TRADITIONALISM.*   As already indicated, many psychoanalysts, even when radically deviant on some points, have shown a general tendency toward an ultra-conservative cultism; moreover, when they are challenged on this score, their theoretic assertions have tended to become even more defensively dogmatic.† Outmoded concepts are clung to in the face of later clinical observations, not because the original formulations have proved to be heuristically or pragmatically advan-

---

* "It is the fate of rebels to found new orthodoxies"—B. Russell in *The Psychoanalyst's Nightmare.* "The doctrines which best repay critical examination are those which for the longest period have remained unquestioned"—A. N. Whitehead.

† Such tendencies are not exclusive to psychoanalysts, but may be found in the enthusiastic protagonists of any school which has made important contributions, e.g., Gestalt psychology, behaviorism, psychobiology, existentialism, etc.

tageous, but because Freud or some authorized disciple proposed them in writings which, apparently, must be reverently and forever quoted by chapter and verse. This is particularly evident in the perennially cherished handicap of a fanciful and outworn terminology, much of which has lost its original meanings and become confused, vague or ambiguous.

THERAPEUTIC LIMITATIONS. This adherence to traditions has been particularly marked in the field of analytic "pschotherapy," which is still conceived by many analysts as a ritualistic series of sessions four or five times a week for an indefinite number of years during which "interpretations" are made of "analytic material" consisting almost exclusively of the verbal behavior of the patient during the prescribed fifty-minute period. The objectives of the therapy are still, through free association, dream-memories, "abreaction" and transference-analysis, to "make conscious" the patient's "Id tendencies," "complexes" and repressions or other defense mechanisms, on the sanguine supposition that, once he is made aware of what was previously inaccessible to his "consciousness," his motivations, adaptations and social behavior patterns would somehow automatically change for the better.* And when, as not infrequently happens, they do not, the therapeutic failure is ascribed either to an inevitably "incomplete exploration" of the patient's "Unconscious," or is passed off by some other rationalization such as his "unanalyzable character" or "resistance to working-through." Less frequently, claims of subtle therapeutic success are made despite the disappointed protests of the patient's family, his friends, or the patient himself that no real improvement has occurred or is in the offing. So also, when some orthodox analysts are forced to do "brief psychotherapy" by the exigencies of practice, they still fail to utilize the variegated resources of a truly dynamic psychiatric armamentarium and persist in attempting "abridged analyses," the sole objectives of which are again to impart verbal "insight" into the "psychogenesis" of the illness as rapidly as possible. Here, too, the tendency is merely to "interpret" the patient's presenting difficulties in terms of his remote or infantile past, instead of dealing with such of his *current* problems and maladaptations as are amenable not only to rational understanding but to active and constructive solution by every means at the command of patient, physician, family and community.† Viewed solely at face value, the classic rationale of analytic

---

* Operationally, the concept that "expressions of non-judgmental interest" or, for that matter, "psychoanalytic interpretations" have *specific* evocative or alterative effects on a patient's thought and behavior must be qualified in the light of experimental data (L. Krasner, J. Greenspoon). Thus, ostensibly neutral interjections by the therapist (such as "Mmm-mm" or the incidental flash of a light) also reinforce the coincidental content of a subject's "free associations" and thereby increase a topical frequency and its "significance" to the patient, even though he is not aware of this process of *operant conditioning* (Skinner). On the other hand, D. Ewen Cameron has demonstrated that explanations and instructions frequently repeated by a tape recorder connected to earphones placed on a sleeping subject's head can alter the behavior even of withdrawn schizophrenics.

† In this connection, Wortis has justifiably criticized the passive fatalism with which many analysts disregard the social inequalities and injustices that face many people they too glibly call neurotic—conditions to which, in fact, no "normal" person can be expected to "adapt" without some form of protest.

therapy would be akin to the proposition that, for instance, all that is necessary to cure pneumonia—also a complex disease of the total organism—is to trace its origin to the patient's susceptibility and type of infection and then let the sufferer work out his own recovery without further expert and concerted aid. Fortunately, most experienced analysts, in actual practice, no longer adhere to the monothetic techniques they still seem to advocate in their publications*; nevertheless, this very circumstance confirms the advisability of broadening psychoanalytic therapy to include other than the purely interpretative methods of influencing behavior.

For clinical exemplification of this discussion a survey of psychoanalytic concepts of the psychoses is presented in Appendix 3, and a fairly detailed account of a "complete" psychoanalysis in Appendix 4. In concluding this review, however, it should be made explicit that the criticisms outlined no longer apply to either psychoanalytic theory or practice as revised and taught by Alexander, Grinker, Rado, Salzman, Maskin, Rioch and other progressive psychoanalysts. In fact, except for differences in terminology and breadth of biologic application, modern analytic formulations do not differ markedly from the biodynamic principles of behavior presented later in this volume and in the *Practice*. Unfortunately, the new developments of psychoanalytic theory, scattered as they are in technical journals, have not as yet been assembled and made readily available in integrated form†; as a result, the unguided student too often becomes immersed in the older, overpopularized literature of psychoanalysis, unaware that much of it is now only of historic interest. It is primarily for this reason that the author—who counts his own formal psychoanalytic training and experience as an indispensable preparation for dynamic psychiatry—has not only inserted this orientative critique, but has outlined modern analytic theory in juxtaposition to relevant biodynamic concepts in Chapters 3 to 6 of this volume.

Meyerian psychobiology

Adolf Meyer's leadership in guiding American psychiatry from its nineteenth-century incarceration in mental hospitals to its present role as one of the most progressive and useful of medical specialties earned him an undisputed preeminence among his academic and professional contemporaries in the first half of this century. But his scientific standing rests on an even greater contribution: a philosophic reformulation of the theory and practice of psychiatry as expressed in a system of concepts

---

* Other critiques have been published by the following prominent psychoanalysts (qq.v.): of Freudian energetics, by Colby; of libido, by Bieber; of orality, by Grinker; of transference, by Orr; of Ego psychology, by Kris, Hartmann and Loewenstein; of esthetics, by Beres; of anthropology, by Kardiner; of psychoanalytic education, by Szasz, and Lewin and Ross; of therapy, by Franz Alexander, Clara Thompson, Frieda Fromm-Reichmann, Melitta Schmideberg and many others.

† Except, hopefully, in the Proceedings of the Academy of Psychoanalysis, published annually in recent years as a series of volumes entitled *Science and Psychoanalysis*, under the editorship of the present author (cf. Bibliography).

that he termed "Psychobiology." Unfortunately, Meyer himself never published a complete exposition of this multiphasic approach, whereas some of his pupils who have recorded his teaching have seen fit to continue using a terminology even more recondite and unnecessarily obscure than that of psychoanalysis.* However, the most significant tenets of Meyer's psychobiology may be summarized as follows.

Concepts of psychobiology. *Behavior is to be regarded as a psychobiologic expression of the whole organism,* and not as a compendium or the sum total of separate "physical" and "mental" part-reactions. To encourage the clinical use of this holistic concept, Meyer proposed that the statically descriptive nosology of Kraepelin be supplanted by a dynamic terminology based on the Greek root *ergon* for work or behavior. Thus, sweeping disturbances in behavior of psychotic degree were to be designated as *holergesias;* mood aberrations were called *thymergasias,* and schizophrenic reactions were divorced from the concept of merely "thinking" disturbances and more properly termed "parergasias" (i.e., deviated energies). A peculiar exception in this nosologic system was the term *merergasia* for neuroses, to indicate that these were "part-reactions"—a concept that in some ways contradicted Meyer's otherwise holistic approach to all behavior, normal or abnormal.

Behavior is both constitutionally and developmentally determined and must therefore be studied in historical and multi-vectorial "long-section" rather than in the phenomenologic "cross-section" of the moment. For this purpose Meyer utilized a chronologic life chart in which important data as to the genetic endowment, intellectual and social development, and the special environmental vicissitudes of the patient were to be recorded in objective detail, so that a comprehensive survey of the subject's entire life span could be made and evaluated in relation to his current problems. In this way, all possible factors—genetic, physiologic, pathologic, experiential—were to be investigated and given their proper etiologic weight. However, it was to be kept in mind that these influences did not act separately, but as vectors in an environmental field to which, in turn, the individual reacted as a whole.

Finally, *therapy, too, was to be as eclectic as possible,* and designed to utilize every available physical, pharmacologic, environmental and psychotherapeutic technique that could prove empirically advantageous. Here Meyer relied greatly on the intuitive "common sense" of both the physician and the patient to select, pursue and accomplish the treatment.

Critique. As may be seen, psychobiologic psychiatry is attractively rationalistic, inclusive and essentially dynamic—qualities which have made many psychiatrists, including the author under Dr. Meyer's tutelage—grateful students of the Meyerian tradition. And yet the very breadth of psychobiologic thought has tended to make certain areas of it somewhat diffuse and impalpable; certainly, it becomes difficult to derive from psychobiology a set of principles sufficiently specific and concrete either to constitute a general conceptualization of behavior or to provide a scientific rationale of clinical therapy. In this connection, the

---

* Outstanding exceptions are Muncie, Strecker and Hardin Branch; the writings of the last are particularly recommended.

covertly contra-psychoanalytic emphasis on "common sense" has sometimes had the unfortunate effect of encouraging superficiality of observation and formulation of clinical problems, with the result that deeper human motivations, subtle symbolizations and complex behavioral interactions and expressions have been either overlooked or else denied their theoretic and practical significance. All in all, the psychobiologic teachings of Adolf Meyer have reaffirmed the unity of mind and body, the holistic nature of all conduct, its multiple interrelated determinants, and the wealth of procedures available to both the investigator and therapist; nevertheless, psychobiology has not fulfilled its promise of furnishing a consistent organon of normal and abnormal behavior as a basis for effective therapy, and its identity and specific influence are therefore waning.

Existentialism and phenomenology

Existentialism (L. *ex sistere,* to emerge) is a protean term which refers nebulously to a consciousness of one's own being through "unfathomable sensitivities" to the "immediacy of experience." This poetic and poignant theme had long been sensed in nearly all spheres of human thought: i.e., by innumerable writers from Homer and Virgil through Anatole France and Dostoevski to Kafka, Rilke and Camus; by dramatists from Sophocles through Shakespeare to Sartre; by artists from the Mousterian cave painters to van Gogh, Cezanne and Kandinsky; by composers from Palestrina through Bach and Franck to Schoenberg; by "intuitive" metaphysicists from Pythagoras through Bacon to Bohr and Heisenberg; by philosophers from Anaximenes through Spinoza to Dilthey, Whitehead and Santayana; and by theologians from Buddha through Aquinas to Tillich, Niebuhr, et al. It was therefore inevitable that in Romantic metapsychology too, Sören Kierkegaard (1813–55) would equate almost all aspects of the human condition—personal, social and religious—with "primal anxiety,"* or that Karl Jaspers (1883–) would dedicate his *Daseinsanalyse* ("the essential of being there") to the task of compromising man's developmental ("ontologic") heritage of *angst* by a recourse to these four "fundamental subjectivities": (1) *I am,* (2) *I am becoming,* (3) *I am aware* and (4) *I deny death.* Heidegger, in his *Sein und Zeit,* then took the predictable additional step (long since taken for granted in other disciplines) of denying sharp distinctions between observer and object and reaffirming, again somewhat redundantly, the subjectivity of all experience. Moreover, these viewpoints were only partially saved from the paradox of solipsism by assuming a material universe of reference (Binswanger's "being-in-the-world") and by admitting the parallel existences of "Others." This, then, permitted human

---

* "And no Grand Inquisitor has in readiness such terrible tortures as has Anxiety, and no spy knows how to attack more artfully the man he suspects, choosing the instant when he is weakest, nor knows how to lay traps where he will be caught and ensnared, as anxiety knows how, and no sharp-witted judge knows how to interrogate, to examine the accused, as anxiety does, which never lets him escape, neither by diversion nor by noise, neither at work nor at play, neither by day nor by night"—Kierkegaard, *The Concept of Dread,* 1844.

beings to commingle, and, in a sense, unite for the relief of mutual for-lornness through a *Begegnung* (the *Ich-du* meeting and invitation of Buber) or by a quasi-mystic *Einfühlung* (the "one-feeling" of Medard Boss).

If the reader accustomed to precision of thought and clarity of language remains somewhat puzzled after this brief sampling of existentialist fantasy, he may be cautioned that studying most of the other *be*-mused and *is*-toxicated writings in this field might furnish a temporarily diverting excursion into amorphous mood-music, but would hardly dispel his semantic or scientific perplexity; on the contrary, Binswanger strikes both the keynote and dominant of the movement in his characterization of the ideal of existentialist ideology as "precisely ambiguous." However, some comfort may be derived from the fact that Earle, in a philosophic critique, points out that Jaspers repeatedly insisted that his own key concepts of *existanz* (existence), *welt* (world) and *transcendanz* (essentially, God) cannot and should not be defined, and that therefore no one can or should know even approximately what he is talking about.

Phenomenology as a parallel psychiatric movement, integrated with existentialism by Binswanger, sprang from Husserl's renewed warning at the turn of the century that psychological data should be observed, recorded and evaluated without preconception and prejudice—a bit of advice manifestly impossible to follow. Since then, some of his disciples (e.g., Minkowski, Strauss) have interpreted the procedure to mean the direct symptomatic diagnosis of Kraepelinian psychiatric entities such as "melancholia"—purportedly evident to clinical inspection, or "schizophrenia"—admittedly a bit more difficult to prehend.

Finally, phenomenologic-existential psychotherapy, again as nearly as can be gathered from the remarkably obscure writings of its proponents, is either frankly fatalistic, or else consists essentially of expressions of empathic understanding, hortatory advice (cf. Frankl's "*Logotherapy*"), or indirect restorations of the same forms of personal "identity" or social and cosmic confidence that, as we shall see, underlie all methods of effective psychotherapy.

Communication theory

This is a rapidly developing field of behavioral science* which has already helped clarify the all-important "normal" transmission of information (cf. Chapter 13) and promises also to contribute greatly to a deeper understanding of deviations of behavior related to disturbances of communication. The primary possibilities may be reviewed as follows:

Information underload or disturbed feedbacks. D. Hebb, J. Lilly, J. Shurley and others have shown that if a normal subject is confined for from 3 to 36 hours to a dark, warm, quiet room or in any other situation in which sensory stimuli are kept to a minimum or held con-

---

* As do all sub-fields, communication theory has developed a lexicon of its own: e.g., "bits" (units) of information, "noise" (irrelevant, supernumerary or ambiguous data), "channels" (avenues or categories) of transmission, etc. A not particularly surprising finding is that most human communication is multiple-channeled noise.

stant,* the effects—depending on the subject's personality—may vary from mounting anxiety through resentment, fear and rage to a quasi-psychotic state characterized by persistent depersonalization and disorientation with or without hallucinations and delusions. On the other hand, deprivation of sleep (L. J. West, G. Morris) or of dreaming (W. Dement) may likewise induce severe disturbances of orientation, thought and judgment. An imbalance of sensorial input, rest and expression may thus account for a class of experiences that range from borderline normal to seriously psychotic: e.g., the vivid illusions and reactive irrational impulses that beset truck-drivers on long, monotonous hauls and not infrequently lead to accidents, or the "breakoff point" experienced by stratosphere pilots when, after several hours of viewless, soundless, apparently motionless flight, they suddenly feel divorced from their former selves and all other earthly matters and may react with trance or panic.† Since, as we have seen, such omissions of contact and stimulus are particularly devastating in early life, we may have one explanation of the fact that human infants seriously deprived of individual love and attention may become indifferent, withdrawn and stereotyped children (the *autism* of Kanner), or avoid human contacts and manifest other somatic disturbances that end in serious physical and behavioral deterioration (the *protophrenia* of Bourne).

Information overload.   Equally significant are the effects of the opposite extreme—a rather more common condition in this era of mushrooming technical cacophony and social intrusiveness. Communications engineers equip computers with automatic fuses that protect their mechanical brains from stimulus levels above tolerance, whereas our human counterparts are quite ineffective: mainly our eyelids, our stapedius muscles, or total bodily escape. And yet J. G. Miller has demonstrated experimentally that when any subject is required, within a given time, to perceive, process and respond to what is for him an overload of incoming information—even when the data are partially of his own making—his reactions may again range from "normal" to striking paradigms of the psychotic. Briefly, the following disturbances may occur:

1. *Omission of intake,* as in functional disturbances of sensation and denial of perceived reality.

2. *Errors of interpretation,* as in illusional or hallucinatory behavior.

3. *Queuing of input*—i.e., "compulsive" ordering and categorization, as in obsessional thinking or false generalization.

4. *Filtering data and limitation of reaction,* as in inhibited, self-constricted character formation.

---

* Please note that the trauma in these experiments arises *not* from "sensory deprivation" (since buzzers may be loud and lights bright and continuous) but from the subject's devastating sense of impotence in reading meanings and reestablishing human communication and influence.

† It is probable that one factor in the induction of psychotic states by so-called "psychotomimetic drugs" such as mescal (H. Klüver, A. Huxley), LSD-25 (H. Fabing, H. Solomon) or recent atropine-like synthetics (L. Abood, B. Böszörmenyi) is the action of these substances in excluding or distorting retinal (J. Apter) or other sensory perceptions.

5. *Multiple channelizations,* with partialing and fragmentation of response or projective delegation of action to others, and finally,

6. *Abandonment of the stressful milieu,* analogous to the geographic, affective, pharmacologic and suicidal escapisms employed by patients when, in their estimation, life's demands become overwhelming.

Following quite other lines of investigation, L. Chapman, L. E. Hinkle, H. G. Wolff and others infer that informational overload or conflict may directly result in organic and cerebral tissue damage.

References*

Adler, A.: The Practice and Theory of Individual Psychology.
Alexander, F., French, T., et al.: Psychoanalytic Therapy.
Allport, G.: Personality, a Psychological Interpretation.
Ashby, W. Ross: An Introduction to Cybernetics.
Corrie, J.: ABC of Jung's Psychology.
Frolov, J. P.: Pavlov and His School.
Fromm-Reichmann, Frieda: Recent Advances in Psychoanalytic Therapy.
Gesell, A. et al.: The First Five Years of Life.
Grinker, R. R.: Psychosomatic Research.
Hilgard, E. R., and Marquis, D. C.: Conditioning and Learning.
Hull, C. L.: Modern Behaviorism and Psychoanalysis.
Hunt, J. McV: Personality and Behavior Disorders. (Chapters 1, 16, 17, 19, 30.)
Jaensch, E.: Eidetic Imagery and Typological Methods of Investigation.
Lewin, B., and Ross, Helen: Psychoanalytic Education in the United States.
Liddell, H. S.: Conditioned Reflex Method and Experimental Neuroses.
Lief, Alfred (Ed.): The Commonsense Psychiatry of Dr. Adolf Meyer.
May, R.: Existential Therapy.
Meyer, A.: The Psychobiological Point of View.
Muncie, W.: Psychobiology and Psychiatry.
Murray, H. A.: Explorations in Personality.
Nicole, J. E.: Psychopathology.
Pavlov, I. P.: Conditioned Reflexes and Psychiatry.
Sonnemann, U.: Existence and Therapy.
Sullivan, H. S.: The Modified Psychoanalytic Treatment of Schizophrenia.
Thompson, Clara: Psychoanalysis: Evaluation and Development.
Tomkins, S. S.: Contemporary Psychopathology.
Walter, W. G.: The Living Brain.
Watson, J. B.: The New Behaviorism.
Wheelis, A.: The Quest for Identity.
Wild, J.: The Challenge of Existentialism.
Zilboorg, G. and Henry, G.: A History of Medical Psychology. (Chapter 10.)

* Cf. References to Chapter 3 for other psychoanalytic source-books.

Chapter 8

Development of a general
biodynamic theory of behavior

Criteria of biodynamics

As has been indicated in the preceding chapter, a comprehensive *biodynamic* theory of behavior should fulfill the following criteria:

1. Be in accord with biologic principles as inferred from the evolution and the structural and physiologic relationships of living organisms.

2. Cover the range from ameba to man, yet not neglect the quantitative or qualitative complexities that distinguish the behavior patterns of one organism from another.

3. Deal with holistic observations of behavior rather than with "physiologic," "psychologic," or even "psychosomatic" part-concepts, which either isolate artificial aspects of the whole or attempt post-hoc correlations.

4. Transcend the spurious dichotomy of "organism versus environment," and instead consider the latter as selectively integrated into the organism's field of action.

5. Trace the variations of *individual* behavior that occur during alterations in the organism-environment totality such as are produced by physical, pharmacologic and pathologic influences, without *a priori* distinctions as to what shall be categorized as "normal" or "abnormal."

6. Account for the phenomena of organismic interaction from simple aggregates to complex social relationships.

7. Be consistent and prognostically valid.

8. Finally, remain pragmatic; i.e., furnish a rationale for various methods of influencing behavior that are demonstrably effective in clinical therapy.

It is evident that these criteria constitute counsels of perfection; certain it is that no existing theory of behavior yet approaches their fulfillment, nor is it likely that human thought will develop one that does so in the foreseeable future. For that matter, no serious claim can be made that the criteria themselves would measure the "ultimate truth" of any behavior theory that could be postulated. *In science, "truth" can perhaps be defined only as the broadest, the most precise and preferably the most concise expression of the extent of confirmed observation*;* ergo, "truth" about behavior, however penetrating, currently inclusive

---

* R. Oppenheimer points out the contingency thus: "Truth is so largely defined by how you find it."

or accurately predictive, is eternally contingent on incomplete data, and until man becomes omniscient all criteria and all theories are merely expressions of his relative ignorance. But to minimize this, zoologists, anthropologists, experimental psychologists, sociologists, clinicians—and for that matter, nuclear physicists and humanist philosophers—are breaking down the artificial barriers among their various disciplines, pooling their specialized techniques and concepts, reuniting "structure" with "function" and "substance" with "mind," and gradually evolving generalizations couched in a terminology significant for all biodynamics. From these joint scientific efforts, three principal approaches to the study of behavior have emerged.

First, the *historical*, dealing with the origins and evolution of man's notions about himself, and placing his current ideas and practices in their proper context and perspective. For example, it is a fascinating and highly instructive exercise to trace the insights and errors of currently popular systems such as "psychoanalysis" or "existentialism" to far clearer statements by ancient philosophers or Renaissance poets, and to recognize that there is hardly a form of psychiatric treatment used today the essence of which was not also employed in the Asklepiad Sanatoria of Greece and Rome (cf. Chapter 1 and the *Practice*, Chapter 21).

Second is the *comparative* method, in which the essential unitary phenomena and consistencies of behavior are discerned by translating the babel of special lexicons and partial formulae of all the various behavioral sciences, ranging from electronics through biology and esthetics to theology, into more definitive terms and broadly meaningful equations. This is the aim of the modern "systems theory" of J. G. Miller, Anatol Rapoport, et al. and is implicit throughout both this volume and the *Practice*.

The third technique is the *experimental*, in which the variations of a segment of behavior are correlated as closely as possible with relatively few co-variant conditions. Optimally, every transaction of a psychiatrist with a patient could constitute a meaningful experiment if it were carefully conducted, objectively recorded, adequately analyzed, and thoroughly compared with previous and later experiences; however, the number of factors involved would be so close to infinity that, with our present limitations of input and comprehension, experimental investigations of behavior are usually confined to much more restricted clinical situations and even more rigidly "controlled" laboratory observations of human or animal subjects. This technique will be dealt with explicitly in the following sections.

An experimental approach to biodynamic formulations

The author's own interests in a possible resynthesis of behavior theory with the biologic sciences led him many years ago to supplement his medical and psychiatric observations by direct animal experimentation. The chronologic development of this research is perhaps of some interest, since it illustrates the scope such studies must attain before their general significance and limitations become evident. Initially, the work was

Plate III

The apparatus consists of a chamber measuring 31 x 30 x 22 inches surrounded on three sides by smaller detachable compartments. Spring-balanced Plexiglass doors provide entrances and exits among the compartments and to transport-cages (far right). Push-pull levers are used by the animal to activate motors and latches which operate the doors or the stimuli and reward systems described below. The apparatus is ventilated by replacement of its entire air content every 30 seconds.

Rewards. A gear-driven rotary magazine provides automatic delivery and removal of dishes containing foods or liquids at the rear of each compartment; these rewards may be presented directly or behind opaque lids. Other goal objects such as toys, mates, offspring, other animals, etc., can also be utilized.

Associated Stimuli. Visual: Light signals exhibited directly in front of the levers or behind or over the goal objects are used in the control and variation of multiple visual dimensions. In addition, each compartment can be illuminated by pictures projected on a translucent screen.

Auditory: Bells, buzzers and speakers for tape-recorded material are synchronized with the clock employed in the measurement of response latencies.

Olfactory: Volatile substances singly or in combinations can be injected into the ventilating air stream of each compartment.

Somesthetic: The size of door openings, their levels and other spatial orientations can be varied.

Conflict-Engendering Stimuli. These include air blasts, the release of artificial or real small reptiles, physiologically harmless electroshocks through the grid floor, etc.

Central Nervous Stimulation. Distant stimulation of cerebral structures can be effected by radio waves which activate stereotactically implanted electrodes.

Activity and Response Recording. "Spontaneous" or learned activities and responses to electrical stimulation are registered on noiseless counters and kymographs activated by an adjustable photoelectric cell in each compartment. The cinematic recording of all events is directly subtitled in the illuminated panels arranged below the experimental chambers.

This apparatus (cf. Masserman, J., Aarons, L., and McAvoy, T., 1960) is an improved version of similar ones used in the studies of normal and deviant animal behavior described below.

Plate III. An apparatus for studying normal behavior and conflict-induced neurosis in small animals

concerned with testing the validity of a typically dualistic "psychoso-matic" postulate then current: namely, that certain portions of the dien-cephalon were the neurologic locus of behavioral "drives" and "emo-tions," or, as some psychoanalytic authors had it, the "seat of the Id was the hypothalamus." This assumption had been based mainly on previous observations by Bard, Ranson and others that electrical excitation of the hypothalamus in animals produced somatic and motor reactions resem-bling those of fear and rage, whereas its destruction induced temporary apathy and indifference to emotional stimuli. Bard himself had care-fully designated the reactions elicited by direct electrical stimulation of the diencephalon as *sham* rage, but this qualification had been conven-iently overlooked by those who were so anxious to "correlate body and mind" that they failed to realize that this in itself presumed that they were disparate variables.

Our own experiments, which utilized Horsley-Clarke stereotactic techniques for precisely localized stimulation and destruction of the hypothalamus in cats, demonstrated (a) that the pseudo-affective reac-tions produced by its electrical or pharmacologic stimulation, unlike rage or fear, ended abruptly with the cessation of the stimulus; (b) that sensory signals associated as many as 480 times with hypothalamic stimuli did not induce emotional responses when given alone; and (c) that animals which recovered from the severe metabolic disturbances caused by hypothalamic lesions concurrently regained their normal emo-tional reactivity. These and other findings (Chapter 2) led to the inference that, although the hypothalamus was undoubtedly a coordinating center for the sympathetic and motor pathways of emotional expression, it could not be shown to be either the source or the seat of experience of affective states—a conclusion borne out by a critical examination of the anatomic, neurophysiologic and clinical evidence in the literature. More-over, further experiments on the motor cortex yielded corresponding results: localized electrical or other artificial stimuli produced peripheral responses that, however dramatic, were apparently unmotivated, unadap-tive and evaluated by the animal only through indirect kinesthetic experi-ences.

These findings led to a significant change in the general methods of our research; dissective and internal-stimuli techniques were discon-tinued in favor of a study of the total behavior of the animal in relation to physiologic needs, goal-seeking, frustration, modes of learning, adap-tational conflicts and aberrations, the influence of drugs and cerebral lesions, and many relatively controllable variations of the physical and social milieu. The rationale, methods and results of these experiments have been recorded on various motion picture films (see Appendix 2) and re-ported in detail in a monograph (*Behavior and Neurosis*, 1943) and subsequent publications. Certain of these experiments will also be cited in later connections, but it may be anticipated here that when the experi-mental observations as a whole were analyzed in relation to data in other fields of biologic investigation and correlated with corresponding obser-vations of human behavior, certain general principles emerged which were broad and meaningful enough to justify their assembly into what we may designate as a "biodynamic" theory of behavior. For purposes of clarity, it may be advisable first to state these principles in bare outline as follows:

1. *Principle of Motivation.* Behavior is directed toward the satisfaction of the variable needs of the organism.

2. *Principle of Experiential Interpretation and Adaptation.* Behavior is contingent upon, and adaptive to, the organism's *interpretations* of its total milieu, in accordance with its capacities and previous experiences.

3. *Principles of Deviation and Substitution.* Behavior patterns become deviated and fragmented under stress and, when further frustrated, tend toward substitutive satisfactions.

4. *Principle of Conflict.* When in a given milieu two or more motivations come into conflict in the sense that their accustomed consummatory patterns become incompatible, kinetic tension (anxiety) mounts and behavior becomes hesitant, vacillating, erratic and poorly adaptive (neurotic) or excessively symbolic and regressive (psychotic).

The remainder of Part Two will be concerned with the experimental demonstration, theoretical development, clinical relevance and therapeutic applications of these principles to the field of psychiatry.

References

Angyal, A.: Foundations for a Science of Personality.
Cannon, W. B.: Bodily Changes in Pain, Hunger, Fear and Rage.
Goldstein, K. L.: The Organism.
Katz, D.: Animals and Men.
Lewin, K.: A Dynamic Theory of Personality.
Masserman, J. H.: Behavior and Neurosis (Chapters I and II, and appended references).
Pearson, K.: The Grammar of Science (Chapters I–IV).
Sears, R. R.: Survey of Objective Studies of Psychoanalytic Concepts.
Skinner, B. F.: The Behavior of Organisms.

Chapter 9

Biodynamic
formulations of behavior

IN THE previous two chapters we reexamined various hypotheses about human conduct and proceeded to sketch certain principles of a comprehensive biodynamic theory of behavior. These principles and their corollaries will now be more fully stated and illustrated at both experimental and clinical levels.

The principle of motivation

Principle I: Behavior is directed toward the satisfaction of various physiologic needs.

It is herewith proposed that psychologic abstractions such as "instincts," "drives," "urges," "libidinous tensions," "wishes," "goal-vectors," "valences," etc., are, in essence, conative inferences used to describe various manifestations of the fundamental homeostatic tendency of all organisms not only to maintain physiologic equilibrium (Bernard, Cannon) but to develop and evolve (Loeb, Simpson). From the standpoint of comparative biology, the "needs" of an organism depend on its biologic avidities: for instance, primitive plants which can exist on minerals, air and sunlight will show correspondingly simple geo-, aero- and heliotropic behavior; at the other extreme, the intricately organized mammal has many physiologic needs which must be satisfied by behavior patterns of much greater complexity. For example, phosphorus-depleted cattle will begin to eat bones or even small animals (Green, 1915); a deer starved for salt will, at great hardship if necessary, travel scores of miles across mountain ranges to reach a salt lick; a man even remotely threatened by thirst will abandon all other interests and activities and use every resource of his skill and ingenuity to secure water. Again, physiologic needs may be made even more pressing or complex by trauma or disease, thus rendering their satisfactions more imperative. Curt Richter (1939, 1941) showed that adrenalectomized rats which required large amounts of sodium to keep alive avidly sought and drank salt solutions, whereas parathyroidectomized rats invariably preferred fluids containing calcium.* Even more intricate patterns involving the elements of anticipa-

---

* Such behavior need not depend entirely on special-sense functions, as Richter (1939) contended; thus, blind, anosmic rats choose the same foods as their intact littermates (Harlow, 1932).

tory behavior could be elicited by other artificially induced physiologic needs: for instance, rats made sensitive to cold by the removal of the thyroid or pituitary gland spent their time collecting nesting materials and building thick shelters to insulate them from changes in temperature. At a more complex "level" of function, Clara Davis observed that a rachitic infant in physiologic want of vitamin D spontaneously selected cod-liver oil from other possible food choices and thus "medicated" itself until recovery.

    Role of consciousness. These observations help to clarify the question as to the relative "consciousness" of needs and wishes. Obviously, it is an accepted linguistic custom to state that Richter's rats were "unconscious" of their need for sodium, calcium or warmth, and that Davis' infant was not "consciously" aware of its avitaminosis; nevertheless, the significant fact is that the physiologic need was apprehended with sufficient specificity to make the behavior operationally adaptive.

    In the human adult, similarly, most behavior is actuated by bodily needs rather than conscious wishes. In fact, the former emerge into greater or less awareness (ranging in expression from vague impulses to formulated "intentions") only when the needs become pressing or when they demand specifically integrated and mobilized skills for their satisfaction. We are, for instance, ordinarily not conscious of our need for oxygen until respiration is impeded beyond "unconscious" adaptations; then, and then only, do we become dimly or specifically enough aware of the threat of suffocation to take "deliberate" action. At various stages of this need for air—depending on its duration and urgency, our response capacities and the available circumstances—our conscious reactions may range from merely loosening our collars or opening a window, to highly intricate patterns for improving our internal respiratory functions or our external milieu. For example, we could spend much of our time following complex medical directions to compensate for heart or lung disease, or, in special circumstances, employ great technical skill diving a damaged stratocruiser to better oxygen levels.   · ·

    Role of channelized consummatory patterns and "anticipation." However, these correlations between relatively simple biologic "needs" and complex ranges of response leave other behavioral phenomena unexplained. A male child castrated in early infancy rarely develops sex "drives," but if castration occurs after he has had satisfactory heterosexual experiences, he may continue to seek and consummate intercourse despite the absence of the specific hormonal stimulants (Levy, 1942). Or, to take a simpler example of the role of experience in "anticipation," after a full meal we return to work to earn money to have ready for more food when next our hunger recurs. Modes of need-satiation once formed by an organism, then, tend to persist as patterns not immediately dependent on the purely physiologic wants that originally actuated them. The biodynamic correlates of such secondary "fixations" of behavior are as yet speculative, as indeed are the chemistry and physics of any protoplasmic processes; however, it is possible that repetitive patterns become governed by cyclic reflexes such as have been described by Laurente de Nó, Dusser de Barenne, McCulloch and others. In a later connection we shall consider the experimental basis of this concept and its application to the clinical phenomena of repetition-compulsions and stereotypy.

Survival of species. But the "physiologic needs" of an organism are not always compatible with its *individual* existence. The male praying mantis (*Mantis religiosa*) will copulate while being eaten by the female (Fabre); animal mothers will fight and die to defend their brood —and indeed, the homologues of such patterns, fortunately for our posterity, are far from unknown in the human species. And yet, there is experimental evidence to show that these patterns, too, are physiologically need-fulfilling; i.e., they are dependent on sex and maternal hormones which serve race rather than individual survival.*

Complex motivations in terms of physiologic needs. Perhaps the greatest resistance to the biodynamic principle that all motivations express physiologic needs will spring from an understandable reluctance to attribute complexly determined "altruistic" behavior to such elemental sources. For instance, the student may wonder what "physiologic needs" are really being satisfied by reading this book. Then why is he reading this book? To gain, or at any rate seek, knowledge. To what end? To be a more capable—or at least a more widely read—psychologist, physician, social worker or whatever. But why be one? Here the replies may consist of protestations, more or less vehement or sincere, that he wants to prepare himself for future research, enlighten the current darkness of his chosen field, serve suffering humanity, and so on. But franker and advisedly private introspection will reveal that beneath such euphemisms lie somewhat more mundane, though still quite complex, strivings. These may be actuated by desires for economic and social security, a favorable environment for a future family and other quite realistic—and withal quite human—motivations. Yet, even these "social" strivings, however displaced, rationalized or sublimated, can be traced to more nearly elemental sexual or parental drives and, lastly, needs for sustenance, shelter, protection from injury and other such determinants. True, what civilization we have is comprised of these cultural elaborations of our basic needs, and studies of such processes are of paramount concern to the social sciences; nevertheless the individual biodynamic conations remain fundamental.

We may, then, append the following corollaries to the first biodynamic principle of motivation:

Corollaries to principle I

Corollary 1. Physiologic determinants of behavior are mainly "unconscious," but enter awareness when the need becomes acute, or when complex and highly organized patterns of adaptation are required in the given milieu.

Corollary 2. "Physiologic" needs may serve race survival in apparent contravention to that of the individual.

* Cf. Warden, Ceni, et al. For a more extended discussion of the ethology of instinct and individual and species adaptation, see Appendix 1.

Corollary 3. The forms of behavior evoked vary with the nature and interplay of needs, and their complexity and effectiveness are contingent on the perceptive, integrative and reactive capacities of the organism.

Corollary 4. Behavior patterns may persist as a function of biologic organization after the original, direct physiologic determinants are in abeyance.

Corollary 5. Socially adaptive patterns often represent complexly contingent expressions of relatively simple needs.

Various other modifications and amplifications of the principle of motivation will be considered in relation to other biodynamic principles in succeeding sections.

The principle of environmental evaluation

Principle II: Behavior is contingent upon, and adaptive to, the organism's interpretation of its total milieu, in accordance with its inherent developmental capacities and experiences.

Metapsychologic considerations. This principle does not necessarily adopt the solipsistic position that there are as many projected "universes" as there are individuals to interpret them; in fact, it avoids any assertion whatever as to the ultimate nature of physical "reality." However interesting such metaphysical exercises may be, the natural scientist must relinquish them to the philosopher and return to the more prosaic methods of observation, comparison and induction used in science.* But with these techniques it may be shown that the reactions of an organism depend not on the *external* observer's concepts of "reality," but on the *organism's* perception, interpretation and evaluation of its milieu in relation to the satisfactions or frustrations of its own "narcissistic" needs. Thus, a termite eating away at the timbers of a

---

* Perhaps a personal anecdote may in part illustrate this distinction between the operationalism of science and the preoccupations of phenomenology. Long ago, while I was studying at the Phipps Clinic under Dr. Adolf Meyer, that inspiring teacher, in a seminar group on psychobiology, propounded the thesis that perhaps the only absolute agreements among different observers arose from a community of sense perception: e.g., a "red" object was red to everyone; a "square" one square, a "soft" one soft and so on. The author, then more ardently concerned about such arguments than he is now, objected that, after all, this seeming unanimity was only a social convention. Thus, it was perhaps convenient, in an Aristotelian sense, to assign absolute qualities to objects, whereas, "actually," one observer might have an internal image quite different from another: i.e., A might perceive an object as "green," "oblong" and "prickly," B as "brown," "oval" and "hot," and C as "white," "square" and "soft" and yet all three non-blind elephant-observers would learn to call the same object "silver," "round" and "hard" (e.g., a silver dollar) as a matter of social convention. Dr. Meyer's reply to this sophistry was typical; said he, "My dear Masserman, the Swiss have an old proverb that here applies: 'Where it doesn't itch, don't scratch.'" It took a number of years for me to realize that whereas some scratching could be justified by an honest intellectual itch, other forms of metapsychologic pursuits remained outside the area of scientific attack until some direct way of comparing the postulated "inner image" of one person with that of another could be devised.

concert hall during the performance of a symphony has no "concern" whatever with whether the composer is Mozart or Stravinsky—unless, possibly, the more vibrant bassoon passages of the latter symphonist happen to resonate on its ligneous lunch. Similarly, a dog in a so-called "conditioning" experiment pays no "attention" to the sound of a bell or a metronome unless (a) he is hungry, thirsty or restless, (b) he has learned that the sound signalizes the availability of food, water or escape, and (c) he is not otherwise interested* in the satiation of another more pressing need at the moment. Man himself, utilizing his almost incomparable versatility of sense perception, his abilities to remember, compare and abstract, and his "reasoning" by manifold operational tests, has explored the universe in more directions and more thoroughly than has any other animal—and yet no two men agree exactly in concepts or in actions as to the nature of that universe. Judged by the phenomena of behavior, therefore, "reality" is a highly relative set of postulates contingent on the particular sensory, apperceptive, mnemonic, integrative and operational capacities and experiences of the organism in question.

Symbolism and generalization. Two interrelated applications of the principle of milieu-interpretation may be considered immediately: the formation of "symbols" and their "projective" generalizations. To begin with simple experimental examples:

EXPERIMENT 2. **Sign and symbol formation**

A kitten learns that depressing a disc connected to an electric switch causes a pellet of salmon to drop into a food box. When hungry, the animal enters the laboratory voluntarily, approaches the experimenter confidently, leaps into the feeding-cage when the door is opened and repeatedly works the switch to obtain food. The switch, the cage, the experimenter and the laboratory have, in that order of generalization, come to "symbolize" to the animal satisfaction of its needs, and it "attends to" and manipulates these proximate configurations (whatever their "representation" may be in its so-called "consciousness" or "unconscious mind") until it reaches the ultimate "goal" of food. Moreover, various spreads of symbolism occur; the kitten shows no fear of food-boxes, experimental apparatus or human beings "in general" unless or until one of these frustrates or hurts it. Then, depending on the animal's interpretation of the nature and circumstances of this hurt, either it will react with a generalized aversion to all food-boxes and their associated configurations, or it will gradually work out whatever distinctions it can make between "satisfying" and "hurtful" food-boxes, cages or experimenters, and adapt to them according to its behavioral potentialities under the circumstances (see Experiments 9 ff.).

EXPERIMENT 3. **Generalization of symbolic aversion**

Another normal kitten of the same age is permitted to play about in a small cage. It steps on the same disc-switch which this time causes a

---

* In this sense, *"inter-est"* has the significant meaning of *existing* or *living among* only those evaluations of organismic-environmental relationships (the "biosphere" of Angyal) that have motivational and apperceptive reference to the participant organism.

light to flash and the kitten to receive a physically harmless but frightening condenser shock. Several repetitions of this experience are enough to produce a marked change in behavior. The kitten stops its free play in the cage, cowers away from the switch and escapes from the experimental cage at the first opportunity. Even outside the cage it avoids anything that looks or smells like the switch, runs away from sudden light flashes or other sensory elements in the traumatic configuration and will not approach the experimenter in the laboratory. Moreover, these active aversions may appear on retest after twenty months of absence from the original experimental situation.

Obviously, we cannot know in what gray universe, or in what peculiarly feline space-time axis, these two animals formed their individual associations: all we observe is that, operationally speaking, the same "objects" which we call "switch, cage, experimenter," etc., come to symbolize opposite "qualities" if not actually "things" to the two animals. Consider now these behavior phenomena at a different level of evolution.

Case 28. Symbol-generalization; "positive transference"

A child is raised by parents who shower him with affection and shield him from all possible disappointments and frustrations. The child is outgoing, bold to the point of "unrealistic" audacity, and friendly though demanding with strangers. Sooner or later, of course, he makes other extrafamilial contacts and is forced to face the difference between his doting parents on the one hand and outraged teachers or unsympathetic truant officers on the other. On the whole, nevertheless, he will tend to act according to his predominant evaluation of grown-ups and continue to expect tolerance and indulgence.

Case 29. Symbol-generalization; "negative transference"

Another child early in life learns to associate his parents, and particularly his father, with deprivations, frustrations or physical hurts. He becomes distrustful of all adults, resentful of authority and defensively hostile. During his schooling the child will tend to regard his teachers as parent-surrogates who must be overtly placated but covertly regarded with suspicion and treated with counter-aggressions; similarly, should the child be sent to a psychiatrist, the latter too will initially become the victim of the same prejudices. Moreover, false semantic generalization of mistrusted parental "imagos" may spread to the point at which the child, grown to adulthood, may feel an irrational antagonism to Catholic priests because of the adverse connotation of the term Father; so also, he may become a militant advocate of obligatory state care for all children from birth through adolescence or beyond.

MASOCHISM. Patients who ostensibly arrange to be frustrated or hurt in their sexual or other social relationships have been regarded either as expiating some unconscious guilt in a "need for punishment," or else as directly expressing the "death instinct" by "self-mutilation." From a biodynamic standpoint, however, neither of these somewhat strained and paradoxical explanations is necessary, since masochism implies merely that certain experiences, though they may appear unpleasant or painful to an observer, are sought by an organism when it associates them with previous satisfactions of quite normal needs (cf. p. 58f.). The biodynamics of this process may be illustrated by the following observations:

Erofeyeva (1916) observed that if a hungry dog were fed only after a mild electric shock to its leg, it would soon learn not only to withstand the pain calmly, but would give various indications of welcoming the experience preliminary to the feeding. Significantly, however, if the current were made so strong as to cause tissue destruction, the dog's reactions to the shock signals were rapidly reversed, and a contrary generalization supervened in which the dog would not tolerate even weak electrical stimuli (in Pavlovian terms, an ultraparadoxical reaction). In effect, the animal could be said to show "enjoyment" of mild pain only insofar as the latter mediated the eventual satisfaction of its hunger; conversely, the animal actively avoided any painful stimuli that resulted in a tissue injury which overbalanced the total gain of the feeding situation.

"Regression to masochism" may likewise occur. Levy (1933) tenderly nursed a puppy with a broken leg to complete recovery; six years later, when jealous of another pet brought into the home, the animal began limping again as though literally in physical pain.

In our own laboratory (Exp. 1, p. 58), cats were taught not only to feed after a mild grid-shock, but to depress a switch to administer the shock to themselves before feeding. In these experiments the spread of symbolization appeared even more clearly, in that when barriers were put in the way of the food reward some animals depressed the switch repeatedly as though to experience at least the intermediate goal of the painful shock in the uncompleted feeding-situation. If, however, the food was indefinitely withheld or the electric shock was made too severe, this "self-punitive" behavior rapidly disappeared.

Humans, too, will undergo great discomforts—and may do so with "masochistic" enthusiasm and gusto—to achieve symbolically valued goals. Herewith a range of examples:

Slutskaya (1928) demonstrated that human infants could be made to show pleasurable anticipation of a previously resented needle-prick if it were repeatedly followed by feeding, provided only that the stimulus was not made excessively painful.

An avidly "henpecked" husband cheerfully endured—and indeed provoked—tongue-lashings or even physical attacks from his wife not because of the intrinsic charm of such experiences, but because of regressive attempts to hark back from stressful adult living to a childhood state in which the severe discipline of his parents, however unpleasant in itself, nevertheless symbolized protection and security.

A "sexual masochist" attained his first orgasms under circumstances of discomfort or pain and reenacted these experiences through flagellation or other "perverse" erotic practices.

A draftee who had avidly accepted from his overprotective parents many warnings of the physical and social dangers of army life "accidentally" mangled his hand in a machine just before a call to military service.

A Hindu fakir inflicts physical torture upon himself so that after many reincarnations, he may at last attain the ineffable peace and beatitude of Nirvana.*

TRANSFERENCE RELATIONSHIPS. Another biodynamic principle of projective milieu-interpretation is that no patient ever approaches a therapist—even one of whom he "knows" nothing—with completely unbiased attitudes. Instead (cf. Cases 28 and 29), the physician, however

* Other aspects of masochism and the dynamics of suicide are discussed in Appendices 3 and 4.

neutral, is inevitably invested with the qualities of character that the patient had attributed to other persons on whom he had previously been dependent, or who had been in positions of welcome or conflictful authority over him. Inevitably, since the patient formed his patterns of interpersonal relationships in his childhood, he tends to cast the therapist mainly in the role of a parent-surrogate, and to "transfer" to him the complex mixtures of dependence, trust, fear, rivalry or hate that characterized the patient's own early familial relationships. In fact, an analysis of the patient's unconscious prejudices in this regard often yields indispensable data as to his generalized interpersonal relationships and social conflicts. Accordingly, the recognition, interpretation and skillful handling of the patient's *transference relationships* constitute perhaps the most useful techniques not only in formal psychoanalysis (cf. Appendix 3) but in general psychiatric therapy.

Corollaries to principle II

The following corollaries may, then, be appended to the biodynamic principle of experiential interpretation and adaptation:

Corollary 1. This principle has no metaphysical bearing on the "ultimate" or "real" nature of the universe, nor does it have teleologic or eschatologic import.

Corollary 2. An organism "recognizes" and reacts only to those stimuli (1) to which it is physiologically sensitive, and (2) which concern its needs.

Corollary 3. "Masochistic" behavior may be manifested by an organism when such behavior mediates the satisfaction of concealed needs.

Corollary 4. The interpretations of stimuli may be spread by experiential association to related configurations and thus predetermine generalizations of "meaning" and attitude.

Corollary 5. This spread is manifested socially in the sphere of "interpersonal" relationships and in the clinical phenomena of transference.

References

Leeper, R.: The Role of Motivation in Learning.
Landis, C., et al.: Sex and Development.
Maslow, A. H.: A Theory of Human Motivation.
Masserman, J. H.: Behavior and Neurosis (Part III with selected references).
Pavlov, I. P.: Lectures on Conditioned Reflexes; 25 Years of Objective Study of the Higher Nervous Activity (Behavior) of Animals.
Richter, C. P.: Biology of Drives.
Ryans, D. G.: Motivation in Learning.
Skinner, B. F.: The Behavior of Organisms.
Stekel, W.: Sadism and Masochism.
Stevens, S. S.: A Handbook of Experimental Psychology.
Thorndike, E. L.: Human Learning.
Tolman, E. C.: Purposive Behavior in Animals and Men.
Warden, C. J.: Animal Motivation.
Watson, J.: Hedonistic Theories from Aristippus to Spencer.

Chapter 10

The principle of substitution

Principle III: Behavior patterns tend to become deviated or fragmented under stress and, when further impeded, assume substitutive and symbolic forms.

Interrelationship of various adaptive patterns

In most animals, the physiologic economy is sufficiently versatile so that the frustration of one need can, in part at least, be offset by the satiation of another. At the metabolic level lack of carbohydrates may be balanced by an increased intake of proteins, from which the body can then manufacture part of its sugar requirements. Conversely, various types of activity may be evoked by the same biologic need: a chilled animal may secure its required warmth by building a nest, by an added intake of high-caloric foods or by increased muscular movement. Obviously, obstruction of one of these patterns will favor attempts to channelize behavior into the others.

Summation of need-satiation. There may also be a minimal level of composite satisfactions so that the thwarting of one mode of gratification will lead to overemphasis on another. For instance, rats given insufficient water to drink will eat or hoard unusually large quantities of food even though the latter cannot supply the necessary body fluids (Hunt, 1941). Similarly, animals will partially compensate for sexual deprivation by excessive feeding, fighting or other activities only remotely related to erotic or procreative goals.

Substitution of part-activities to represent or "symbolize" complete satiation. Under more general frustration, the organism may select from a previously total pattern of adaptation some segment on which it then concentrates in lieu of the unattainable whole. The following experiment exemplifies this fragmentation and fixation:

EXPERIMENT 4. **Fixation on part-patterns**

An animal is trained to press a large disc switch that operates a mechanical feeder. When the way to the food is barred, the animal persists in working the switch, and may even sit on it for long periods as though in partial compensation for the lack of food. The animal may also walk about the cage pressing other objects even though they offer little direct resemblance to the switch: e.g., pulleys, pieces of paper or even the tails of other cats.

However, an animal accustomed to work the switch for food may occasionally take apparent satisfaction in doing so even after its hunger is completely satiated—much as humans continue to labor, apparently for the sheer joy of piling up "profits," long after these can no longer gratify any "realistic" personal needs. In this way the *mode* of satisfaction may in itself take on a conative role that in some respects seems to become independent of the original physiologic objective.

Substitution of intermediate goals. Behavior may also become deviated toward *proximately associated* or *intermediate* goals, as illustrated in an extension of one of the experiments already cited:

EXPERIMENT 5. Substitutive goals

An animal learns to work a switch that flashes a light and deposits a pellet of food in a hinged food box. When the feeder is disconnected, the animal continues to manipulate the switch for the light alone; in fact, it may nuzzle the switch repeatedly or reach for and manipulate the bulb (though never attempt to "open" either) as though they objectively represented the food-box itself.

Similarly, Pavlov reported that when his dogs did not receive their food reward after an accustomed light or sound signal, they would show substitutive interests in, and direct their part-consummatory activities toward, the "conditioned" signals as goals in themselves; e.g., they would actually lick the signal bulb, or, when the bell rang, snap at the air as though to swallow the sound.

The cherished lock of hair (natural or false), the pounded table in a heated argument, the religious fetish treasured as an augury of heaven—these and other symbolic substitutives in human behavior may be mentioned as paradigms.

Aggression. Another easily observed characteristic of human behavior is the hostility directed against any frustrating object or person, sometimes including one's own body. Destructive and concurrently self-injurious expressions of this tendency are so common that a universal drive toward dissolution and death (Thanatos) became part of Freudian theory. However, that "aggressive" (Latin, to move toward) behavior is economically intended merely to eliminate physical or animate obstructions from the path of satisfaction is indicated by experimental observations such as the following:

EXPERIMENT 6. Frustration, aggression and dominance

PHYSICAL. A cat or monkey trained to press a switch, open a door and lift the lid of a reward box to secure food will, if these objects are rendered experimentally inoperative, attempt to manipulate them with increasing strenuousness, and may finally attack them so viciously as to injure its own snout, teeth and claws.

SOCIAL. When two animals are trained together to respond to a signal by opening a food-box, the more alert and agile of the two—though not necessarily the stronger—will generally secure the food reward, whereas the other will gradually cease to respond to the signal. During this period little or no fighting occurs; each cat simply adapts to its own abilities to control the situation. If, however, the successful cat becomes accustomed to being dominant, but is subsequently prevented from securing the food either (a) by the introduction into the cage of a still more preemptive animal or (b) by being made neurotically phobic to the signal or the food itself (cf. Exp. 9), the experimental subject becomes definitely aggressive, particularly toward the newly dominant cat. Conversely, if the displaced or neurotic subject is permitted to dominate the situation again, this aggressivity abates as the original food-directed behavior becomes reestablished.

Aggressive patterns, then, appear when needs are frustrated (1) by external obstacles, (2) by interorganismic rivalries or (3) by "internal" conflicts; conversely, they tend to disappear when these are overcome.

Human complexities

Such experiments lead to a much needed pruning of the theory of aggression in line with the principle of parsimony; nonetheless, it remains true that so many influences converge on ("overdetermine" is the peculiar psychoanalytic term) human behavior that simple formulae, however attractive, may be misleading. For instance, as has been shown by Razran experimentally and Benedek and Rubinstein clinically, the "maternal instinct" is correlated with the menstrual hormonal cycle, yet witness in the following example the widely divergent expressions of this drive as affected by personal and cultural experiences, derived techniques and values, and current milieu:

Case 30.   Range of substitutive and symbolic patterns

A married woman with strong conscious or unconscious maternal cravings finds herself incapable of bearing children. To begin with, if she is unaware of the reasons for her sterility, she may consult a gynecologist for a physical examination and diagnosis, have the fecundity of her husband's semen checked, follow any indicated medical or surgical procedures to correct his or her sterility, and then have intercourse under conditions most favorable to impregnation—an elaborate but direct and progressive course toward her final goal of maternity. Or, still acting "normally," she may accept her own sterility as an inevitable frustration and attempt to satisfy her maternal longings by substitutive means: e.g., adopting a child, or becoming a kindergarten teacher. If these outlets are blocked by external circumstances or by inner conflicts involving covert aggressions toward children, her behavior may become more deviously symbolic: she may keep cats or parrots, or found a pet hospital, or promote an antivivisection society—in all of which activities her behavior could range from "normal" to the borderline of what most observers would characterize as idiosyncratic or fanatic (cf. footnote, p. 38). Or, if such substitutive gratifications prove inadequate, she may abandon all direct or indirect efforts to resolve her specifically maternal needs and attempt instead to seek substitutive satisfactions for alternative narcissistic, erotic or other para-maternal urges: e.g., in regressive dependency, sexual promiscuity, multiple marriages, racial or economic hostilities, or various other displacements and deviant consummations.

Her behavior as thus far postulated may as yet have remained within the limits of the socially acceptable—unless, of course, it is complicated by an excessive resort to drugs or by a furor of anxious activity reaching the hypomanic level (cf. Case 20). However, if these diversions alone should prove inadequate while the repressed maternal drives continue strong and undeniable, their satisfactions by more abstractly symbolic, fantastic or "dereistic" devices might be attempted, in which case her behavior will become "neurotic" or "psychotic." For example, the woman, still driven by her unconscious desires to be pregnant, may express them "psychosomatically" by developing functional amenorrhea, morning nausea or even pseudocyetic abdominal and mammary enlargement and false labor pains at her supposed "term." If, on the other hand, her wishful fantasies harden into delusions, she may insist that she is pregnant despite all external evidences to the contrary, and invest her belief with various grandiose, persecutory, religious or other ideational content; e.g., that she had been "drugged and raped," or that she is destined "to give birth to a new Messiah" (cf. Case 21).

It is evident, then, that the progressive deviations of behavior sketched above range from the "normal" through what various observers would call "socially unadaptable," "borderline," "neurotic" or definitely "psychotic," depending on the latitude of the substitutive satisfactions or symbolic equivalences permitted to fall within the "meanings" of these designations. The relativity of all diagnostic terms will be more fully discussed in their clinical context, but it is important to note here that the biodynamic principle of substitution and symbolism subsumes an almost infinite diversity and complexity of human behavioral patterns.

Hedonic level.   It has sometimes been assumed in analytic theory that every form of gratification can be assigned a "libidinal" weight, and that the total satisfactions from all sources must reach a necessary minimum before the individual can attain contentment and stability. Clinically, however, it may be observed that the pleasures derived from any particular activity differ widely from person to person and that the minimal level varies even more; further, these presumed quanta also vary from day to day in the same individual. Thus, to take a commonplace example, a person may sincerely state that he "would rather play [tennis, bridge, string quartettes or at love] than eat," whereas his choice at any given moment would actually depend on a multitude of intercurrent factors, and in any case would hold true only within fairly narrow limits. For example, four hours of quartette-playing generally makes even the most ardent chamber musician demand a muscular and prandial respite before a Haydn viola part can reexert its charms. So also, Brozek has shown that the thoughts and dreams of college students on a near-starvation diet change rather quickly from their usual competitive or erotic preoccupations to persistent images of prosaic food.

Regression.   In psychoanalysis, this term is applied to the readoption of "earlier" or more "primitive" behavior patterns when later ones are frustrated or rendered conflictful. The term *earlier* is obviously redundant, since the organism, frustrated in some current mode of behavior, can evoke only from its past experiences some other pattern to fill the void; nor need this substitution actually be a more *primitive* type of activity. Here again a simple experimental example may illustrate the point.

EXPERIMENT 7. "Regression" to more complex adaptations

A cat is taught to depress a switch three times in succession to secure a pellet of food—a bit of "counting behavior" that most cats can easily learn.* The animal is then given food only if it presses the switch a single time, and this secondary retraining is continued until the triple-depression response apparently disappears and the single-depression one becomes well established in its stead. If now the food-box is held shut so that the animal cannot feed, several interesting phenomena appear. After numerous single depressions of the switch, sometimes with increasing violence, the animal eventually abandons it, plays vigorously with other objects, drinks much water, courts petting, attempts to leave the cage, or shows other substitutive activity. Eventually, however, it returns to the switch, but instead of depressing it only once, reverts to the triple-depression technique before seeking the food reward, and if food is forthcoming returns to the triple response indefinitely. In effect, the frustrated animal, after trying various substitutive activities, regresses to an earlier pattern, but *not* one that is simpler or more "primitive."

This example, elementary as it is, raises an important issue in clinical biodynamics; namely, that moderate frustration of "adult" adjustments does not necessarily result in "regressive" deterioration of conduct; on the contrary, it is a matter of common observation that behavior of even greater complexity may be evoked to maintain the over-all level of need-gratification. Thus, a wealthy man may elect to live in idle luxury, but should he lose his wealth he may again muster previously learned skills and develop complex social adaptations rather than starve, depend on charity, or become neurotic or psychotic. Which of these courses he takes will be determined by his level of necessary satisfactions, his capacities, and the ingrained though latent adaptive tendencies developed in his earlier life experiences.

Cultural factors in hedonic level

The culture with which a subject identifies has an obvious influence on the number, type and intensities of the satisfactions to which he becomes accustomed. Moreover, since cultures vary widely in these respects this consideration, too, has important clinical applications.

For example, many an exchange student from Oriental or other comparatively leisurely cultures who matriculates at an American university is bewildered by the furor of scholastic, athletic, social and recreational activities and may need a long period of adjustment or adaptational guidance before his mode of living can be made elaborate and hurried enough to suit his new cultural milieu.

So also, an "upper class" civil servant accustomed to a wide variety of cultivated satisfactions in his home country cannot easily encompass a sudden

---

* Monkeys, as Levitt, Aarons and I have also shown, can be taught to select as a cue for a food reward only that object in five that differs subtly in color, form, size or design from all the others in rapidly varying tests—thus showing an ability to grasp a highly abstruse principle of "oddity" (Levitt, Aarons and Masserman, 1960). In control studies, this problem baffled human competitors, some of whom continued to claim an exclusive capacity for "abstract thought."

shift to the primitive life of some colonial outpost. Under such circumstances he may keep the symbolic forms of his culture by having four-o'clock tea, importing a grand piano and dressing for dinner in the wilderness. This denial of isolation and nostalgia may or may not be sufficient to keep him from substitutive license, liquor or lechery, or from finally breaking under the strain of continued social deprivations.

Fortunately, the human organism seems capable of adjusting to major changes in the nature, amounts and modes of his gratifications, provided only that the adaptations required are gradual and do not give rise to too much internal conflict.

Substitution of part-activities in lieu of total patterns

This device, too, has a wide range of applications. Some of these have already been noted, and the following may be added:

Expression and gesture. As Darwin has shown, "emotional expression" in animals and men consists of movements of the face and body that convey the intent of the subject to an alert observer. For instance, a person "looks suspicious" if his narrowed, shifting glance and wary restless posture reveal an apprehension of expected danger; or he "looks angry" when his dilated pupils, flushed face, set jaw and tensed musculature indicate that he is suppressing or repressing aggressive action. However, gestures and rituals may also take on highly complex symbolic and cultural mimetics.

The ardent communist may not dare to put into practice his plans for violent revolution, but he can raise his clenched fist in unison with his comrades in signification of a threat against the "oppressive capitalist-imperialist" world. Similarly, the captured Nazi officer, unable to relinquish his fantasies of invincibility, arrogantly raises his right hand high in the Fascist pose to indicate that he is of a race "superior" to those who salute by a "decadent" arm-to-brow movement reminiscent of pulling the forelock. But gestures (kinesics) and auxiliary speech-sounds may differ widely from culture to culture: an extension of the tongue may be a token of respect in China, and a hiss in Japan—unpleasant to Western ears—is a signal of sibilant submission.

Part-goals. Among many obvious exemplifications are these:

Too many students in our preparatory school system (and too many in college) concentrate on getting good marks in their "courses" as though such grades were significant ends in themselves, and give little or no thought as to the purposes and goals of educational experience.

Adolescents barred from direct erotic gratification spend a good deal of time and energy in mastering dance forms permitting much physical contact and freedom of motion, and thereafter remain intent upon such partial contrectative devices.

The aging bookkeeper who, after years of failure, has relinquished his ambitions to rise to office manager continues to waste his narrow efforts on getting the neatest possible page completed precisely on an irrationally rigid schedule.

In fact, a tragic proportion of human living seems to be concentrated on the relatively insignificant part-goals of the moment: preoccupation with the spotless pantry, the exact overtime pay, the bridge score. A person in our culture must be inhibited and conflictful indeed before his preoccupations with minutiae and ritual are considered obsessive-compulsive enough to be labeled "neurotic."

"Symptom" formation. The substitutive significance of many syndromes is often evident even on superficial examination. For instance, the exhibitionism, masturbatory movements and climactic tempo of a hysterical pseudo-epileptic attack (cf. Case 14) deviate and partially relieve the erotic tensions which the patient must otherwise repress; similarly, vomiting, diarrhea or other "psychosomatic dysfunctions" (cf. Case 39) often indicate rejecting, aggressive or other unconscious desires not permitted to reach more direct and pervasive expression (*Practice*, Chapter 12).

Aggression. Experimental approaches to the dynamics of this response pattern have already been examined. Clinically, the etiology of reactive hostility may emerge for direct interpretation during the course of psychotherapy when the patient becomes irrationally angry because the therapist cannot fulfill the role of parent, slave, love object, wizard or other desired functionary wishfully assigned (psychoanalytically, *transferred*) to him in the patient's fantasies. Under these circumstances, the patient may also become more intensely involved in special forms of work, recreation, sexuality, sports and other activities in which his hostility finds overt or covert expression* in a variety of displaced interpersonal relationships.

Corollaries to principle III

The following corollaries may, then, be appended to the biodynamic principle of substitutive behavior:

Corollary 1. The substitution of behavior patterns is facilitated by the partial interdependence of bodily needs and the interchangeability of their modes of satisfaction.

Corollary 2. The minimal hedonic level is contingent on variable personal, cultural and intercurrent factors.

Corollary 3. When end-goals are difficult of attainment behavior is directed toward proximate or subsidiary goals.

Corollary 4. In circumstances of frustration, part-satisfactions may serve symbolically in lieu of total consummatory patterns.

Corollary 5. Under such circumstances conations may also be deviated into substitutive aggressivity. This phenomenon, however, cannot be directly translated into terms of group behavior.

---

* The forms of social aggressivity, of course, also vary widely from culture to culture. For instance, the Kwakiutl Indian of the Pacific Northwest, when he felt wronged, gave away all his property at a ceremonial *potlach*, whereupon the person who wronged him was forced by tribal custom to do the same (Young, 1943).

References

Alexander, F.: Our Age of Unreason (Part II).
Allee, W. C.: The Social Life of Animals.
Barker, R., Dembo, T., and Lewin, K.: Frustration and Regression.
Dollard, J.: Hostility and Fear in Social Life.
Kardiner, A.: The Individual and His Society.
Luria, A. R.: The Nature of Human Conflicts.
Masserman, J. H.: Behavior and Neurosis (Part III, with selected references).
Murchison, C.: Handbook of Social Psychology.
Simmel, E.: Self-Preservation and the Death Instinct.
Sullivan, H. S.: Psychiatry: Introduction to the Study of Interpersonal Relations.

Chapter 11

The effects of conflict

Principle IV: When, in a given milieu, two or more motivations come into conflict in the sense that their accustomed consummatory patterns are partially or wholly incompatible, kinetic tension (anxiety) mounts and behavior becomes hesitant, vacillating, erratic and seemingly maladaptive (i.e., neurotic) or excessively substitutive or symbolic (i.e., "psychotic").

Various concepts of conflict

Reflexologic. The role of conflict in neurotic behavior has been recognized in many psychologic theories. In Pavlovian reflexology, neurosis was explained on the basis of an opposition between cortical "excitation" and "inhibition," with the following experiment (performed in 1913 by Shenger-Krestovnikova) as a paradigm:

EXPERIMENT 8. Conflictful "discriminatory reflexes"

A dog was shown a circle marked on a card and was trained to salivate in expectation of a food reward given after each display of this "conditional stimulus," thus establishing an "excitatory reflex." As a differential response, the animal was trained *not* to salivate ("inhibitory reflex") if the card was marked with a definitely oblate ellipse. When the differential discrimination between the two "conditional" signals was well established, the ellipse was gradually made more circular until its axes approached the ratio of 8:9, a point at which the dog could apparently no longer distinguish the "excitatory" circle from the "inhibitory" ellipse. At this stage of the experiment the animal showed erratic salivation, ceased to feed, howled, and struggled against the harness and became restless and uncooperative in further training.

Gantt, Liddell and their associates produced similar behavioral aberrations in animals by the process of exceeding an animal's capacity to make discriminative adaptations to "conditional signals," and also recognized some of the neurotigenic effects of the monotony, frustration and restraint necessitated by the usual "conditioning" procedures. Unfortunately, since motivation, environmental configurations and interpretations, interorganismic transactions and many other contingent influences were traditionally excluded from consideration in Pavlovian theory, other reflexologists did not exploit the full biodynamic significance of their illuminating findings. Instead, they continued to regard experimental neuroses exclusively in terms of cerebrocortical disturbances created by opposing "discriminative reflexes"; in this monothetic approach, the many adaptive tribulations of an animal physically restrained by a previously trusted experimenter and inescapably forced to face an insoluble problem were largely ignored. Nevertheless, the key Pavlovian concept of "conflict between excitatory and inhibitory processes" remained cogent, and was eventually translated into biodynamic terms by expanding "reflex" to include total response, amending the meaning of "inhibition" to its actual behavioral connotation of *positive* (i.e., "excitatory") action in a direction opposite to some former pattern, and, finally, recognizing the conflict as occurring when two or more incompatible patterns of total response are elicited simultaneously in an ambivalent field. The advantages of this translation of terms and meanings will emerge more clearly in later connections.

Psychoanalytic concepts of conflict.   In psychoanalytic theory, too, conflict is given a leading role in the etiology of neuroses. Freud made the penetrating observation that "anxiety is the source of all neuroses," and then, in effect, defined anxiety as an inner sense which warns the "Ego" (adaptive capacities) to "defend itself" against an impending and dangerous "intrapsychic" conflict when the latter threatens to erupt in disruptive behavior. Unfortunately, the essential nature of this conflict was not traced more clearly to its biodynamic roots in incompatible needs and adaptations and was left at the figurative level of "complexes" or clashes between disparate "portions" of the personality such as "the Id" (comprised of primeval "drives" or "instincts") and the "Superego" (the assimilated, or "introjected" precepts and patterns of the culture, especially as mediated through the parents). Unfortunately, this attractively simple but conceptually rather naive system of "metapsychology" (Chapter 3) can be applied theoretically only to human beings, and even so omits, excludes or contradicts much in neurophysiology, ethology, communication theory, sociology and other disciplines that is essential to an understanding of human behavior. Apart from this, and from a more basic scientific standpoint, it is not amenable to direct experimental or empiric demonstration and therefore can be correlated with total behavioral phenomena only when it, too, is translated into operational terms as discussed below.

Biodynamic correlations.   In review, both reflexologic and psychoanalytic theories can be clarified biodynamically as follows:

REFLEXOLOGY.   In biodynamic theory the concept of "reflex" is expanded to include the *total* reaction of the organism to its perceptions of its milieu, and all "conditioning" is a progressive adaptation of behavior to cumulative experience. Similarly, "excitation," "extinction," "inhibition," etc., are regarded as *positive and total* adaptive patterns, which, however, cannot be directly equated (as conditioning theory contends) with simple *neurologic* patterns of "excitation" or "inhibition" of specific pathways or areas in the cerebral cortex, but rather are part of the integrated functioning of the entire organism.

PSYCHOANALYSIS.   On the other hand, biodynamic theory can be correlated with psychoanalytic metapsychology if "instincts," "libido" and other such conative terms are traced to their sources in biologic

Plate IV

A. *Control Observations.*   A cat has been trained to pass a barrier at a signal light (upper right flash) and open the food-box for a pellet of food. The animal's behavior is goal-directed and efficiently adaptive.

B. *Conflictful Experience.*   At a later feeding signal the cat is subjected to a mild air blast at the moment of food-taking. The animal is shown recoiling from the unexpected, uncontrollable and thereby potentially threatening (i.e., "traumatic") situation.

C. *Neurotic Behavior.*   After five such experiences at irregular intervals the animal refuses to feed or approach the box and develops other neurotic aberrations of behavior described in the text (pp. 134 ff.). Although starved for 48 hours, the animal is here shown in a typical phobic response to a feeding signal: crouched away from the food in cataleptic immobility against an impassable barrier.

D. *Transference Retraining.*   After four months of neurosis, the animal is retrained by manual feeding and gentle guidance once again to feed from the box. At first, the animal does so only when being petted by the author; later, feeding responses may be reconstituted in response not only to the light but even to the air blast (nozzle shown in deep left corner).

E. *Therapeutic Result.*   After 18 days of such retraining the animal's neurotic reactions largely disappear and it once again passes barriers for food at the light or air-blast signal.

F. *"Masochistic" Patterns.*   Another animal, trained to depress an electric switch for its feeding signals, and also given mild, then increasingly strong electric shocks at the time of food-taking, is here shown manipulating the switch with spontaneous avidity to experience the shock as a symbolic part-satisfaction with or without the food reward.

Plate IV. **The biodynamics of an experimental neurosis***

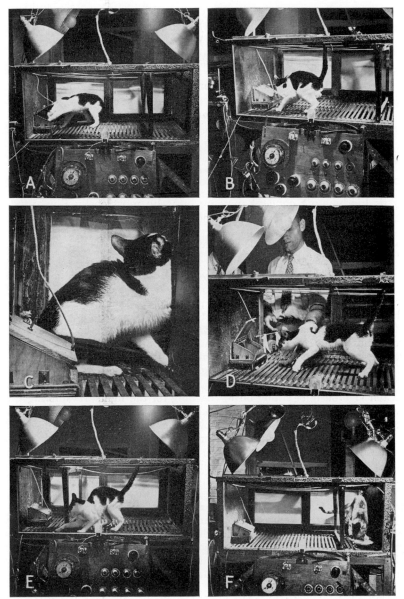

 * For a description of motion picture films of these and other experimental studies
see Appendix 2.

needs, and if the Ego is considered to be merely a generic term translatable as the integrated adaptive capacities of the organism. Similarly, the Superego is equated with (a) mnemonically patterned aversions to repeating past sufferings or adverse experiences (provided "suffering" and "adversity" are weighted according to the organism's own behavioral evaluations), as opposed to (b) a tendency to strive toward need-satisfying identifications (Ego-Ideal). As may be seen, this translation of terms offers certain conceptual advantages: data in any field of human or animal behavior may be recorded in terms of objective biologic observation, comparisons may be made from field to field with an operationally meaningful terminology, and tentative "principles" can be derived which, since they do not constitute a rigid *a priori* system, may be expanded or modified as new facts are discovered and new correlations emerge (cf. Chapter 8).

Incompatibility of adaptive patterns

This biodynamic concept may perhaps be most easily illustrated by citing its direct application in the production of an experimental neurosis:

EXPERIMENT 9   (cf. Plate IV).   Production of an experimental neurosis

A cat (or a rat, dog, or monkey) is trained to respond to the flash of a light and/or the sound of a bell by opening a box to secure a pellet of food, and is then further trained to depress a switch to operate these feeding-signals at will. During the period of its training the animal is friendly to the experimenter, enters the training cage eagerly, and operates the switch readily and effectively; indeed, the animal sometimes continues to do so even after its hunger is satiated. When the feeding responses are prevented by disconnecting the switch, interposing barriers, locking the food-box, or failing to drop the food after the signals, the animal indulges in substitutive behavior such as striking the disc switch vigorously or sitting on it, reaching for the lights, reexploring the cage, playing with the wires and barriers, or attempting to attract the experimenter by approaching as close as the cage will permit and scratching or mewing for his attention. Soon, however, the animal adapts to the new situation by ignoring the signals and the food-box, although without developing any signs of aversion to the switch, the signals, the cage or the experimenter. Moreover, the animal can easily be retrained to abandon its substitutive activities and resume working the switch whenever the food-reward is again made regularly available.

If, however, on several irregularly spaced occasions the animal is permitted to work the switch and reach for the food, but is at that moment subjected to a mild, physiologically harmless but unexpected air blast or electric shock, the situation obviously becomes motivationally conflictful. The switch-signal configuration still represents the possibility of satisfying hunger, providing the animal responds with its learned adaptive behavior of taking the food deposited in the box, but the same configuration now also threatens the animal with an unpleasant experience which can be avoided only by an exactly opposite pattern of behavior. In effect, then, equally urgent but contraposed needs and their incompatible patterns of expression are in conflict. Under these circumstances, remarkable changes in the total behavior of the animal occur along lines that so clearly correspond to neurotic patterns in the human that, for purposes of comparison, the two classes of observation may be juxtaposed under the following headings.

ANXIETY. The animal crouches, trembles, shows horripilation, dilated pupils and retracted nictitating membranes, breathes rapidly, shallowly and irregularly, has a fast, pounding pulse and a markedly increased blood pressure. Special studies reveal increased epinephrine and 17-ketosteroid content and gastrointestinal stasis, diminished clotting time and other bodily changes indicative of the mobilization of various physiologic resources and "emergency mechanisms." These manifestations of motor and sympathetic tension, then, parallel those that accompany the subjective experience of normal and neurotic anxiety in the human.

PHOBIAS, STARTLE REACTIONS AND HYPERSENSITIVITY TO STIMULI. The manifestations of anxiety above noted increase markedly when the light or bell signals are given, when the animal is forced toward the food-box by a movable barrier, or when, though hungry, it is offered food pellets similar to those that it formerly secured in the box. Moreover, these aversions quickly become more generalized: the animal resists being put into the experimental cage and immediately attempts to escape from it; it avoids the experimental room and, in many cases, the experimenter himself. Similarly, even when it is replaced in its accustomed home cage it shows severe startle reactions and phobic aversions to sudden lights or sounds, to constricted spaces or to restraint, and especially to any sensory stimuli in the modality associated with its "traumatic experience": e.g., the click of an electric switch, or even the scarcely perceptible sound of an air current from an insect sprayer used in the animal room.

The most trenchant examples of similar reactions in the human being occur in the so-called "acute war neuroses." Consider, for instance, the following hypothetical, though clinically typical case:

Case 31. Acute combat neurosis

A military trainee without adequate preparation or "seasoning" is suddenly subjected to the carnage, destruction and immediate personal danger attendant on front-line combat. All his motivations are, of course, self-preservative, but he cannot implement them through immediate escape because, at the same time, deeply ingrained and contrary patterns of self-preservation through patriotism, group loyalties, hostility against a common enemy and considerations of his social safety confine him to the battlefield. He is, therefore, torn among insistent but apparently mutually exclusive patterns of adaptation which make it impossible for him to resolve the situation by the usual devices of compromise, flight or fight. If, then, his integrative capacities are further weakened by fatigue, he becomes incapable of handling the disruptive internal stresses so engendered and begins to suffer overwhelming anxiety accompanied by severe physiologic dysfunctions such as tachycardia, tremors, gastrointestinal dysfunctions, motor disturbances, alterations of consciousness, etc. At this point, he may actually welcome even a moderately serious wound or inflict one on himself, and feel euphoria instead of pain while being evacuated. Thereafter, any threatened return to the site of his traumatic experiences, actual or fancied, induces a recurrence of his anxiety to the point of panic; and even in the relative safety of the base hospital he shows hypersensitivity and phobic reactions to any perceptual configurations symbolic of these experiences. For instance, bed-sides cannot be tolerated because they are reminiscent of the inescapable confinement of the fox-hole, and the buzz of a fly or the striking of a match produces reactions comparable to those produced by the dive of a strafing plane or the explosion of a mortar-shell (cf. Ross, Gillespie (1941), Grinker (1943), Glass (1952)).

Inhibitions and repressions. As was indicated previously, animals with severe experimental neuroses may refuse to take food in or out of the experimental cage and may, indeed, starve themselves into a state of morbid inanition. Those with less severe neuroses will show incomplete inhibitions of feeding: they will eat only food pellets of a shape or composition other than those used in the experiment ("food faddism") or they will feed spontaneously only if outside the experimental or home cage. Another type of inhibition of activity is highly suggestive of a process of "repression." For example, neurotic cats which do not actively avoid the feeding-switch will treat it as if they had never known its function; i.e., in contrast to their pre-neurotic eagerness to reach it, they will walk around or over it as if they were hardly aware of its presence. In animals only mildly neurotic, phobic reactions to the light or bell may be replaced by a similar behavioral "amnesia" for the previously well-learned significance of these stimuli as signals for food.

Amnesias and inhibitions in human neuroses, similarly, may range from bewildered confusion, loss of memory, fugue states and motor disturbances (especially with regard to handling weapons, v.i.) of the acute war neuroses, to the highly specialized and symbolic avoidances and ritualizations of behavior that will be discussed in later clinical connections.

Motor disturbances and compulsive behavior. An animal with a severe experimental neurosis may show gross aberrations of motor function ranging from cataleptic immobility to continuous, apparently aimless, hyperactivity. Between these extremes lie patterns with more specific "compulsive" content; e.g., a hungry neurotic animal may "counter-phobically" hide its head in the food-box in response to a feeding signal, yet refuse to eat; another may turn on its back and claw at the light in a peculiarly stereotyped manner, a third may show an "hysterical paraplegia," i.e., drag its hind legs in the experimental cage but use them normally elsewhere, and a fourth will show aversion amounting to to fear of a harmless white mouse that had been placed in the experimental cage during a conflict-engendering experiment. One neurotic dog developed the elaborate ritual of circling the food-box three times and then bowing on its forepaws before attempting to feed.

Corresponding patterns in human behavior are readily observable. Acute traumatic neuroses may be expressed in severe motor disturbances such as *semi-catatonic stupors* (an occasional characteristic of the syndrome of so-called "three-day battle schizophrenia") or in a harrowing anxiety-ridden restlessness that soon exhausts the patient. Phobic compulsions are a frequent aftermath of these reactions; e.g., the patient will automatically cover his head or body at any unexpected noise, or dive under the bed despite every resolve not to do so, or *counter-phobically* spring into hypertensive alertness to face the non-existent danger. In human beings, of course, the compulsive acts may also become highly abstract and unconsciously symbolic: for instance, a soldier in a fugue state kept throwing out his arms in a peculiar gesture that could not be explained until, after Amytal hypnosis, he recalled that in the heat and excitement of a night battle, he had machine-gunned a friend, and had suffered remorse so great that his last memory was an overpowering wish to throw away his gun and to run blindly from the unbearable horror of the situation.

"Psychosomatic" disturbances and "organ neuroses." The physiologic expressions of "anxiety" and the feeding inhibitions or substitutive polydipsia of acutely neurotic animals have already been mentioned. In addition, many animals, despite adequate artificial feeding, show disturbances of gastrointestinal function in the form of diarrhea or constipation with a persistent loss of weight. A neurotic monkey may eat only while defecating, or develop gastrointestinal hypermotility of such severity that undigested food will be excreted within an hour. Concurrently, the animal becomes increasingly susceptible to serious pulmonary, dermal and ophthalmic infections and generalized allergic reactions.

Sexual aberrations. These may consist of complete abolition of discernible interest or activity, indiscriminate intensification or persistent perversion; e.g., neurotic monkeys may become exclusively homosexual or autoerotic. One female vervet continuously manipulated her axillae, anus and genitalia, and her male companion almost flayed his penis by nearly unremittent autofellatio over a period of weeks.

Gantt also observed pollakiuria, incontinence and ejaculatio praecox in his neurotic dogs and wrote of one of them (1944): "If Nick had been a patient his symptoms would have been referred to as anxiety neurosis, merergasia, phobias, functional tachycardia, palpitation ... (and/or) gastric neurosis."

Regressive behavior. This, of course, is difficult to observe in most neurotic animals,* although there were some indications of it in a tendency to isolation and surrender of dominance in the group hierarchy. Similarly, cats often showed an excessive preoccupation with interminable licking and preening, as contrasted with a carelessness in the disposition of excreta that is rare in this species. Neurotic animals also showed "regressive" changes in their "transference" relationships to the experimenter: i.e., they became either unpredictably aggressive or, much more frequently, reverted to a prehensile clinging sometimes accompanied by nestling and nursing movements.

Changes in general behavior characteristics. These took the form of an emergence of behavior patterns suggestive of generalized uneasiness, suspiciousness, restlessness and impulsivity. In less neurotic animals, the "transference" relationships of the animals to various experimenters were often differentially significant; the animal would continually court excessive attention and petting from one member of the

---

* However, cf. D. Levy's observation (p. 120) of a recurrence of puppyhood limping in an adult dog under stress.

laboratory staff, and at the same time become viciously antagonistic to another member more directly associated with the animal's traumatic experiences. Liddell and Gantt have noted more elaborate developments of such "paranoid" reactions in the sheep and dog respectively. Thus Gantt's neurotic dog Nick would fawn upon strangers, yet refuse to recognize Gantt himself even outside the laboratory.

CENTRALITY AND PERVASIVENESS OF CONFLICT. It may, at first thought, appear peculiar that motivational conflicts, however intense, engendered at a few feeding responses should occasion the dramatic, generalized and persistent neurotic aberrations in the animals here described. However, it must be remembered that the daily handling and feeding of the animals in the experimental apparatus really constituted the main activity, and perhaps the most meaningful experience, in their otherwise very routine existence, so that conflicts induced in the feeding and transference situation were correspondingly traumatic and severe in their effects. Conversely, animals given free run of their quarters, permitted to chase mice, mate at will, etc., showed fewer and milder neurotic aberrations when subjected to the experimental neurotigenic experience than did control animals kept isolated and otherwise inactive. The human parallel is again obvious: people with multiple interests and many satisfying modes of self-expression can withstand frustration and conflict in one field of endeavor far better than those whose entire existence revolves about a single vulnerable adaptation.

References*

Durbin, E., and Bowlby, J.: Personal Aggressiveness and War.
Guthrie, E. R.: The Psychology of Human Conflict.
Miller, N. E.: Experimental Studies of Conflict.
Murchison, C., Ed.: Handbook of Experimental Psychopathology.
Rosenzweig, S.: An Outline of Frustration Theory.
Underwood, B. J.: Psychological Research.

° Cf. Selected references, Appendix 1.

Chapter 12

The biodynamics of therapy

If the fourth principle of biodynamics as thus far derived is valid, then it follows that neurotic aberrations of behavior would increase in number, intensity and pervasiveness when the underlying conflict of motivations and adaptive patterns is exacerbated, and, conversely, should diminish as the motivational impasse is resolved. These important corollaries to the principle are borne out in the following experimental and clinical observations.

Exacerbation of neuroses during increased conflict

Neurotic animals show the greatest anxiety, the most marked startle and phobic reactions and the severest disturbances of sensorimotor and organic functions when maximally felt needs are opposed by reinforced fears; e.g., when the air blast and/or shock are repeated on the second or third day of neurotic self-starvation. A similar exacerbation of neurotic symptoms can be produced by making the total situation more pressing and inescapable in other ways, such as blocking off accustomed avenues of egress from the cage, gradually forcing the animal against the signal-switch by a movable barrier, or displaying delectable pellets in an open food-box near the source of the air blast or the electric shock.

Clinically, the direct correlation of neurotic aberrations of behavior with external vicissitudes and the resultant variations in intensity of internal motivational conflict is a matter of common psychiatric observation. Thus, a woman who is markedly ambivalent about her sexual or maternal functions may, under ordinary circumstances, construct various defenses against such conflicts and so make fairly "normal" and nearly adequate adjustments, but it will be noted that during menstruation or before and after sexual intercourse changes of mood, general irritability, "psychosomatic" dysfunctions, "conversion" headaches, compulsive behavior or other neurotic symptoms break through as indices of exacerbated unconscious conflicts. Or, should her ambivalences be further increased by pregnancy—and especially if an intercurrent toxicity weakens the patient's integrative capacities—, her neurotic phobias, sensorial disturbances, flights into fantasy and motor aberrations may increase to the level of a "psychosis gravidarum." The clinical course in the latter case might then be as follows:

Case 32. Psychosis gravidarum

Typically, there may be progressive disorientation, mounting agitation, and symbolic delusions that some abhorrent phallic or embryo-like creature such as "a snake," "a lizard" or "a monster" is gnawing at her "vitals." Parturition may be prolonged and difficult and will not necessarily produce an improvement in the patient's psychosis; instead, the patient may insist either that she never gave birth to a child, or that the one presented to her is not her own. If, however, before such psychotic patterns become fixed, the pregnancy, though physiologically "normal," is aborted* and the intensity and immediacy of the patient's unconscious conflicts are thus in part resolved, she may gradually resume her milder pregravid patterns and thus show partial clinical recovery. Her neurotic susceptibilities will, nevertheless, persist, and should a later pregnancy once again exacerbate her conflict and her defenses, psychotic behavior may be re-precipitated.

Case 33.   Homosexual panic

Similarly, a man in civilian life may be able to repress his homosexual tendencies by diverse but fairly acceptable substitutive devices, such as compulsive heterosexuality, avoidance of close friendships, or arrogant self-assertiveness to overcompensate for passive dependent wishes. But should he enter the military services where such defenses are no longer readily available and where, instead, he is forced into intimate and exhibitionistic associations with other men in barrack or trench, he may react with severe disturbances of behavior up to and including paranoia and psychotic panic.

Such examples, however, need not be multiplied, since the exacerbation of neurotic and psychotic behavior under environmental stress appears in almost every psychiatric history and is a cardinal clue to one important factor in the etiology of these disorders.

Resolution of conflict and modes of therapy

This heading covers the converse of the phenomena discussed in the preceding section, and introduces those applications of the fourth biodynamic principle that are, perhaps, of the greatest clinical significance: namely, the rationale of the various methods of resolving neurotic conflicts and of directing behavior into more favorable or "normal" patterns of adaptation. The present discussion will be confined to a review of the basic procedures as they have been found to influence favorably the course of experimental neuroses in animals, with brief comparisons to similar methods used in the clinical treatment of patients.

Prolonged removal from the neurotigenic situation. If a neurotic animal is kept away from the experimental situation and permitted to rest in favorable surroundings for several weeks or months, its manifestations of anxiety and its aversive, compulsive and other neurotic behavior patterns gradually diminish. Unfortunately, however, if it is then replaced in the apparatus, required to feed there, or given a few feeding signals even without repetition of blast or shock, its neurotic behavior patterns in most cases return with remarkable rapidity and intensity. The following experiment is illustrative:

---

* But therapeutic abortion on psychiatric grounds is explicitly prohibited by law in 27 states.

EXPERIMENT 10. **Effect of removal from conflictual situation**

A female kitten was made experimentally neurotic (cf. Exp. 9) at the age of four months, and was then kept in the author's home under the best of care for eight weeks. During this period her general restlessness and suspiciousness, her phobias of lights and sudden or unusual sounds, and her aversions to constricted spaces gradually diminished, although, unlike a normal pet, she continued to be a feeding problem, did not keep herself clean despite sporadically intensive self-grooming, could not be taught to use a sand box for elimination, was vicious toward a non-neurotic litter-mate kept as a control, and was so unpredictably destructive that to conserve the author's domestic tranquility she eventually had to be returned to her home at the University.

Here she remained another ten months during which there was some additional, though incomplete, improvement. At the end of the year, she was deprived of food for a day and then replaced in the experimental cage. At first she showed only a slight increase in her usual wariness and hesitancy; in fact, she even essayed to work the signal switch twice for a pellet of food. The third time, however, and with no repetition of the air blast or shock, she began to show phobic reactions to the feeding signals and then aversion to the switch. Next occurred mounting general uneasiness, mewing and restless pacing; finally, she remained huddled motionless in a corner as far away from the food-box as possible. A light signal given by the experimenter at this point induced marked physiologic manifestations of anxiety and a frantic attempt to escape from the apparatus. Replaced in her home quarters, she again showed feeding inhibitions, startle reactions and phobic behavior almost as intense as those after the first induction of her neuroses a year previously. Similar experiments confirmed the fact that even after months of "rest" in favorable circumstances, animals exhibit a rapid reconstitution of their neurotic responses when replaced in a situation associated with a previous conflict, even though the original trauma is not repeated.

CLINICAL APPLICATIONS. In psychiatric practice, removal from the immediate scene of conflict is a therapeutic procedure frequently, though often ineffectually, employed. The physician is inclined to advise that the hypochondriac housewife be sent away from her troublesome husband and children "to a quiet nursing-home to rest her nerves"; the executive with obsessive worries, insomnia and functional colitis is told offhand to "go to Bermuda and play some golf"; the soldier with emotionally cathected "combat fatigue," however mild or responsive to immediate therapy, is too readily evacuated from the battlefield to a base hospital. Such measures undoubtedly produce marked amelioration—though never complete relief—of clinical symptoms, but it is frequently forgotten that the patient's conflicts and neurotic behavior tendencies cannot be shed in a railroad station, on a golf links or in an army ambulance. If nothing else is done, he is prone to persist in many of his neurotic patterns, to show evidences of all of them whenever his conflicts are reactivated by untoward circumstances in his new environment, and to resume his aberrant defenses on his return to the original or some related neurotigenic milieu. Moreover, if the patient's futile attempts to escape geographically (and regressively) from his conflicts are sanctioned and even encouraged by the physician, the former will keep trying futilely to solve his problems by this means alone rather than cooperate in other forms of therapy more likely to produce lasting recovery.*

Diminution of the conflictful drives. If the severity of a conflict is dependent on the relative strengths of one or more of the opposing motivations, the diminution of any one of these should ameliorate the neurotic symptoms. This may be demonstrated experimentally as follows:

EXPERIMENT 11.   Diminution of a conflictful need

An animal with an experimentally induced aversion to food is fed by stomach tube to satiate its nutritive needs. If the animal is then replaced in the experimental apparatus, it shows a marked decrease in its phobic reactions to feeding signals and to constriction against the food-box. The next day, however, when its hunger is again intense, these and other neurotic reactions return in full force. However, in some animals the unpleasant experience of the tube-feeding itself becomes associated with the conflictful situation and tends to exacerbate the neurosis.

CLINICAL APPLICATIONS.   Some of the manifestations of this phenomenon in human behavior are fairly direct; for instance, the "fainting spells" and other dramatic conversion symptoms common in sexually inhibited or deprived spinsters of the Victorian era were often pointedly relieved by a healthy marriage—a phenomenon that, incidentally, had been commented upon two millennia previously (cf. Hippocrates, p. 5).† Nevertheless, since conflicting motivations operative in human neuroses are exceedingly more complex than those in the cat, the efficacy of clinical therapeutic procedures is usually remotely symbolic rather than directly physiologic. Thus, a therapeutic abortion in a patient with a functional "psychosis gravidarum" (cf. Case 32) may relieve few bodily stresses, yet may resolve her intensely conflictful desires to reject the child; similarly, the evacuation of a soldier with a "combat neurosis" (Case 31) may in part mitigate his acute conflicts over patriotism and loyalty versus self-preservation, resentment of military authority, longing for home, etc. Conversely, measures which transgress symbolic inhibitions (e.g., the forcible feeding of a patient with anorexia nervosa to whom eating signifies cannibalism) may induce more conflict than they relieve, and so—as Soranus remarked in a parallel instance—actually exacerbate the neurosis.

---

* In the military application of this principle Glass, Ranson and others made it an official policy, initially controversial but eventually highly successful, to treat psychiatric casualties *in situ* during the Korean conflict by direct, biodynamically sound measures of temporary physical relief and motivational reencouragement (v.i.) and to evacuate only those combatants whose reactions to stress had reached psychotic proportions.

† Another clinical illustration of the temporary effects of relieving a conflictful drive-tension is that of a sexually inhibited girl who ordinarily stuttered badly but who, after each successful coitus, experienced an hour or two of almost completely restored facility in speech—yet later, because of retroactive repression, could only dimly recall what she had said during such periods.

Forced solution of the conflict through environmental press.
This technique is illustrated in the following experiment:

EXPERIMENT 12.   **Forced solution of conflict**

A hungry animal in which an experimental neurosis had been induced by the methods described in Exp. 9 is forced progressively nearer
to a food-box by a movable partition in the experimental cage. The animal's manifestations of anxiety, its general restlessness and its phobic
reactions to the conditional signals increase rapidly the closer it is made
to approach the box, until the animal is in a state apparently bordering
on panic. If at this point, when no avenue of escape is available, the box
is opened wide to display some especially delectable tidbit such as salmon and catnip, the animal may suddenly make a dive for the food and
begin eating it, at first furtively and finally freely and voraciously. The
animal's behavior under these circumstances indicates that its hunger
drive, until then almost exactly balanced by its fear of the feeding situation, had been increased to such an unbearable intensity that the consummatory feedings finally broke through all their previously counterposed inhibitions and were expressed in direct action. Once this occurs,
moreover, the "neurotic" responses to all stimuli associated with the
previously conflictful situation also gradually become reversed: e.g.,
after a few such "forced seductions" the animal, when removed from
the experimental cage, again seeks to re-enter it, once more responds
favorably to the feeding signals, and either spontaneously begins *to react
to the air blast itself as a signal for feeding* or can readily be trained to
do so. In other words, the adaptational impasse has not only been
broken by blocking from expression one of the contending forces (fear)
and overweighting the other (hunger), but the relief experienced by
the animal has apparently re-invested the total situation with a newly
favorable connotation extending to all its associated experiences, including even the previously "traumatizing" air blast. It must be noted, however, that such salutary effects were not produced in all animals by the
method of inescapable environmental press; on the contrary, some animals with severe neuroses, when subjected to the methods here described, entered into a state of panic and thereafter showed a marked
exacerbation of their neurotic reactions both in and out of the experimental cage.

CLINICAL APPLICATIONS.   Perhaps the closest parallel method of
treating a phobic state in a human subject would be the practice—formerly a favorite one among somewhat sadistic swimming instructors—of
forcibly throwing a boy with an obsessive fear of water into a shallow
pool and then commanding him to swim. In such an emergency the boy
may suddenly learn that self-preservation often depends on an ability
to master the new environment and that, after all, his phobia was fantastically exaggerated. Should the situation take this favorable turn, the
boy's reactions to water may change remarkably; glorying in his conquest
of a previously harrowing fear, he may elect to spend his summers at
swimming beaches, join water-skiing and skin diving clubs, and indulge
in all manner of aquatic activities which in former times he had anxiously
avoided. But on the other hand, if the boy's hydrophobia has been deeply
and firmly rooted in early traumatic experiences, and if he lacks the

integrative capacity and adaptational flexibility to withstand heroic forms of "treatment," the forced immersion at the hands of a swimming instructor may only increase his fears to the point of blind panic and lasting resentments against teachers and disciplinarians in general. Nevertheless, if such reservations are kept in mind, environmental press may often be used with relatively good effect in treating neurotic reactions of specific causation, recent onset and relative fluidity of expression and course. A pertinent example is the following:

Case 34.   Reconstitutive press therapy

An air force pilot emerges physically unhurt but in a state of extreme tension after crash landing his damaged plane at his home base. More or less consciously, he is torn between reawakened fears of flying and counterposed desires to rejoin his group, retain his prestige and reestablish himself as a competent officer. If now, before his anxiety becomes channelized into specific phobias, compulsions, motor dysfunctions, etc., he is forced by custom or kindly authority to take up another plane immediately, with or without a trusted friend of equal rank and competence as a reassuring "standby" but preferably in regular formation with his echelon, his motivational conflicts may be favorably resolved, his normal illusions of invulnerability, security and mastery restored, and a chronic and disabling neurosis thus avoided.

INTERHEDONIC STRAINS. One other type of relationship between neurotigenic conflict and environmental press may also be considered here: namely, that the motivations involved need not be as diametrically opposite in sign as are hunger vs. fear, passivity vs. aggression, directly "narcissistic" vs. indirectly "group-motivated" conations, etc. On the contrary, severe neurotic states may be induced when the opposing drives are conflictful *only* in the sense that their behavioral expressions, while equally positive and desirable, are nevertheless incompatible. The legendary prototype of this in animal behavior is expressed in the parable of the indecisive donkey who starved to death exactly midway between two stacks of hay because he could not bear to choose only one of them; manifestly, the donkey's life would have been saved either by removing one haystack or by the "environmental press" of forcing him toward the other. The principles here involved may be illustrated clinically by the following vivid example:

Case 35.   Interhedonic anxiety

A senior medical interne, of excellent intelligence, attractive personality and high ambition, complained to his staff advisor that for the preceding week he had hardly been able to sleep, had eaten poorly, had been so preoccupied and irritable that he had deliberately avoided his friends for fear of offending them, and had been unable to concentrate on his studies or clinical work despite all efforts to do so. On inquiry, he readily revealed the circumstances that had induced these reactions: Several months previously he had followed the usual custom and had filed separate applications for residencies at two university hospitals, with the intent of securing one position or the other and so beginning a career that, he hoped, would lead to special training and a permanent teaching post with whichever academic institution appointed him. Ten days before his interview with the faculty advisor, he had received a telegram from one of the hospitals located in New York informing him that he had been selected for a highly desirable residency there and requesting his acknowledgment of the appointment. Proud and elated, he was in the very act of drafting his acceptance when another wire arrived with the information that an attractive post in San Francisco, for which he had also applied, was now likewise open to him. Then began a period of doubt and indecision that, within a few days, became almost unbearably excruciating. Either appointment was eminently desirable, but since, with the dramatic fatality of youth, the interne imagined that the decision "would alter his whole future"—which should he choose? In his dilemma he looked up every scrap of information that might serve to tip the balance. First he concentrated on fairly rational issues such as the relative academic standing of the two institutions and the probabilities of his own advancement in each; when, however, such considerations proved necessarily speculative, he went on to other details: the comparative climates of New York and San Francisco, and even the availability of his favorite sport of skiing. He made tables of comparisons, and tried ineffectively to weigh each item quantitatively and then assay the totals. He spent hours in restless rumination, paced the floor nights, and could find no surcease in any of his usual recreations. He at first plagued his faculty acquaintances with requests for advice until he himself realized that this might undermine their respect for him, and that the decision must be his own. He began to regret that he had ever studied medicine, and indulged in regressive fantasies as to how much better off he would have been had he entered his father's business where he would have been assured of a career that did not require sweeping and hazardous decisions. Next he decided that he "would leave it all to fate" and the single toss of a coin; when New York came up, he tossed it again to make it two falls out of three. New York came up again, but with it all the attractions of San Francisco crowded back into his imagery, and once again he vacillated. Finally, in desperation, he decided to see his staff advisor and leave the problem in "more experienced" hands.

The advisor handled the case as follows: Knowing that any decision he made might later be regretted by all concerned, that the appointments were indeed about equally desirable, and that in any case one of the other hospitals would decide the issue, he simply advised the interne to take a week-end off for a ski trip while the advisor "made inquiries that might aid in the decision." The youth did so, and returned to find a registered letter from New York informing him that since he had not as yet replied to their offer, or even acknowledged it, they had presumed that he was not interested and had appointed another in his place. With a sense of immense relief, the lad immediately wired his acceptance to San Francisco, and, with hardly a trace of misgiving or remorse got assiduously to work on his studies in preparation for his career in the golden West.

This case history, of course, is only a single example of the way in which fortuitous circumstances often resolve conflicts which, if permitted to remain at an impasse, become pervasive and disabling. Indeed, in such states the patient may actually seek, in the words of Fromm, an "escape from freedom" to make difficult decisions, and may plead with the therapist to give him relief by firm unequivocal direction. Sometimes this can be done, although, as will be seen in discussing the techniques of clinical therapy, certain precautions against channelizing this form of inertly passive dependence must be taken—else, to return to the analogy of the donkey, fate or the therapist may remove the wrong haystack, or the donkey, instead of solving his own problems, may always wait to be led.

Employment of transference relationships in guidance and retraining. Despite this last caution, it is very often necessary to use the psychiatrist's "influence" over a patient (i.e., the patient's conscious or unconscious desires to follow the therapist's expressed or implied recommendations) in order to lead the patient to reexplore a situation and find satisfactions that will resolve his conflicts and so relieve his neurosis. For a simple instance of the application of this principle we may again cite an experimental example:

EXPERIMENT 13.   Relief of neurosis by retraining

A hungry neurotic animal is placed in the experimental cage and retested for feeding inhibitions, compulsive behavior, phobic reactions to signals or space constriction and other neurotic manifestations. All such manipulations are then discontinued, and instead the animal is stroked, petted and fed gently in the cage by an experimenter it trusts (or by another person who is an ostensible facsimile) until its manifestations of anxiety abate and it stops trying to escape from the apparatus. During the next few days the hand-feeding continues progressively nearer to the food-box until the animal will take food offered on the experimenter's palm within the box. At this stage, the animal may show several interesting phenomena: it will eat from the box only while being petted, but retreat from it as soon as the experimenter's hand is withdrawn; later, the animal will feed directly from the box only when he sees the experimenter approaching the cage, but abandon feeding when the experimenter passes from view. A conditional signal or a movement of the constricting barrier in *either* direction while the animal is feeding at first re-induces food-inhibitions, and a phobic retreat from the box, but these reactions, too, can be overcome by gently guiding the animal back to the food despite a threatened constriction or while the signal is being given. In the same way, the animal can be retrained to work the switch for its own food rewards and, finally, even be taught to welcome the originally traumatic air blast as a feeding signal. During this whole period the animal shows a gradual diminution not only in its food aversions and phobic reactions, but also in its hyperesthesias, motor disturbances, loss of group dominance and other neurotic characteristics in and outside of the experimental cage. Significantly, however, if the animal is consistently afraid of the experimenter who attempts to retrain him, or if its motivational conflicts are re-precipitated by an air blast or shock too early in the process of retraining, the neurosis recurs and further efforts are far less effective.

This experiment illustrates the biodynamic process which can be outlined in operational terms* as follows: The animal's fears of feeding were mitigated by the presence and guidance of an experimenter who could "influence" the animal by virtue of the fact that he had fed and cared for it in its pre-neurotic state, was thereby associated with the satisfactions of its nutritive needs, and could therefore, by manipulations

---

* Cf. the discussion of "anthropomorphism" in Appendix 1.

meaningful to the animal, again swing the balance of its behavior into goal-directed patterns of need-satiation as the neurotic conflicts abated. With this advantage, the animal could reexplore the conflictful situation, readopt the need-satisfying patterns of switch manipulation and conditioned feeding and so abandon its previously neurotic responses as the latter were found to be no longer adaptive or necessary. If, on the other hand, the experimenter was too closely bound in the animal's experience with traumatic episodes in the experimental cage or elsewhere, he could not be instrumental in mitigating the animal's inhibitive and phobic reactions in the feeding situation. Further, either evaluation on the part of the animal was usually transferred by it to other laboratory-coated bipeds, who then, irrespective of their reciprocal attitudes (countertransference) toward the animal, were regarded by it with "positive" or "negative" *transference* and endowed with a corresponding therapeutic potential.

THE CLINICAL BIODYNAMICS OF "TRANSFERENCE THERAPY." The preceding experiment may be used as another paradigm for reformulating the phenomena of transference in biodynamic and experimental terms. Thus, if the patient more or less consciously regards his therapist as an understanding, capable and kindly parent-surrogate—or can be induced so to regard him—the patient will seek security in a "positive transference" and accept "persuasion," "suggestion" and other forms of "ideologic" retraining. He will then follow the therapist's interpretations and guidance in such a way as to resolve conflictful situations and test out new patterns of behavior, adopt these patterns when they are found to be satisfactory, and so, perhaps, gradually discard neurotic deviations of conduct as these are felt to be more of a handicap than a necessity. If, on the other hand, the patient, consciously or not, associates the therapist with some unsympathetic, rivalrous, tyrannical or punitive figure in his past experiences, the patient will resent or fear the therapist and so develop a "negative transference." Thereafter, even while appearing to cooperate with the therapy he will actually misapply or make a mockery of it, or else express his hostilities in greater conflicts and new neurotic patterns—unless, of course, the dynamics of such "negative therapeutic reactions" are also recognized and the motivations of the patient led into healthier channels of expression.

"Social" interaction in neurosis. Closely allied with the phenomena of "interpersonal" influence and "transference" described above are the effects of the normal adaptive behavior of one individual on the neurotic patterns of another. The following experiment is illustrative:

EXPERIMENT 14. Interanimal influence in neurosis

A hungry neurotic cat is placed in the experimental apparatus together with a normally trained one. At first the neurotic cat reacts phobically to all stimuli associated with the situation, while, of course, the normal animal moves freely, disregards constriction and feeds readily on signal. Gradually, however, the neurotic cat begins to approach the opened box as the normal one feeds after signals, and later it, too, begins to feed furtively until the next signal drives it away. Still later, the signals begin to lose this effect on the neurotic animal until, finally, both cats seek the food. If the normal cat is now removed, the neurotic one will show a renewed inhibition of feeding and a partial return of phobic responses, but, after further associations with the normal animal, all neurotic reactions eventually become diminished— though never, in our experience, completely abolished. Significantly, there was no evidence in our experiments that a normal animal would adopt the patterns of a neurotic partner, since such patterns, in the experience of the normal animal, would serve no adaptive purposes.

THE DYNAMICS OF INTERORGANISMIC INFLUENCE. It must be noted that the results of all experiments of this type (Exp. 15) vary greatly with the severity of the neurosis, the pairing of the animals, their previous dominance relationships (cf. p. 123 f.) and other factors even more difficult to interpret. For example, experiments with animated dummies indicated that the "normal" animal influenced the neurotic one merely through its instrumentality in taking up space in the cage, repeatedly displaying the food after signal by opening the box, creating "topologic valences," or "channels of movement," etc.* This may lead to a generalization of considerable sociologic significance: namely, that organism A does not ever influence organism B by direct "interorganismic" forces, but only by so manipulating the environment of B that the latter's motivations and adaptations are significantly altered. Such a theorem would, of course, be condemned as solipsistic (a current term of opprobrium) by those who prefer more mystical formulations for the concept of "role," "encounter" or "*einfühlung*" in interpersonal relations, but it has the advantages of making unnecessary any assumptions of spiritual or other intangible interactions among individuals, and is, moreover, compatible with the organismically centered concepts of biodynamics. The applications of this concept to the complexities of group relationships and "group therapy" will be further discussed in Chapter 14 and Appendix 4.

DYNAMICS OF IDENTIFICATION. Whatever the modes of interpersonal influence, it is usually demonstrable that person A will emulate (i.e., "identify" with) the behavior of person B if that behavior seems to gain advantages and attain goals that A longs to secure for himself. As we have seen, a child who feels rejected in his own home may develop anxiety, resistance to discipline, reactive aggressions and other neurotic aberrations of behavior which express his hostilities and his deviated seeking for power; if, however, he is removed from his conflictful environment and placed among more "normal" children who have learned to gain their desired goals by being more socially adaptable, he may relinquish his neurotic patterns and tend to adopt their modes of behavior. Early identifications, however, tend to be fantastic and exaggerated. Thus, when urges toward emancipation and self-sufficiency are stirred in a normal boy he will dress and play the part of the roving cowboy, the intrepid fireman or the futuristic space explorer; later still,

---

* Some twenty years after these observations, Harlow demonstrated that infant monkeys prefer approximately monkey-shaped dummies-of-refuge made of wire and soft terry cloth to their more mobile and therefore less predictably available mothers.

in response to his adolescent erotic strivings he will adopt the manner-isms of dress and speech of whichever romantic screen actor or erotic crooner happens to be the current idol of his girl acquaintances. Simi-larly, in adult life, he will continue to "idealize" and attempt to imitate those who, to his thinking, have achieved satisfactions in the particular fields of endeavor that primarily concern him. Thus, depending on the physical and intellectual endowment, culture, training and experience of the individual subject, his idols may be great scientists, saintly mar-tyrs, musical geniuses—or, for that matter, irresponsible "beats" or no-torious criminals—who have achieved the types of successes for which the subject himself is consciously or unconsciously striving.*

DYNAMICS OF "SUGGESTION" AND "PERSUASION." These concepts may now be formulated more specifically with regard to their biody-namic roots in the needs of the individual. From a clinical standpoint it may readily be demonstrated that a patient—even when in the "deeply suggestible" state of hypnosis (Erickson, White)—will act on expressed or implicit direction from the therapist *only if* the behavior suggested is *actually in accord with the balance of his conscious or unconscious needs and motivations.*† So also, in any other form of therapy the patient will respond to "reasoning," "persuasion" or "guidance" only when the course of conduct advocated by the therapist actually promises satisfaction of at least some of the patient's desires, if only those for passive dependence upon, and approval by, the therapist himself. If these conditions are fulfilled, the patient may also "identify" with the therapist and thus spontaneously emulate the latter's patterns of behavior and social adap-tations—a change which, let us hope, would be beneficial to the patient in most instances. Once this process of advantageous identification is well started, it may be utilized to mediate more generalized contacts: e.g., the therapist may gradually direct the patient into recreational, occupa-tional, religious or other group activities to reclaim a habitual niche in the social order.

For example, it has been found that the therapy of a soldier with an acute war neurosis can be greatly expedited if, after he has dissipated

* The "person identified with" need, of course, have no "real" existence, since the traits attributed to him may be purely a function of the narcissistic wishes of the iden-tifier. A striking illustration of a mass phenomenon related to this principle is the fol-lowing: there are about 70,000,000 people of all ages in this country (many million more elsewhere) who avidly read the so-called "comic strips," the characters of which have an amazing but demonstrable influence on popular speech, dress, customs and attitudes. Deaths of such characters have been the occasion of widespread mourning; their pictured enlistment increased the number of volunteers for the armed forces, and more than one otherwise "normal" youngster has been seriously hurt trying to emulate the feats of Popeye or Superman (F. Rodell). Similarly, food habits may be influenced in children by the preferences of human or even animal characters in fairy tales (Duneker, 1938), and racial attitudes may be determined by the nationality of heroes in motion pictures (Thurstone, 1931); (Peterson and Thurstone, 1932). Cf. also Mierke (1933) and Nowlis (1941).

† In this connection, cf. Young's (1940) critique of intellectual "regression" (Pla-tanow, 1933) and other artificial hypnotic phenomena. Hypnotism and hypnotherapy are discussed in detail in Chapters 22 and 35 of the *Practice*.

some of his anxiety and established a good therapeutic rapport with the psychiatric medical officer, the latter places him with a receptive and cohesive group of other patients who are well on the road to recovery and more or less eager for a return to active duty. Under such circumstances, the patient relinquishes as no longer essential the unconsciously escapist and regressive functions of his neurosis and re-identifies his own objectives with the cooperative security of the group and so with military discipline and social collaboration in general. But the experiences of military psychiatrists have made clear that unless the patient himself acquires strong motivations no therapeutic measures—least of all covertly hostile exhortation or command—can make him an effective soldier. "Group therapy" then, no matter how well bolstered by a favorable interpersonal milieu, must still be directed fundamentally toward the individual incentives, defenses and adaptations of the patient.

Experimental "working-through." We may begin the discussion of the dynamics of this mode of therapy with a relatively simple experimental example:

EXPERIMENT 15.   Resolution of conflict by spontaneous working-through

A cat is trained to work an electric switch that automatically actuates a bell or light signal and then deposits a pellet of food in a food-box as a reward. After this feeding pattern has become habitual over a period of several weeks, the animal is made experimentally neurotic by subjecting it to unexpected air blasts at several food-takings (cf. Exp. 9). When the neurosis has been unequivocally established over a period of weeks during which the animal is fed outside the cage, the animal is replaced in the experimental apparatus and permitted free access to the switch, but given no further supplementary feeding. As described in relation to neurotic "amnesia" (p. 34 f.) the animal for a time appears to "ignore" the switch, although a recognition of its presence and significance is indicated by the fact that, whereas the animal may eat pellets of salmon from the hand of the experimenter elsewhere in the cage, it will sedulously avoid them if they are placed directly on the switch pedestal. However, as the conflicts between hunger and fear of switch-manipulation increase during the next ten to twenty hours the animal begins to show mounting anxiety; e.g., it mews more plaintively, drinks excessive amounts of water, and paces about ever more restively seeking attention or escape. Then, as though under undeniable internal duress, it begins to approach the switch at optimum moments and to touch its mechanism gently—although at first so delicately and tentatively as not to close the electric circuit. Characteristically, when the animal acquires sufficient temerity to depress the pedestal firmly enough to actuate the bell or light signal, its first reaction is to beat a hasty retreat from the switch and make no attempt to secure the food pellet won by is renewed efforts. However, once the animal has progressed this far, its pre-neurotic feeding patterns become re-integrated with increasing rapidity and effectiveness until, in another few days, the animal is once again depressing the switch, answering the signals and securing the food freely. The re-introduction of the air blast at this point causes some return of neurotic behavior but the animal, as though appreciating the circumstance that it can secure food only by manipulating the switch whatever the hazards, eventually reverts to feeding after switch-manipulations and learns that, after all, the air blast too, is harmless. When this adaptation is also established by spontaneous trial, the neurotic inhibitions, phobic reactions, compulsive substitutions and other aberrant behavior patterns abate rapidly—although, as noted, subtle residua of them never completely disappear.

In the above experiment, then, the animal employed the one advantage it had over a neurotic animal untrained in the use of the switch: i.e., it utilized its partial manipulative control to reexplore a conflictful situation and "work through" a solution that once again met its needs and rendered neurotic aversions no longer necessary.

CLINICAL APPLICATIONS. It is, of course, a truism that in human behavior, too, each person employs whatever perceptive, integrative and manipulative skills he has previously acquired to "work through" his problems to solutions as nearly satisfactory as possible; moreover, it is equally evident that the greater the repertoire, versatility and development of his skills, the more of his problems he is *capable* of solving effectively, when sufficiently motivated to do so and not prevented by fear, anger, awe or other disruptive reactions. The fundamental significance of this principle has perhaps been most clearly emphasized by Meyer in his "psychobiologic therapy of the ergasias" (pp. 102 ff.) in which an important issue is made of evaluating the patient's assets (i.e., education, talents, capabilities) as well as his special handicaps and "liabilities." However, it is the patient's *effective utilization* of these capacities and resiliencies which determines whether he can "work through" his own problems with or without the aid of special therapy. Even in the latter case the patient, whether he is aware of it or not, utilizes the therapist as a social tool for reexperiencing and retesting his interpersonal relationships; only later, under the therapist's guidance, does he begin to reexplore more directly what seemed to be a baffling reality. Finally, as the patient's anxieties diminish he revises his customary ("unconscious") motivations, values and symbolisms, and "works through" and adopts various new ways of achieving his goals through less neurotic, more lastingly satisfactory and more socially adaptive patterns of behavior.

In this connection even orthodox psychoanalysts are beginning to realize that the mere verbalization of previously "unconscious" conflicts or their symbolic "acting out" in the therapeutic situation alone (cf. Chapter 14) is not enough; in addition, the patient must spontaneously apply his "insights" to a gradual reconstruction of more nearly "normal" patterns in his daily living, and then he must adopt these patterns as *intrinsically* preferential to his previous inhibitions and neurotic compromises. For instance, a phobia or a compulsion, no matter how complete the analysis of its origins and symbolic meaning, is never effectively mastered by the patient until he has begun to test out and assert his emancipation from it in his everyday life; i.e., until he has gained what may be called *operational insight*. Moreover, such therapeutic readaptations, especially of less deeply rooted and rigidly fixed neurotic reactions, need not necessarily be approached only by way of a symbolic "psychoanalysis," but may often be secured by directly reexploratory behavior. Thus, as in Case 34, aviation psychiatrists have learned that when a previously stable flier, though unhurt, is threatened by a neurosis after a crash, it is best not only to have him take another plane aloft immediately but also to induce him to reassert his cherished mastery over the ship's controls, to glory in the sense of freedom, power and group-belongingness that his special skills give him and, finally, to learn that he can, after all, once more enjoy such experiences safely and advantageously. If all this is done, a neurosis is not only averted, but the flier becomes more calm, skillful and confident than ever; i.e., though no verbal "analysis" was involved, the subject "worked through" his problem to a personally and socially successful solution.

Resolution of conflict through disintegration of precept formations. As we have seen, a neurosis is resolved when the environment is no longer interpreted as symbolically threatening and conflictful: e.g., when, to the cat, the switch and the conditional signals mean "food" instead of "food plus (feared) shock," or when, to the flyer, an airplane and its manipulation mean success, prestige, freedom or other desiderata, rather than all these plus the chilling shadow of injury and death. These, of course, are still relatively simple examples; much more complex and pervasive are the conflictful motivations, symbolisms, fantasies and elaborately defensive adaptations of the longstanding clinical neurosis.

DRUGS IN NEUROSES. The very abstruseness and complexity of neurotic reactions render them subject to yet another defense against anxiety—namely, the use of drugs that cloud consciousness, disintegrate painful symbol-associations and partially resolve motivational conflicts by mitigating both their component drives and their counterpoised repressions and inhibitions. Clinically, indeed, neurotic individuals so frequently become addicted to alcohol, the so-called tranquilizers and energizers, the barbiturates, marihuana or the opiates that it has become a therapeutic principle to assay and treat the underlying neurosis as an indispensable part of the therapy of any chronic drug addiction.

It seemed at first that this relationship of drugs to neurosis, because of its complexity, would be difficult to demonstrate in any but human behavior. And yet recent work with animal neuroses has given so direct a clue to the universality of the biodynamic corollary involved that again a typical experiment may be illustrative:

EXPERIMENT 16a.   Effects of alcohol on normal behavior*

An animal is trained in progressively more difficult adaptive patterns: first, it learns to open a box to secure a pellet of food dropped by a feeder; then it is taught to delay this response until various conditional signals have been given; next it learns to manipulate an electric switch to work the signals and feeder; and finally it solves increasingly difficult problems of how to work the switch despite changes in its position and the intervention of various partial barriers. If now the animal is induced by thirst to drink a small amount of a dilute alcohol solution (dose 0.5 cc. to 1.2 cc. of 95 per cent alcohol per kilo) the most com-

* Cf. Appendices 1 and 2, and films 1, 4, 5 and 8.

plex and recently learned adaptive patterns disappear first: for instance, the animal can no longer solve a difficult approach to the switch, but can still work the latter if it is made more easily available, after which the animal responds to the signals and opens the box with only a minimal loss of efficiency. However, if progressively larger amounts of alcohol are given or absorbed, the animal gradually loses the perceptive-manipulative capacity to work the switch in any position; next, the discriminated "meaning" of the feeding signals as announcing the deposition of food becomes impaired; then the animal can no longer find or open the food-box, although it may avidly take food offered directly; finally, the animal enters into a stupor in which all stimuli—even the food itself—cease to have any apparent experiential significance. Conversely, as the animal recovers from the drug its responses return in reverse order: first, it begins to take food from the box; then to respond to the feeding signals; next, it recovers its ability to work the switch in simple positions; and, finally, it regains its capacity to solve increasingly complex approaches to the switch and food-box. In short, alcohol apparently contracts the perceptive-reactive field into simpler and more primitive configurations until only the most elementary associations remain; conversely, as the animal recovers, it regains its perceptive-integrative-manipulative abilities in their order of learned complexity and efficiency.

EXPERIMENT 16b.   Alcohol as a preventive of neuroses

A normal animal trained as above is given 1 cc. per kilo of ethyl alcohol and while thus mildly intoxicated is subjected every second day over a period of months to various intensities of unexpected air blasts and/or electric shocks at the moment of food-taking. These ordinarily neurotigenic traumata, if sufficiently severe and frequent, may induce mild and transient hesitation in feeding, but the animal develops none of the dramatic and persistent symptoms of the usual neuroses. However, if the preventative doses of alcohol are then discontinued and the animal subjected to the same conflictful experiences for a few more days, a full-blown neurosis develops with high statistical probability.

Human analogies hardly need elaboration. Neolithic man discovered, brewed and drank beer to diminish the impact of his daily dangers; wine was administered or demanded to cloud the imminence and mitigate the horrors of primitive surgery; and some of us still are inclined to take a "bracer" before some experience that might otherwise leave intolerably vivid mnemonic residues of dread and sorrow.

EXPERIMENT 16c.   Effects of alcohol on neurotic behavior

A sober animal is permitted to work the switch for food and is made neurotic by a series of air blasts or shock (Exp. 9). As previously described, the animal develops a highly complicated set of behavioral aberrations: various inhibitions, aversions, phobias, compulsions, regressions, etc. If now the animal is again forced by thirst to drink about 1 cc. per kilo of an alcohol solution, these complex reactions are also partially disintegrated, permitting earlier, simpler and more directly goal-orientated (i.e., more "normal") responses to break through. Thus, when a neurotic animal is mildly intoxicated, its phobic aversions are sufficiently diminished so that it may spontaneously work the switch and feed on signal, and may thereafter be more easily induced to do so when sober.

Plate V.   The effects of alcohol on neurotic behavior (Exp. 16)*

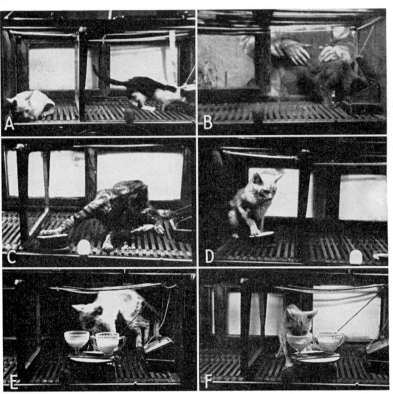

* The photographs in this plate are enlargements of 16-mm. stills from the motion-picture film "Neurosis and Alcohol" (Film 5, App. 2).

Plate V

A. Control observations on the role of differential experience in determining contrasting signal-reactions: The white kitten on the left had been trained to feed at a bell signal and had then been made neurotic by the air-blast technique as described in Exp. 9; she is here shown cowering at the feeding signal given simultaneously with a mild air-blast. In contrast, her black-coated litter-mate had been trained to react to the bell–air-blast configuration as a *signal for food,* and is here shown feeding avidly in response to the same configuration of stimuli that sends her neurotic partner into a crouched, palpitant, phobic rigidity.

B. A neurotic animal which, when sober, consistently manifested marked feeding inhibitions, startle-reactions and phobic aversions to the experimental situation (cf. Exp. 9 and Plate IV, C and D) is here shown once again feeding spontaneously in response to a light signal 20 minutes after the oral administration of 3 cc. of alcohol in 27 cc. of milk.

C. However, alcohol disorganizes not only the intricate patterns of neurotic behavior, but also the relatively complex components of normally goal-directed responses. For instance, during the preceding two days, the animal shown had starved itself rather than approach the phobically avoided signal-switch. However, after being given 1 cc./kg. of alcohol, the animal operated the switch repeatedly but, as illustrated, he often remained poised for as long as 12 seconds midway between the switch and the food-box without completing the sequentially integrated act of feeding.

D. With the switch moved behind a barrier away from the food-box, another neurotic and mildly intoxicated animal, after 24 hours of hunger, remained standing on the signal-switch for 60 seconds or longer without seeking the food-reward at all.

E, F. Nevertheless, about half the experimental animals eventually learned that alcohol relieved some of their neurotic tensions and inhibitions, and thereafter chose to empty the cocktail-shaped glass that held milk spiked with 5 per cent alcohol in preference to the plain milk in the eared mug. This preference was not affected by any variations in the position of the two glasses on the rotary stand, and remained statistically significant as long as the animals remained neurotic (Masserman and Yum, 1945).

Of course, the alcohol has no specifically selective effect on the neurotic symptoms; on the contrary, all behavior patterns are partially disintegrated. As a result, intoxicated animals, whether normal or neurotic, show ataxia, confusion, repetitive movements, fragmentation of whole responses and disturbances in goal-orientation.* Nevertheless, along with these general effects there occurs a particular disorganization of the highly complex neurotic patterns themselves, so that, with small doses of alcohol, more nearly elementary and better-established reactions such as dominance-assertion or simple feeding on signal remain relatively intact and reappear in overt behavior.

EXPERIMENT 16d.   Neurosis and alcohol addiction

Of all the animals who experience relief of neurotic symptoms during repeated mild intoxications about half apparently associate the smell or taste of alcohol with this surcease and begin to prefer food or milk containing alcohol to plain milk; i.e., they show behavior characteristic of "alcohol addiction."

In most animals, of course, neurotic behavior returns in great part when the pharmacologic effects of the alcohol wear off, but a few seem able to utilize their temporary bravado during mild intoxications to re-explore the switch-feeding-shock conflict and so gradually reestablish more nearly normal response patterns. Similarly, when the animal's neurosis is sufficiently relieved either through such pharmacologically aided "working through" or by other methods of therapy, the animal's preference for alcohol diminishes or disappears. It is also significant that mild alcoholic intoxication is more effective in alleviating aberrant manifestations in animals with relatively recent and fluid neuroses than in those in which the neurotic patterns had become chronic and fixed, and "normal" adaptations correspondingly submerged and unavailable. In the latter case, marked alcoholic addictions do not develop, but other forms of spontaneous or manipulative adaptations are also less successful in restoring "normal" behavior.

---

* ALCOHOL AND ACCIDENTS. M. S. Schulzinger in Industrial Medicine and Surgery (October, 1956) writes as follows on another important aspect of alcoholism: "The intake of alcohol is an important factor in accident causation. As the amount of alcohol in the blood increases so does the likelihood of an accident. In some individuals, one ounce of whiskey or one bottle of beer is sufficient to cause sensory or motor impairment. Alcohol tends to dim the vision, dull the senses, and produce deleterious effects on perception and cognitive abilities. Alcohol causes impairment of attention, concentration, memory, judgment and reasoning, but worst of all is the loss of insight into the presence of the extent of the impairments. Alcohol also induces neuromuscular incoordination and stimulates aggressive behavior when the individual is least able to cope with it. The intake of alcohol, even in small amounts, is thus incompatible with skilled or hazardous activity. Yet reports show that from 25 per cent to 40 per cent of all auto fatality victims had been drinking. The effects of alcohol vary with individual tolerance and length of usage. In an individual of average weight, two ounces of whiskey are enough to produce a blood alcohol level of 0.05 per cent—an amount sufficient to produce an average impairment [e.g., of driving skills] of 25 per cent. Alcohol is eliminated from the blood at the rate of about one-third of an ounce per hour. Physiological impairments thus are likely to last for hours, depending on the amount consumed."

CLINICAL ACTION OF ALCOHOL. Studies of addicts have shown that from a psychiatric and psychoanalytic standpoint, the ingestion of alcohol or other hypnotic drugs* clouds anxiety-cathected symbol-reactions, ameliorates tension by partially dissolving repressions and inhibitions (i.e., unconscious fears of the consequences of an act) and thereby permits previously repressed drives to find release in action. Many of the behavior patterns that thus find expression are, as may be expected, regressive in nature: the alcoholic titillates his "oral" desires from his bottle, becomes maudlin and sentimentally dependent while drunk, and may continue to intoxicate himself into an autistic, fantasy-ridden torpor—which, unfortunately, the concurrent toxic effects of the drug may change into a delirious nightmare. Homosexually tinged camaraderie and other repressed tendencies also appear during the process of intoxication. In many cultures, behavioral aberrations under such circumstances receive some measure of social sanction, in that alcoholism is accepted to a considerable degree as a mitigating circumstance for the expression of erotic, aggressive or destructive behavior that would be severely condemned in the completely sober individual. Small wonder, then, that a neurotic who has found these escapes from intrapersonal and social conflict—however illusory and evanescent such escapes may be —should continue to misuse the drug to the point of chronic alcoholic addiction.

EXPERIMENT 17.   Effects of other drugs

Experiment 16 can be repeated with other drugs, such as Nembutal, morphine and the bromides, each of which also disintegrates neurotic behavior patterns and so permits previously inhibited goal-directed responses to reappear. In contrast, rauwolfia and phenothiazine derivatives disintegrated neurotic patterns less effectively and produced undesirable sympathomotor disturbances more frequently than did alcohol, barbiturates or opiates, whereas meprobamate and lysergic acid diethylamide had almost no effect even in large doses.† The disorganization of behavior produced by drugs was generally less pronounced in intact animals than in those with cortical injuries. *Most significant of all, every experiment indicated that the effects of all medications and their attendant manipulations depended not only on the drug, dose and mode of administration but also on complex combinations of factors comprising the genetic, physical and metabolic constitution of the animal, its unique experiences, its material and social transactions during and subsequent to the procedure in question, and configurations of many other*

* Morphine, codeine and marihuana addicts (v.i.), when they cannot secure these drugs, frequently resort to alcohol or the barbiturates for comparable, though not equivalent, biodynamic effects (cf. Tatum, and Marcovitz and Myers).
† Cf. Pavlov (1932), Dworkin (1939), Masserman (1943) and Masserman and Pechtel (1956). The only addiction in animals to any drug other than alcohol has been reported by Yerkes, whose chimpanzees presented themselves with apparent avidity for injections of morphine. However, Yerkes believes that his animal subjects developed a pharmacologic craving similar to that experienced by human morphine addicts, independent of possible neurotic factors apt to develop in apes kept in captivity. Morphine differs in this way from alcohol, for which no direct tissue avidity has thus far been demonstrated.

relevant influences, including the beliefs and interpretations of the observer.

In the discussion of Principle I (cf. pp. 114 ff.) it was emphasized that behavior is fundamentally actuated by physiologic needs and that when the organism experiences various modes of gratifying these its behavior becomes correspondingly channeled. Experiments 16 and 17 illustrate an extension of this principle to "neurotic" patterns, in that neurotic animals apparently can learn that hypnotic drugs may ameliorate conflicts and tensions and so temporarily facilitate behavioral readaptations. In view of its clinical importance we may proceed to examine the biodynamisms of this avidity more specifically.

CLINICAL APPLICATIONS. Although there is some evidence that alcohol in doses of less than 0.5 cc. per kilo may have a transient stimulant effect on the central nervous system (Masserman, 1940), there is little doubt that alcohol, morphine, the barbiturates and bromides, most of the so-called ataractics and similar drugs used in "psychopharmacologic doses" act as cortical depressants, causing impairment of finer perceptions and discriminations, constriction of the integrative field and progressive disorganization of adaptive responses. As has been seen, however, precisely these effects, once experienced, would continue to be "desired" by a neurotic individual to whom the environment had become pervasively threatening and poignantly conflictful, since under such circumstances transient but welcome relief would be afforded by ingesting a drug that blurred and disorganized apperceptions provocative of anxiety, diminished inhibitions and facilitated a regression to relatively elementary need-fulfilling behavior. As already indicated, mankind has nearly always and everywhere concocted and consumed various nepenthics (e.g., volatile ethers and alcohols, and substances allied to mescal, marihuana and the opiates) to guard or release him from real and fantasied threats of disappointment or injury. We therefore have a long experiential precedent for prescribing, under proper conditions and adequate controls, sedative (sitting) or hypnotic (sleeping) drugs in measured doses to troubled patients to dull their perceptions, blunt their fears and give them temporary but welcome surcease from anxiety until we can help them resolve their underlying conflicts. However, we must recognize that drug therapy is inextricably associated with each patient's unique fantasies of dependent allegiance ("my doctor's special remedy"; "a toast to the Queen"), group-belongingness through "social drinking" and mystic connotations (religious rituals, "miracle drugs," etc.); indeed, such symbolisms may far overbalance the pharmacologic actions of the drug itself. Because of these connotations and the ready availability of many drugs, neurotics readily become habituated: there are at least five million alcoholics and uncountable numbers of addicts to barbiturates, ataractics and opiates in the United States alone.

ELECTROSHOCK. Neurotic animals subjected to cerebral electroshocks corresponding in frequency and intensity to those used in clinical therapy showed a disintegration of recently acquired inhibitions, phobias, compulsions and other behavioral deviations, while earlier, simpler, more normally effective patterns reemerged. As with neurotic animals given effective drugs, their adaptations could then be further improved by environmental manipulations, "transference" training and other corrective procedures. However, all electroshocked animals—even those subjected to the comparatively mild unidirectional Leduc current—showed a permanently impaired capacity for complex learning even when no detectable histopathologic changes in the brain had been produced.

NEUROSURGERY. Obviously, any cerebral operation will (a) produce a transient general disorganization of response patterns which, like the effects of drugs or electroshock on recently acquired neurotic deviations, may be temporarily salutary, and (b) result in a circumscribed but permanent defect in the organism's response capacities. The latter seems always to be true, although it may require highly specific demonstration; for example, lobotomized animals may appear even on careful testing to have retained elaborate skills and to be otherwise perfectly normal until subjected to a few days of isolation and sensory understimulation. Under such circumstances, unlike unoperated animals, they may become confused, wildly aggressive or develop other marked deviations of behavior. For such reasons, neurosurgical studies in both animals and humans are difficult to interpret*; nevertheless, our work has indicated that lesions in the ventromedial thalami or amygdalae—and far less so in the cingulate gyri—may disintegrate experimentally induced neurotic patterns and overbalance the corresponding organic loss in adaptive skills by a sufficiently wide margin so that, from the standpoint of survival and apparent contentment, the animal may be said to be benefited. However, *the effects of apparently identical lesions in different animals again varied with the preceding experiences of each.* For example: lesions in the dorsomedial nucleus of the thalamus in normal cats impaired their acquired skills and relearning ability but rendered them relatively passive and friendly; in contrast, identical lesions in cats which had previously been made experimentally neurotic produced similar effects on learned behavior, but released unmistakable patterns of hostility and overt aggression. So also, kittens or young monkeys subjected to bilateral amygdalectomies were relieved of previously acquired neurotic patterns to a far lesser extent, and remained much more disorganized and diffusely erotic and "unrealistic" in their behavior than was the case with the adult animals. Here, then, was further evidence that the effects even

---

* Among the difficulties are (1) the unique genetic and experiential background of each animal; (2) its subtly but necessarily different handling by different experimenters, no matter how purportedly constant the procedure; (3) the impossibility of absolutely objective observations, grading or reporting of complex behavior patterns; and (4) the surgical impracticality, in view of variability in blood supply, projection pathways and other anatomic features, of producing exactly delimited cerebral lesions. Finally, from the standpoint of comparative neurophysiology, the troublesome question remains as to whether homologous lesions in animals can yield accurate information about functions in the human central nervous system, in which such marked encephalization and other shifts of function have occurred. Nevertheless, the studies here cited reemphasize an important clinical maxim: that the permanent effects of a cerebral lesion depend perhaps less on its site and even its extent than on the personality of the patient, his significant pretraumatic or preoperative experiences, and the physical and psychiatric care given him during the crucial period of rehabilitation.

of discrete physical traumata can be understood or treated *only with reference to the permanent physiologic engrams left in the central nervous system by the previous experiences of the organism.*

CLINICAL PARALLELS.   It is probable that the various "shock therapies" and the operations of lobotomy and leucotomy as used by some neurosurgeons for the treatment of psychoses act in part by producing temporary or permanent decorticating effects: i.e., rendering the individual no longer capable of fine-spun fantasies or elaborate delusions and reducing his repertoire of reactions to more simple and easily controlled patterns. Unfortunately, the diffuse or localized decerebration produced by anoxia, electrical shocks or operations on the cerebrum, however minimal, differs from that induced by most drugs in moderate dosages in that the damage produced by the former methods is permanent, with the result that the patient's higher intellectual functions may be irretrievably sacrificed. In less gifted patients, these finer capacities can be spared with scarcely noticeable loss, but in patients with special intellectual abilities and highly developed talents and skills (e.g., scientists, artists, professional musicians) the permanent impairments produced by shock or cerebral surgery may be a tragic personal and social price to pay for the use of such drastic methods, especially in the treatment of transient anxiety states, depression or pseudomanic reactions, which are amenable to more constructive therapeutic techniques.

In effect, then, each person behaves differently from every other because (a) he was differently constituted at birth and (b) because he has had different experiences: ergo, (1) he will react uniquely to any given drug or cerebral lesion and (2) he will subsequently need rehabilitative therapy specially tailored to fit his frame and modes of action, hide his defects and best utilize his remaining capacities for optimal adaptation. Moreover, in human imagery, the experience of an operation or of induced convulsions or comas may have the added symbolic significance of disruptive psychologic cataclysms, of expiations of unconscious guilt, of mystical survival, and of final rebirth under the welcoming aegis of a kindly and seemingly omnipotent therapist. None of these interrelated factors can be left out of consideration in comprehensive and thereby effective therapy.

Interrelatedness of therapeutic methods.   The clinical variations, contraindications and applications of each of these therapeutic approaches is further developed in succeeding sections of this volume and in the *Practice,* but it is important to note here that the methods outlined are not really as discrete or independent as their necessarily linear verbal exposition might seem to indicate. As a review example, a monkey subjected to experimentally induced conflicts between hunger and an apparently innate "symbolic" fear of a toy rubber snake will develop serious "psychosomatic" dysfunctions and become progressively more inhibited, compulsive, phobic, pervasively suspicious (paranoid) and unrealistically stereotyped (delusional) in its behavior. "Method 4," say, can then be used in therapy: i.e., the animal's confidence in some mentor is rewon and it is then gently but progressively retrained to resolve its conflicts and once again to seek and secure food. However, this necessarily also implies (1) a "psychologically" altered milieu, (2) the concurrent alleviation of an impasse between hunger and supposed self-preservation, (3) an externally facilitated solution of the problem and (4) a change in behavior pattern exemplified by the mentor—hence all five "methods of psychotherapy" are involved simultaneously. But the therapeutic contingencies may be rendered even more complex by "constitutional" or other biodynamic factors. For example, Method 4 can be employed only in spider monkeys or in relatively young macaques, since only these will respond by becoming dependent on the experimenter's ministrations; in contrast, a neurotic vervet is comforted most effectively by the presence of a mate, whereas the group-oriented adult cebus is helped most by re-participation, perhaps necessarily in an altered role, in the life of the cebus colony. Nor are the therapeutic effects of drugs, electroshock or lobotomy to be regarded as more specific, since their actions vary not only with the particular drug or procedure and the physiologic status of the organism, but also with its concurrent motivations and adaptations, its life experiences before and after the procedure in question and, for that matter (though more subtly), the beliefs, attitudes and derived actions of the experimenter-observer. Laboratory data, then, may help to clarify effective therapy, but at the same time their proper interpretation also reveals how intimately interrelated at all levels all treatment procedures are.

Corollaries to principle IV

We may now summarize the preceding two chapters as follows:

The concept of conflict has been a leading *motif* in both the reflexologic and psychoanalytic theories of the neuroses, although the operational referents of the concept in these theories have usually not been as inclusive as in the biodynamic formulations here proposed. Specific corollaries, however, must be added to the biodynamic principle that neurotic aberrations of behavior occur when motivations and their expressive patterns are incompatible and conflictful. Among these are:

Corollary 1. Under circumstances of conflict, physiologic and motor disturbances typical of anxiety and the various "psychosomatic" disorders appear, and total behavior becomes ambivalent, phobic, regressive and compulsive.

Corollary 2. The neurotic behavioral phenomena covered by these terms vary in complexity, symbolic "meaning" and forms of expression with the perceptive, experiential, integrative and expressive capacities of the organism.

Corollary 3. These neurotic reactions are accentuated when the underlying motivational conflict is intensified and, conversely, are mitigated when the conflict is diminished.

Corollary 4. Among the methods of alleviating conflict that have clinical therapeutic connotations are these:
   1. Prolonged rest from the conflictful situation.
   2. Diminution of one or more of the conflictful drives.

3. Forced solution of the conflict by "environmental press."
4. Employment of "transference" and other influences in guiding and retraining the neurotic organism to adopt more advantageous patterns of behavior.
5. The use of "interorganismic" or "social" relationships for similar purposes.
6. Spontaneous "working-through" of the conflictful situation.
7. The use of drugs which disintegrate complex neurotic patterns and diminish tension by permitting a partial release of goal-directed behavior charged with lesser degrees of conflict.
8. Securing such effects, but with permanent residues of functional impairment, through the use of physical agents such as electric currents or anoxants, to produce cerebral shock and diaschisis.
9. Direct surgical attacks on the central nervous system.
10. The multivectorial integration of each of these and probably many other influences.

And yet, despite our analysis to date, all behavior remains unique and elusive in a most intriguing manner, and its vicissitudes can be completely covered by no set of principles thus far formulated. The necessary extensions of clinical theory into the realms of man's imagery and communications, and the evolution and current expressions of what may literally be termed his *Ur-defensive systems of make-believe*, will be the topics of the next two chapters.

References

Burrow, T.: The Biology of Human Conflict.
Diethelm, O.: Treatment in Psychiatry.
Henderson, O. K., and Gillespie, R. D.: A Textbook of Psychiatry.
Jessner, L., and Ryan, V. C.: Shock Treatment in Psychiatry.
Kubie, L. S.: Manual of Emergency Treatment for Acute War Neuroses.
Masserman, J. H.: Behavior and Neurosis (Part IV, with appended Bibliography.)
Solomon, H. C., and Yakovlev, P. I.: Manual of Military Neuropsychiatry.
White, R. W.: A Preface to the Theory of Hypnotism.

Chapter 13

Language and "verbal" therapy

Comparative approach to language function

As we have seen, philosophers and linguists have, until recently, been inordinately proud of man's ability to communicate by words and signs, and often seemed to think that this differentiated him from the rest of all creation. On the other hand, unprejudiced observers, from primitive hunters and herders to modern professors of ethology, have not failed to note the elements of gestural and vocal expression and the occurrence of meaningful communication among animals less self-exalted than man (cf. Bierens de Haan, 1934), and have consequently not been so certain as to man's monopoly of the essentials of language. As both philosophers and biologists man's physicians have enjoyed an unequaled opportunity to observe the behavioral correlates of "language in action" (Hayakawa) in their patients, and have traditionally found it is necessary to employ "action in language" as an indispensable tool of therapy. Nevertheless, like other artisans with a practical and often urgent job in hand, physicians have been prone to be less interested in the dynamics of their too-familiar tools of communication than in the ever-new clinical problems to which they must be applied. As a result, only recently have psychiatrists begun to pool their special knowledge and research skills with biologists, anthropologists and linguists in a comprehensive study of language—a study necessitated by the intimate participation of communication in all forms of "normal" and "abnormal" human behavior. It may therefore be important to re-examine some of the former concepts of semeiology and linguistics in the light of the newer knowledge of behavior and perhaps in this manner approach an integration of these intriguing sciences with certain fundamental principles of biodynamics.

An analysis of language functions

We may begin with a critical review of the "elements" of communicative reference as traditionally classified under the following semeiotic categories:

Signals. These are generally defined as sensory stimuli which actuate relatively simple responses in a sensitized organism. Thus, in Pavlovian reflexology, signals were differentiated into *unconditioned* as opposed to *conditioned* or learned; for example, it was stated that the "unconditioned" sight or smell of food "caused" salivation in an untrained dog, whereas an animal accustomed to receiving the food after the clang of a bell would eventually also salivate at this "conditioned" signal. As we have seen, these formulations neglected the intrinsic factors of motivation, meaning and total adaptation; in fact, such considerations were deemed superfluous in a system of peripheralistic and mechanistic reflexology. It was soon noted even by Pavlovian workers that satiated, ailing or frightened animals might show marked aversion rather than anticipatory salivation at the sight, smell or preliminary signal of food, and that the same bell sounded under other circumstances produced quite different effects, e.g., barking and struggling when the animal was closely confined or otherwise prevented from reaching its goal. From a purely experimental standpoint, therefore, signals gradually came to be assigned the more contingent and dynamic significance to be considered below.

Signs.   Signs are usually distinguished from signals in that the former are complex in connotation, invoke generalized patterns of behavior, and cannot be as easily traced to directly associated experience. For example, the "sign" *Fire! Exit Quickly!* suddenly flashed on the screen of a motion picture theater will actuate in most of the audience almost the same behavioral responses that would be induced by the sight of flame or the smell of smoke, and yet the printed letters "F-I-R-E" need never have been associated in contiguity of time, space or "causation" with the actual experience of being burned. The relativity of such distinctions will be more fully considered in a later connection.

Symbols.   These are customarily distinguished from signs as being yet more generalized and abstract in nature, and thereby even more remote from the basic experiences to which they refer. Perhaps the best illustrations of the genesis of symbols come not from their formal philologic derivation, but from the exploration and correlation of their meaning with the behavior patterns of patients under psychoanalysis. A clinical example may be cited as follows:

Case 36.   Symbol-derivation; acrophobia

A male patient complained of a generalized fear of all objects associated with height: e.g., skyscrapers, mountains, airplanes and especially elevators. The patient consciously dated his severe acrophobia to a vivid experience during adolescence in which he came close to being seriously injured in an elevator accident. Despite the seeming rationality of this explanation, further analysis revealed that the patient's conflicts reached much deeper motivational levels and were based on more devious and symbolically threatening associations: namely, elevators—elevation to heights—attainment of prominence and success—early competitiveness and rivalry with father—fear of castrative retribution from a powerful authority and, finally, phobic reactions in adult life to any object or concept that might symbolize, however indirectly, a situation that the patient had considered extremely dangerous as a child.

Or to take another clinical example:

Case 37.   Symbolic derivations; schizophrenic

A schizophrenic girl invariably fought as though in panic if any attempt were made to remove a piece of dirty white cloth she habitually wore in her hair. One day while under Amytal hypnosis she explained circuitously that this cloth represented a nun's cap and thereby symbolized "renunciation of mortal sin" and a life of asceticism and depersonalized atonement.

Such representations may be termed deviant and bizarre, but to appreciate the semantic derivation of all symbols from personal and group experience it need but be remembered that "normal" individuals react with even more complex behavior patterns to more abstruse symbols every waking (not to mention dreaming) moment. Thus, the sign of the quarter-moon evokes as rich an assembly of religious, ethical and cultural reactions in the devout Mohammedan as does the adoration of the crucifix in the reverent Catholic or the sight of the Torah in the Orthodox Jew. In each case, of course, the mere sensory stimulations of crescent, cross or scroll would have little intrinsic significance were it not for their resonance with the individual experiences, current motivations and wishful aspirations of each member of the respective religious sects. Symbols, then, however complex and remote, are in essence abstractions and generalizations of experience, and as such remain exquisitely personal even when similar experiences and symbolizations are shared in a common culture (v.i.).

WORDS AS SYMBOLS. As has just been seen, any configuration and permutation of sensory "stimuli" may constitute a symbol: i.e., a "cross" of any material, the picture of a cross, the gestural "sign of the cross," the feel of the cross to a blinded person, and the word *cross* all give rise to nearly equivalent conceptual resonances. Words, then, like all other symbols, also have "meanings" only with reference to their specific connotations for each individual, and even these meanings may vary widely not only with the context of the phrase, sentence, paragraph and oration, but also with the current circumstances and emotional state of the writer, speaker, reader or hearer. Nevertheless, however variable their denotations, words, being economical of effort and easily transportable in space and time, have become the most widely used (as well as most widely misunderstood) forms of communication. Parenthetically, it may be noted that the rapid evolution of human thought in the last three centuries has far outdistanced the development of verbal symbol-systems with which to express it, with the result that old words have been confusingly used for new and more complex meanings, or else verbal language has been abandoned as too limited for scientific discourse in favor of a symbolic logic capable of expressing subtler and more transcendent relationships. Much effort is now being expended by philosophers, logicians and semeiologists, e.g., Rashevsky, Rapoport, et al., toward the desirable goal of creating a more adequate and meaningful "language of science," and so make possible among scientists "precise" communication and "concerted" thinking and research. Unfortunately, we must consider the disturbing contention that, until all scientists are born identical twins and subjected to exactly the same experiences, this goal can be only asymptotically approached.

Language as communication

In order to give expression to the essentially kinetic and operational processes of thought—a dynamism inherent in even the most leisurely of descriptive passages—various types of "substantive" and "operational" word-symbols are required for communication. These have usually been grouped about as follows:

(a) words that metaphorically point, such as the article "the"
(b) those that "denote" objects such as "man" or "fortune"
(c) those that "modify" these objects, e.g.: "indolent" or "large"
(d) those that express relationships: "his" or "inherited"
(e) those that connote translation in time* or space· "run" or "through"
(f) those that modify such movements: "quickly," "thoroughly"
(g) those that "belong" to various other "classes" which can be abstracted from the richness of human thought in numbers apparently limited only by the taxonomic ardor of the categorist.

In the actual expression of an "idea" the literal examples given above might then be operationally juxtaposed thus:

"The indolent man ran through his large fortune quickly and thoroughly."

Be it noted, however, that even in this simple sentence we already have a further complexity of formulation recognizable as a *figure of speech;* obviously a man—especially an "indolent" one—can be said to "run" (in the sense of rapid ambulation) "through" (in the sense of pierce) "a fortune" (an abstract monetary concept) only if these words be given a fantastic latitude of connotation. It is, of course, within this penumbra of symbolic intersignification that the art and poetry of language lie; indeed, virtuosity in any medium of discourse often reveals the essential wholeness of being by removing artificial distinctions among various modes of experience. Unfortunately, extreme spreads of symbolic meaning may also be translated into behavior sufficiently aberrant to require psychiatric attention. For instance, the man referred to in our example might spend a small inheritance lavishly on the basis of a wishful fantasy that it was indeed an inexhaustible "fortune"; moreover, should he continue to be thus "unrealistically" extravagant, his spree could well be terminated by custodial care in a psychiatric hospital.† Or conversely, if the man's wife were the author of our sentence, and she meant by it that her husband was "squandering" sums which, though actually small, were nevertheless causing her inconsolable grief and agitation, then she herself might be committed to an institution as a

---

* "Time," too, is a highly individualized concept, dependent on the integrity of the nervous system (especially the functions of the thalamus) and the past and current experiences of the subject. Cf. W. Goody, and Spiegel and Wycis.

† Such "individual languages" are termed *idiolects* by Paul Ziff (*Semantic Analysis,* Cornell University Press, 1960).

ruminative and agitated melancholic. In this connection, a literal-minded "semanticist" of the Korzybski school might be tempted to think that the abnormal behavior in both instances actually arose from a relatively simple source: a "misinterpretation" on the part of either the man or his wife of the "true referent" of the word "fortune"—a mistake to be directly corrected by rational-sounding explanations to the patient of the material "reality," "extensibility" and "time-bindedness" of the *particular* "fortune" under consideration.* Unfortunately, as every psychiatrist soon learns, such an exercise in what might be termed paracommunicative dialectics is as theoretically naive and, in most cases, as clinically useless as pointing out to the acrophobic patient previously cited that his fear of elevators is "really unnecessary" because elevators, actuarily speaking, "are not dangerous." Obviously, such "explanations" and "reassurances" would not apply to this particular patient's interpretation of the concept "elevator" as a castration-threatening and fear-inspiring symbol. Similarly, in the case of the irresponsible man or his melancholic wife, the futility of a purely intellectualistic and verbal approach would arise from the circumstance that their linguistic "fallacies" are not the cause, but simply the symbolic expression, of much deeper unconscious conflicts. Thus, the man may be recklessly squandering an inheritance of whatever size in fearful expiation of guilt over the death of his father and in an unconsciously determined renunciation of the latter's legacy; conversely, the melancholic woman may be so insecure and preemptive in her attitudes toward her husband that the smallest expenditures on his part engender feelings of deprivation of psychotic intensity. The advantage each takes of the opposite extremes of meaning of the term "fortune" is therefore no simple "misuse" of language, but rather a coherent part of a total behavior pattern rooted in previously established attitudes and derived experiential syllogisms. In this sense, it may well be contended that, to the man, the word "fortune" *means* "something I must get rid of," whereas to the woman it represents "my husband and all of his possessions, all of which must be used for my exclusive benefit." Lewis Carroll epitomized the issue admirably:

"'When *I* use a word' . . . Humpty Dumpty said, in rather a scornful tone, 'it means just what I choose it to mean—neither more nor less' "†

---

* Such "semantic" therapy is often sought and readily accepted by many neurotic patients who are avid of "systems," since it threatens few of their defenses, stirs or creates little anxiety, and may incidentally serve as a medium for transference-manipulations, therapeutic guidance and a partial working-through of the patient's personal and social problems. If, however, the "therapy" is limited to such intellectualized rationalizations, results are likely to be evanescent, or else the neurosis may become complicated by an obsessive-compulsive preoccupation with "semantics" itself or other verbal expressionisms.

† The passage continues: "'The question is,' said Alice, 'whether you *can* make words mean so many different things.' 'The question is,' said Humpty Dumpty, 'which is to be master—that's all.' Alice was too much puzzled to say anything."

Language and behavioral adaptation

Perhaps the first question that arises in this connection is whether the distinctions among signal, sign, symbol and sentence are differences in kind or merely in the complexity of denotation and connotation. Certainly, the factors of motivational reference, "meaning" and operational adaptation are present in each case from the most "elemental" to the most complex. Thus, as was seen in our simple Pavlovian example, the dog will salivate neither at the sight of food nor in response to a conditional signal, should he happen not to be hungry. To the dog, then, the signal does not really "mean" food *qua* food, but represents an opportunity to satisfy a physiologic need or to please its master by some desired action; when neither is present, the signals induce little overt response.

In the same way, too much stress should not be laid on the differences between a unimodal bell or light "signal" and the use of a spoken or even written "sign." Every dog or cat owner knows that his pet will "understand" and respond to any gesture, call or combination of words customarily used as a signal for feeding, release from confinement, etc., and most experimental animals from chicks up can readily be trained to react similarly to signs printed in configurations of "words" as well as those discriminated by color or shape.* The following are simple experimental examples:

EXPERIMENT 18.   **Experimental signal-sign equivalence**

Cole taught racoons (a) to climb their cage for food at the sight of a card representing an appropriate "invitation"—and (b) to refrain from doing so when a different card was shown. Significantly, if the animals did not receive the anticipated reward after responding to the proper "sign," they tore up the card with a displaced fury comparable to a maiden's attack on the previously cherished letters of a newly faithless lover. So also, cats can be taught to "read" and distinguish "signs" saying FOOD or NO FOOD and to react with corresponding adaptive "anticipations" and responses.

Equivalence of symbols. The relativity of signals, signs and symbols in meaning function can also be demonstrated by showing that they may be substituted for each other—or even altered radically—and yet evoke similar behavioral responses *if the motivational referents of the total situation are held constant.* The following simple experiment is illustrative:

EXPERIMENT 19.   **Experimental substitution of signals**

Finch and Culler trained dogs to flex their forelegs off an electric grid at the sound of a bell, and then were able to substitute various other conditional signals in succession (a light, a stream of water to the nose and an air blast) by the simple device of shocking the dogs with an

---

* For the developmental analysis of this language process in children, cf. Luria, Piaget, Markey and Lewis.

electric current to the chest if they did not flex their forelegs in the desired way.

An even more significant experiment with human subjects was performed by Hudgins on the basis of preliminary observations by Cason:

Case 38.   Establishment of an "unconscious psychosomatic reflex" in human subjects

Hudgins began by sounding a bell while he flashed a light into his subject's eyes, and was able in this manner to establish involuntary contraction of the pupils in response to the bell sound alone. He next required his subjects to ring the bell at the spoken command "contract!" and thus produced pupillary reactions in response to the combination of this command and the subject's own muscular activity. Next, in successive stages of transfer from "voluntary" action to abstract "idea," the subjects themselves spoke, whispered, and then merely "thought" the word "contract," with the result that a remarkable effect finally appeared: not only could each subject cause his pupils to contract by a particular mode of "thinking"—a form of sympathetic control ordinarily considered to be beyond the reach of "the will"—but 10 of the 14 subjects were quite unaware of the specific bodily expressions (i.e., unconscious "psychosomatic" reactions) that accompanied their thoughts.

Hudgins, then, had created in a group of people a highly individualized configuration of visceral reactions* to the cognate symbol "contract" —a response which could be traced through their special experiences to an apparently remote but actually basic physiologic source: in this instance, simply the protection of the retina from excessive light. The significance of such experiments for biodynamic research and communication theory hardly needs further elaboration.

Change in behavior responses.   On the other hand, an adequate change in the motivational referents of a "constant" configuration of stimuli can produce a complete reversal of the animal's responses, since any "stimulus," "sign" or "symbol" has meaning only as a part of a continuous series of total perceptions each of which has been modified by all preceding experiences and adaptations in the life of the organism. This may be illustrated by various experimental observations as follows:

EXPERIMENT 20.   Changes in the motivation-symbol-behavior complex

A cat or dog trained to open a food-box in response to a bell or light stimulus shows no aversions to the signals at any time, and will avidly welcome them when hungry (Exp. 1). If, however, the animal is shocked or frightened unexpectedly a few times at the moment of "conditioned" food-taking, it will thereafter react to the food signals with severe manifestations of anxiety, and may show a phobic generalization of these responses to other elements of the conflictful situation: the cage,

* For other experiments in establishing "psychosomatic responses" cf.: heart (Anderson and Parmenter, 1941; Gantt and Hoffman, 1940); respiration (Allen, 1942); spleen volume (Hargis and Mann, 1925); vasomotor responses (Menzies, 1937); galvanic skin reflex (Bass and Hull, 1934; Switzer, 1934; and Cook and Harris, 1937).

the experimenter and even the food itself.* Moreover, if the motivational conflict is made sufficiently intense and persistent the animal will also develop peculiar ritualistic compulsions, loss of dominance in groups, food-inhibitions to the point of cachexia, and other somatic and motor disturbances comparable to the corresponding "symptoms" of severe human neuroses (Exp. 9).

"Meaning" under such circumstances can likewise be extended to olfactory and gustatory cues; for example, a neurotic animal which experiences transient but repeated mitigations of its neurotic symptoms when given alcohol will thereafter choose foods or fluids smelling and tasting of this drug, and so become an alcohol "addict" until its neurosis is permanently relieved by other means (Exp. 16). In this connection Pechtel and I (1950) have shown that monkeys, though ordinarily not particularly concerned with smell or taste, become atavistically hypersensitive in both sensory modalities when made experimentally neurotic, and that this hyperesthesia is the last symptom to disappear during recovery. A "verbal" response-pattern may easily be added to such experiments: i.e., during a control period a cat can be trained to react to the word "food!" with manifestations of anticipatory relish and "normal" food-seeking behavior whereas, after the induction of motivational and related symbolic conflicts, the same animal may react to the "same" verbal signal ("food!") with crouching, hiding, or even an aggressive attack on the experimenter who had tactlessly uttered it. In the latter case, then, we have a cat "taking umbrage" at a word to which it had become "emotionally" hypersensitized. As we shall see in a later connection, were the shibboleth of "anthropomorphism" to be used in an attempt to cloud the comparative significance of these and other experimental observations, it would obviously reflect more on the philosophic bias of the critic than on the heuristic validity of the data.

To generalize from these and other observations previously cited, then, symbols in both men and animals are significant to the individual only in terms of personal experiences, and their meaning and effects are therefore contingent on the expansions and cumulative modification of individual adaptations. In effect, symbolizations may be assigned almost any mode and spread of individualized "meaning," conative and affective† as well as cognitive. Indeed, political organizations, monetary economies and related "social processes" acquire much of their force and significance as systems of interpersonal symbolization.

* Compare the phobic reactions of an airplane pilot who, after severe and protracted motivational conflicts, develops a "combat neurosis" and thereafter shows anxiety and an exacerbation of somatic symptoms at any "stimulus" that might, however indirectly, be reminiscent of flying or battle. Such displaced symbolizations might then produce phobic responses to the faintly propeller-like whirr of an electric fan, or the distant shell-like scream of a locomotive, or even the gunlike retort of a cork being pulled from a bottle.

† Angyal (1941, p. 73) seeks to define affect operationally thus: "*Emotional experiences are symbols of value-laden ego-relevant facts.* This brings to the fore the processual character of emotion as an evaluative experience." Angyal's thesis, however, differs from the one here presented in his Platonic implication—typical for the Gestalt school (Köhler, 1929)—that both "values" and "facts" have a transcendent, abstract existence.

Significance of linguistics in dynamic psychiatry

The language of the patient. The semantic principles developed in the preceding section may be profitably applied to the relationships between formal psychoanalysis and dynamic psychiatry. As we have seen, classic psychoanalysis is a process in which, through the use of free association, "dream interpretation" and other techniques, unconscious motivations, cognate symbolizations and patterns of current behavior are retrospectively traced through covert concept formations and evaluations to the basically formative experiences and reactions of early life. So revealed, the dynamisms of the patient's conduct, including his linguistics, are more amenable to consciously directed personal and social readjustments. This process may be exemplified with special reference to a patient's symbolic system by the following case:

Case 39. "Psychosomatic" symbolism

An intelligent, thirty-two-year-old woman, who had previously been treated in various medical clinics for a chronic illness vaguely diagnosed as an "endocrine dyscrasia" or "anorexia nervosa," was referred to the Clinics because of persistent vomiting and severe cachexia. The terms in which the patient described her complaints were of immediate symbolic significance: i.e., she stated that for the preceding five years all references to sex had become literally "distasteful" and "disgusting" and that her "inability to stomach" men caused her actually to vomit in their presence. So pervasive was this spread of cognate somatic symbolism that even if she merely heard the telephone ring she became nauseated over the remote possibility that some man was calling her for a "date"; similarly, reading or hearing the word "date" or even seeing the fruit by that name produced abdominal discomforts.

Because of the chronicity and involved nature of the patient's "psychosomatic" disorder and its deep roots in her personality, psychoanalytic therapy was thought advisable. Early in this process the patient, rather too readily, traced her heterosexual aversions and their bodily expressions to extreme guilt over perverse kissing and temptations to fellatio with a suitor five years previously; significantly, however, actual intercourse had not caused such great concern. These analytic "confessions" were accompanied by little emotional discharge, but subsequently, with mounting anxiety, the patient began to recall similar experiences with her older brother during childhood, and equated them with even earlier oral-erotic wishes directed toward her father. These were finally associated with a bizarre but revealing infantile fantasy which she reconstructed as follows: after weaning, but before being ejected from the parental bed, she had, in substitution for her mother's breast, sought and swallowed her father's penis. This imaginary maneuver had also served various ancillary purposes: it removed her father as a competitor, while at the same time the incorporation of his penis made her, in fancy, "masculine" like her favored elder brother and so more likely to regain her mother's exclusive attentions.[*] Unfortunately, however, if she were to avoid retribution by her castrated father and deprived mother, a self-compulsory pattern of "undoing" and expiation was called for: she must reject symbolically and vomit somatically all other "oral" satisfactions not given her freely by her mother. These psychosomatic fantasies, "bizarre" only in their child-like symbolisms, nevertheless had definite experiential referents to the circumstances of the patient's

[*] For significant symbolic parallelisms, cf. Case 40, Appendix 3.

early life. The patient's mother, a domineering, highly emotional woman, had in reality rejected her infant daughter because of her own jealousies and aggressions in the family interrelationships. In this situation the patient had at first made an abortive attempt to seek security in a weak father; when this failed, she regressed to a helpless maternal dependence colored by anxious renunciations of all emancipatory longings. Accordingly, she was particularly sensitive to oral and other erotic temptations toward her father, her brother or later male surrogates, so that her interpersonal relations with them continued to be colored by ambivalence and symbolic "psychosomatic" rejections. Small wonder, then, that the patient had suffered persistent "stomach trouble" throughout childhood, that her gastro-intestinal dysfunctions had increased during menarche and again during an anxiety-ridden courtship, and that even at the time of her analysis she was still living in a child-like dependence on her mother and reacting to every opportunity for emancipation with an exacerbation of her specific psychosomatic defenses. From the standpoint of our present interest, moreover, it need hardly be added that all words, symbols and gestures referable to mother, food, marriage, sexuality or related concepts evoked exquisitely individual and unique connotations and affects which profoundly influenced not only the patient's use of language but nearly every other aspect of her behavior.

No patient's symbolic system can ever be completely "analyzed," nor does one analysis "prove" a general linguistic theorem, but it may justifiably be stated that the type of symbol-derivation just illustrated is fundamental to a dynamic semasiology of linguistic behavior. Evidence from psychoanalytic sources therefore again supports the thesis that symbols do not have a transcendent quasi-Platonic existence *per se*, but are meaningful only in terms of the individual experiences and interpretations of the observer. Further, these symbol-meanings are continually being both expressed in, and modified by, the individual's current motivations, attitudes and environmental adaptations—a corollary that cannot be neglected in evaluating the verbal communications of the patient in relation to his total behavior. We may here, then, lay the groundwork for the clinical applications of biodynamic semantics by considering the limited and contingent role of language in dynamic psychiatry as contrasted to that most traditionally verbal of techniques and therapies—psychoanalysis.

Totality in clinical observation.   Freud was, by many accounts, a shy man and, apparently for reasons of his own, preferred having his patients literally looking the other way during their analytic treatment. Thus was prescribed the standard couch-and-chair tandem in most psychoanalytic offices—an arrangement that has relieved the tensions of many a patient (and analyst) and so contributed to the respective "freedom" of analytic associations and interpretations. Nevertheless, most modern analysts have broken away from custom sufficiently to take the patient off the resting position, look him unabashedly in the eye when necessary, and obtain coherent and realistic data as to his everyday behavior from him or, as occasion requires, from his friends and family. Such heterodox departures are part of a growing recognition even among analysts that the patient's verbalizations, however unrestricted, are only a partial expression—and often not the best index—of his total behavior patterns, and that a consistent account of his current occupational, sexual, social and other adaptations furnishes cogent material for transference interpretations, for "reality testing" and for the therapeutic process as a whole. However, once the patient, spiritually or actually, is back on the couch and "free associating" again, some analysts relapse into traditional habits of treating the patient's word sequences with so constricted a field of reference that a great deal of their diagnostic and dynamic significance may be lost. As an illustration, the question of so-called "dream" analysis may be considered in this connection.

"Dream" analysis.   It may, perhaps, clarify the problem to realize that no dream *as such* has ever been analyzed—or ever can be analyzed—until we develop some almost inconceivable technical device for recording and reproducing the actual dream fantasies. All that can really be done at present is to note carefully the patient's *verbal and other patterns* while he is talking "about" his hypothetical "dream" during some later interview, remembering all the while that his imagery has inevitably been repressed and distorted in recollection, that it is described in words and symbols colored by his experiences not only before but since the "dream," and that in the very process of verbalization his "descriptions" and "associations" are further dependent on his unconscious motivations in recalling and telling the dream at all, his transference situation, his current defenses, his physiologic status and the many other complex and interpenetrating factors of the fleeting moment (cf. Appendix 3). There is, then, no "language of the dream," just as there is no "language of the psychiatric history," of the "hypnotic trance," or of "the Pentothal interview"*; there is only the language of the patient under a fluctuating configuration of interrelated physiologic and symbolic contingencies.† This complexity, of course, makes linguistic observation more difficult and demanding, but so also does it make our understanding of the patient more comprehensive and dynamic, and our therapy thereby more realistic and effective.

The verbal language of therapy

For reasons parallel to those just outlined, the therapist must also couch his communications with the patient in symbols, syllogisms and analogies carefully designed to resonate with the patient's motivations, symbolisms and adaptations, else no material change in the patient's behavior *other than* his verbal patterns will result. Thus, all psychiatrists

---

* The diagnostic aspects of verbal analysis were more fully dealt with by Eva Balken and the author in a series of clinical studies published between 1939 and 1941. Briefly, it was shown that not only does the content of a patient's imagery indicate the nature of his intrapsychic conflicts and their fantasied solutions, but the distinctive combinations of substantive, kinetic or descriptive symbols he uses in his verbal expressions have differential diagnostic significance. For example, anxious patients used many transitive verbs and adverbs; "compensated" neurotics (e.g., "compulsives" and "hysterics") employed, respectively, exact or leisurely descriptive phraseology; paranoid patients stressed personal pronouns, etc.

† Cf. also H. A. Murray (1932) and R. Harrison (1940).

have had experience with neurotic patients who have eagerly adapted to their own uses some physician's careless statement that they had "nervous trouble," and have inadvertently been helped to regress into a life of dependency or invalidism on the plea that their "nerves were all shot" —a rationalization now, according to them, supported by authoritative opinion. On quite the same plane, many analysts now realize, was the patient who, in the exploratory days of psychoanalysis, was given "interpretations" not clearly meaningful at the time even to the analyst, with the result that while the patient could ever afterward talk glibly (or even smugly) of his "Id," his "Superego" and his "complexes," he showed no other significant changes in insight, attitude or behavior. In short, if communications between patient and therapist are to be truly effective, they must reach beyond the verbal level to basic motivations, pressing conflicts and real-life readjustments, else the reorientative process attains little vitality and remains, as we have seen, either an idle exercise in the superficies of fantasy, or, worse, an iatrogenic trauma.

The thaumaturgy of words.   Nor need we be deceived when the mere verbalizations of the patient or our own "interpretations" seem to produce temporary improvements in his behavior. Biodynamically, the sounds produced by the human voice reach so deeply into the formative layers of experience that at times they appear to have almost magical effects. For that matter, nearly all animals try to influence their environment by cries, howls and other vocalizations—certainly human children do. And when food, warmth, protection and other wants are satisfied through the medium of such sounds, the child further cultivates and refines its vocalizations in accordance with the requirements of its milieu, i.e., it acquires a "language" endowed with apparently magic potentialities for satisfying needs. This fantastic belief in the covert powers and uses of words and word-systems is, then, found almost everywhere—in the incantations and prayers of savage religions, in the "secret" languages (pig Latin, Opish, "Double Dutch," etc.—cf. Bender) of adolescents and, clinically, in the ardor with which the neurotic patient importunes the psychiatrist for some particular brand of verbal magic. For such reasons, some "explanations" and "interpretations" can be operationally effective in a limited sense, regardless of their content, provided only that the patient has a sufficiently intense desire to believe in the powers of the physician's words and person. Thus, it is not unusual to see patients equally "enlightened" and "improved" by a Christian Scientist's revelation that "Good is God," by a "clinical neurologist's explanation that "emotions come from the thalamus and not the cortex" or by a pseudo-"analytic" interpretation of the "oral erotic basis" of some neurotic symptom. Obviously, in each of these instances the patient's anxiety is relieved by the therapist's apparent willingness to help, and his confidence-inspiring erudition and reassuring attention; unfortunately, however, the avidly regressive passivity and fantasy-ridden dependency of the patient under such circumstances is an insufficient basis for a stable improvement in his behavior. This important reservation applies even when the patient can be induced to "verbalize" ideas and "insights" undoubtedly relevant to his motivational conflicts and neurotic adaptations, since as long as these "insights" remain merely verbal and are not applied to behavioral readaptations, little effective progress has been made.

Non-verbal communication

Jurgen Reusch has pointed out that gestures and facial expressions establish the essential channels of relationship between child and adult long before mere words take on their secondary "analogic" functions, and that thereafter non-verbal, "non-analogic" modes of communication remain the most effective means of human intercourse. This field has also become of prime interest to linguists, and has recently been applied to investigations of the speech and gestures of psychiatric patients by Smith, Birdwhistell, et al. But we have long since learned to recognize an almost infinite variety of these attitudinal telegrams: the flush and cough of embarrassment; the downcast eyes and pursed mouth of shame; the narrow stare of reproach; the curled lip of distaste; or the taut white facies of grim anger. Nor does it take the perceptive student of psychiatry long to become attuned to his patients' other gestural and kinesic signals which, when combined with a subtle appreciation of the tone, rhythm, tempo, hesitations, interjections, irregularities and interruptions of speech, lead to diagnostic impressions as significant as those derived from the patient's verbal content. These aspects of the psychiatric examination are discussed more fully in Part One of the *Practice,* but the following may here serve as brief examples:

The furtive restlessness and rapid, treble delivery of the anxious patient, as contrasted with the bland, cadenced, practiced, sometimes smug garrulity of the chronic "hysteric" or "character neurotic."

The slumped shoulders, prehensively anaclitic movements and slow decrescendo singsong of the depressed patient—maintained until the ominously quiet desperation of a resolve to suicide.

The stereotyped, unresponsive automatisms in posture, expression and voice of the schizophrenic.

These vignettes, however, should not be taken as the "phenomenologic manifestations" of specific "disease entities" (Minkowski, Strauss, et al.) any more than the verbal and motor expressions of anger should be so regarded. Instead, non-analogic modes of communication—often more precise and poignant than the protean analogues of words—will change continuously with altered circumstances, and by this very token can be used by both patient and physician for understanding and therapeutic communication.

Totality in therapeutic techniques

The topics here discussed are, indeed, relevant to all therapy, whether by orthodox "psychoanalytic" or by briefer and more active techniques. As indicated, symbol-interpretations alone can lead only to grudging verbal acknowledgments by the patient that his infantile anxieties, inhibitions and other neurotic defenses do not, after all, seem justified by current "reality" as described in the language of others. Such verbal comparisons, however, obviously can constitute only a preliminary to more direct experiential reorientations, and must of necessity be condensed in the rapid clinical treatment of patients whose symbol-systems are not so deviant as to make communication too difficult. In these cases the therapeutic task is to resolve the patient's motivational vicissitudes and conflicts as rapidly as possible and then, as his neurotic anxiety diminishes, induce him to undertake new experiences which may lead to more lastingly satisfactory personal and social adjustments. The essential core of therapy may, indeed, be stated aphoristically thus: *render the patient's neurotic compromises and symbolisms—active as well as verbal—gradually less necessary and covertly satisfying to him, and at the same time make more "normal" adaptive patterns increasingly desirable and available.* The main lever for initiating this double reorientation is often the working-through of the patient-physician transference relationships, but other available therapeutic resources, such as somatic therapy and familial, economic and other influences, must be skillfully employed, and certainly need never be slighted simply to maintain any narrowly monistic "physical," "psychologic" or "environmental" approach. For instance, it may be desirable to advise the withdrawal of family overprotection or the removal of secondary gains, and to counter the discomfiting but kinetic effects of these procedures by other recommendations as to an improved home environment, suitable employment, and facilities for more satisfactory sexual, social and recreational outlets. Dynamically, such time-honored measures, even when utilized only over a short period of treatment, constitute much more than merely "superficial" therapy, since if skillfully directed they may reach and effectively mitigate conflicts with or without compulsively verbalized explorations of "the Unconscious." In such instances, too, "insight" on the part of the patient may be non-verbal, but expressed no less effectively in his stable readaptations to his new modes of living and his permanent rejection of the old.

Nor should the therapist be remiss in utilizing this repertoire of non-verbal therapy in the intermediate and terminal stages of even a formal psychoanalysis. For instance, toward the end of her first analytic year the "anorexia nervosa" patient described as Case 39 broke through some of her maternal and transference dependencies and acquired a fair verbal insight into her oral and other defenses. Nevertheless, her ultimate reality adjustments were both expedited and stabilized when, under the active guidance of the therapist, and with the intelligent cooperation of her mother, family and a few friends, she moved away from home, secured self-supporting and satisfactory employment, and cultivated increasingly gratifying social, recreational and, finally, heterosexual contacts. True, she would have found it difficult or impossible to take advantage of such manipulative adjuncts had she not "worked through" her anxieties, inhibitions and neurotic defenses in the preceding analytic process, but the therapeutic principle remains: the analysis of verbal symbols alone is not sufficient, since therapy must deal pragmatically with the total adaptive behavior of patients in their everyday milieu.

Language as "general" communication

But there remains to be considered a final semantic issue of theoretic importance, namely: if signs and symbols are significant only in an individually experiential and highly contingent sense, how can language be used for interpersonal discourse at all? For that matter, how can this book be meaningfully "understood" by anyone but its author? This problem has seriously concerned many a student of language, but perhaps clues to its solution lie in some of the biodynamic principles discussed above. In brief, we develop a commonality of "understanding" of each other's symbolic expressions insofar as we have each experienced comparable (though never identical) motivations, frustrations and adaptations in a physical and social milieu characterized by common goals, vicissitudes and modes of attainment. As a specific illustration, the word for hunger "means" almost the same in any language, since all individuals have experienced the elemental biologic need to which it refers; in contrast, the connotations of "food" begin to vary much more widely from culture to culture. Similarly, symbols with more complex and contingent motivational referents such as "home," "family," "work" and so on (not to mention ethereally elaborate concepts such as "truth," "beauty," "religion" or "the good life") must necessarily have ever wider ranges of meaning among individuals with necessarily different experiences and social backgrounds.* Indeed, we hardly need language to communicate experiences of direct biodynamic significance; thus, we can accurately discern pain, fear or rage in each other or in animals with no expressions at the verbal level at all. Conversely, as the experiences become more specialized to the individual and group, their communication becomes at best only approximately "understood" by those not personally acquainted with them. For instance, many nuances of meaning conveyed by the analytic symbolisms in Case 39 will almost certainly seem bizarre and far-fetched (i.e., "fantastic" in the usual sense of the word) to students who have not as yet had a direct and intimate acquaintance with symbol-formations in their own or their patient's conceptual systems. Disparities of connotation also increase rapidly as social and cultural gaps among individuals and groups become wider; indeed, such difficulties in interpersonal and intergroup communications have constituted barriers to human understanding and fellowship that are sometimes of tragic import. Even on "simple" gestural levels there may be great ethnic differences: to the Chinese the clapping of hands "means" not approval but worrisome concern, rounded eyes "signify" not awe or wonder but anger, and the extrusion of the tongue "expresses" not derision but surprise (Klineberg).† At higher levels of abstraction such

---

* Nor, of course, is the superficially professed reaction to a verbal symbol necessarily an accurate index of deeper attitudes. For example, Stagner (1936) found that the majority of Americans at that time expressed disapproval of the concept of "fascism" yet very many of them covertly subscribed to—and acted upon—inherently fascistic prejudices and policies.

† Direct affective expressions (rage, fear, etc.) are, however, far less variable in general pattern (Darwin) and may be independent of cortical control (Bard, 1934).

disparities increase rapidly; for example, most occidental peoples would find it very difficult to understand the terms the Balinese use for their intricate family relationships or peculiar directional or temporal orientations; conversely, the Balinese find it almost impossible to grasp our everyday words for time and space (Mead).* All in all, the sciences of communication and semantics are highly complex anthropologic and sociologic disciplines which, nevertheless, must be regarded as integral with biology, psychology and psychiatry in the biodynamic organon of human behavior.

In effect, then, language is a form of gestural and vocal behavior which, while most highly developed in human beings, conforms to the biodynamic principles of all behavior as outlined in Chapters 8 to 12. Signs, symbols and their relationships in language function are representative of the personal experience of the individual and can be approximately "understood" only by other individuals with corresponding experience in their own personal and cultural environments. The language of the patient is therefore highly significant, but must be evaluated in the light of his balance of motivations, his adaptive patterns and his current interpretations of his milieu in terms of his past experience. Similarly, symbol-interpretation and verbal "insight" are not therapeutic ends in themselves, but must be employed only as adjuncts to other therapeutic processes that resolve motivational conflicts and direct behavior into more stable and favorable channels.

* The anthropologic literature is so replete with illustrations as to the protean nature of expressive and cultural symbolism that any selection must be almost at random. For example, J. C. Moloney reports that Japanese boys, when frustrated, are permitted to beat their mothers' breasts; as adult soldiers defeated in Manila, they ran their bayonets through the breasts of Philippine women. Leighton and Kluckhohn observed a different effect on the opposite side of the world: "In spite of the fact that Navaho infants receive a maximum of protection and gratification, when they grow to be adults [because of unaccustomed frustrations] they are very moody and worry a great deal." As to the interpenetrations of sexual, familial, social and religious customs: the Shakta sect of India worship *mudra* (grain), *mansa* (meat), *madya* (liquor) and *maithuna* (sexual intercourse). A solemn rite in honor of the goddess Shakti is to put the upper garments of all of the worshipers' wives into a large vase, and then assign each wife to any man who pulls out her garment. According to a recent news report (Time, May 2, 1955, p. 30) a Shakta husband cut off his wife's nose because she would not comply with this holy custom, and she committed suicide because she "regretted her marital unfaithfulness." In contrast, among the Nam Lo Li of Hainan, China (J.A.M.A. 157, p. 62, 1955) when a woman is found guilty of adultery her husband goes to jail. Nor are mass hallucinations unacceptable: X. Fielding reports that, on Crete, the whole village of Frangcastello sees a spectral army of 385 soldiers killed on the anniversary of the Greek war of independence. As implied by Ruth Benedict in her *Patterns of Culture,* an arrogant braggart and snob is the social model among the Kwakiutl; a mystic escapist would feel at home with the Zuñi; a male homosexual would be assigned a respected social role as a *berdache* among the Plains Indians, and a homicidal paranoiac committable in our culture would be regarded as realistic and prudent in a Dobu community. To quote Murdock: "The comparative method is indispensable . . . at most [other methods] can only produce culture-bound generalizations approximately valid for a particular group of related societies during a particular segment of their history. . . . [However] the treasure house of ethnography is so rich and varied that it is relatively easy to support almost any hypothesis."

References

Allport, G. W., and Odbert, H. S.: Trait-names, a Psycho-lexical Study.
Bateson, C., and Mead, Margaret: Balinese Culture.
Bierens de Haan, J. A.: Langue humaine, Langage animal.
Croce, B.: Aesthetic: as Science of Expression and General Linguistic.
De Laguna, G. A.: Speech, Its Functions and Development.
Freud, S.: Analysis Terminable and Interminable.
Gombrich, E. H.: The Story of Art.
Hayakawa, S.: Language in Action.
Katan, M.: Schizophrenic Speech.
Lewis, M. M.: The Beginning of Reference to Past and Future in a Child's Speech.
Markey, C. J. F.: The Symbolic Process and its Integration in Children.
Money-Kyrle, R.: The Psychology of Propaganda.
Morris, C.: Foundation of the Theory of Signs.
Ogden, C. K., and Richards, S. A.: The Meaning of Meaning.
Pear, T. H.: Voice and Personality.
Piaget, J.: The Language and Thought of the Child.
Ruesch, J.: Disturbed Communication.
Sanford, F. H.: Speech and Personality.
Scheibel, H. G.: On the Objectivity of Aesthetic Value.
Smith, H. W.: Man and His Gods.
Vigotsky, L.: Thought and Speech.
Waterman, P. F.: The Story of Superstition.
Wheelwright, P.: The Language of Poetry-Myth-Reality.
White, W. A.: The Language of the Psychoses.

Chapter 14

The evolution of psychotherapy

THERE ARE three principal modes of clarifying any branch of knowledge and setting it in its proper scientific context: the experimental, the comparative and the historical. In a field as broad and complex as psychotherapy, the developmental aspects require special elucidation, perhaps along the lines indicated in this final chapter.

Organismic integration

Herbert Muller, in his *Uses of the Past,* trenchantly remarked that "Our age is notorious for its want of [any deeper] sense of history than the minutes of the last meeting," and in psychiatry particularly we seem to prefer the trivial writings of yesterday to the deathless lessons of five billion years of cosmic and biologic development and relatedness. In contrast, Alfred N. Whitehead, in his masterly *Science and the Modern World,* thus expresses the thesis that there is an unbroken line of past, present and future "events" and "locations" *from nuclear particles to human behavior:*

In being aware of the bodily experience, we must thereby be aware of aspects of the whole spatio-temporal world as mirrored within the bodily life. . . . In a certain sense, everything is everywhere at all times . . . every spatio-temporal standpoint mirrors the world. [p. 93] The event is a necessary link in the pattern of transmission, by which the character of every event receives some modification from the character of every other event. [p. 154]

Or, as John Donne* put it more poetically: "No man is an Iland, intire of itselfe . . . never send to know for whom the bell tolls: it tolls for thee!"

This apprehension of universal interrelatedness apparently stirred the primal Algonkian slime; certainly, the most primitive living things apply the Golden Rule in a way that gives a wry twist of meaning to the phrase "descent of man." For example, the cells of the lowly myxamoeba *Dictyostelium discorideum* ordinarily live a life of rugged individualism; however, should shortages of food or water develop, *a few individuals form the nucleus of a colony and then die to constitute a stalk upon which the others may sporulate and survive.* As Bonner also points out in his *Cells and Societies,* at only a slightly higher level of cellular aggre-

---

* Who, like St. Augustine, Francis Bacon, Descartes and many other less gifted mortals, lived as an individual hedonist through youth (Ur-defense I, v.i.) became a socially conscious adult (Ur-defense II) and ended life as a theologic transcendentalist (Ur-defense III).

gation the Portuguese man-of-war *Physalia pelagica* is at the same time a group of independent cells, a loosely assembled colony of individuals, an "animal" in the biologic sense, and also a fully delegated, organized and functioning society. As to the supposed uniqueness of humans in possessing "consciousness" (or its putative negation "the Unconscious") Simpson comments in his *Meaning of Evolution* as follows:

> I know that some students of the subject deny that any animals below man . . . are 'aware' or 'perceive' anything whatsoever; for the present purpose, this does not matter in the least; all animals *act* as if they had awareness and perception—even the ameba does. [p. 21] The basic fact that all phyla of animals have survived since their origin bothered Sigmund Freud, who could not see why all ancient forms have not yielded to a death wish. [p. 19] Nor, as Huxley remarked, does ascribing evolution to an *élan vital* [cf. libido, Thanatos] explain the history of life [any more] than . . . an *élan locomotif* explains the operation of a steam engine. [p. 131] Struggle is not necessarily or even usually of the essence. Precisely the opposite; selection in favor of harmonious or cooperative group associations is certainly common. [p. 96]

The first three biodynamic principles—those concerned with the motivational milieu-adaptive and compensatory aspects of normal behavior—are thus seen to include fundamental organismic capacities for *interaction* and *aggregation*—names for the "forces" that assemble atoms into men and men into societies.

Anthropologic integration

Available records confirm Simpson's thesis by indicating that the earliest creatures that can be termed *Homo sapiens* were already well advanced in respect to communion and collaboration, in that they lived not only in family groups but in cohesive clans organized for mutual welfare. That such organizations strove to preserve the most intimate of all biodynamic relationships—child to mother and man to woman—is indicated by the figurines of steatopygous females ("paleolithic Venuses") whose huge breasts, bellies and buttocks epitomized the acme of maternity and sexuality. Concurrently there appeared man's projection of wishful imagery into the future, as represented in the cave paintings near Lascaux in France or Altamera in Spain.* Significantly, these Mousterian sketches of tribal hunts and customs depict not only *individual skills* and *aggregate actions*, but also a third reliance fundamental to human behavior and therefore to psychotherapy: namely, that if a yearning hope is but eloquently and insistently enough expressed, some transcendently powerful All-Giver will answer the plea and grant satisfaction to the supplicant. As Mövius in his *Archaeology and Earliest Art* analyzes the evidence, this protoreligious function is the most likely explanation of why these paintings were placed in temple-like alcoves,

---

* Gombrich in his *The Story of Art* regards these scenographs and those of even earlier Acheulean cultures as displaying nothing less than "formalized artistic perfection."

covered over like palimpsests and surrounded by other objects of primitive worship:

> The stenciled or negative hands on the cave walls reflect possession or power . . . the darts or arrows piercing certain animals signify the casting of a spell on the game.

To recapitulate, then, fifty or more thousand years ago man already derived essential comfort from three fundamental faiths to which men eternally cling and which will as eternally be available in psychotherapy. These faiths, which we may call ultimate or Ur-fantasies, are:

First, man's perennial trust in his capacity to control his milieu through various technologies, from chipped flints then to space satellites now.*

Second, a wishful reliance on the collaboration of his fellow-man, and

Third, an arrogation of power to employ one or another form of Supreme Magic to serve his own purposes.

The evolution of clinical psychotherapy

Acting on this triune core of essential faiths, our ancestor in Akkad or Egypt, when troubled by frustrations and conflicts, attempted to solve his problems by his own skills and ingenuities. If these failed he could summon a group of his fellows in a designated Place of Succor for advice and assistance. If lay efforts were insufficient, a general physician or a specialist could be engaged at a standard fee, and with pre-set penalties for failure.† Should all human efforts prove inadequate, final recourse was had to the Temple, where accommodating female attendants were commissioned to comfort him in the name of Mother Ishtar or Isis, and where a priest commanded various supernatural minions to help the needful votary with both his earthly and heavenly affairs. In Eighteenth-Dynasty Egypt, thirteen centures before Christ, temple therapy also included such regressively cathected activities as prolonged ablutions, specially prepared foods, confessional prayers for forgiveness, and a trance to induce dreams for interpretation by the priest. But even more than this was available; by following the magic ritual of the Book of the Dead, Seth, Osiris and all lesser deities could be compelled by the devout Egyptian not only to remove his frustrations and slay his mundane enemies, but also to banish all obstacles to immortal suzerainty in the Land of Ra.‡ We may well ask: could any system of therapy provide

---

* This, too, is not uniquely human: wasps use pebbles to tamp their tunnels, finches use cactus spines to dig insects, ant colonies raise food crops and then aphids for their "milk" and beavers engineer dams and build submarine cities. Moreover, like their intransigent human cousins, they continue to do so no matter how often their activities lead to frustration or catastrophe.

† These procedures and practices were later specified and regulated in the Code of Hammurabi (c. 1250 B.C.).

‡ Then, as now, the magical formulae ended by an invocation to the supreme god Amen!

better escapes from harsh realities, more satisfying recourse to temporarily regressive physical satisfactions, greater alleviations of past and present anxieties, and more glowing promises of everlasting power and glory? By all accounts, the ancient Akkadians and the Egyptians of the middle millennia before Christ were relatively a happy people.

Nor was this empirically acquired wisdom of their forebears altogether lost on the iconoclastic Greeks. Their beautifully situated Asklepiad sanatoria (health* resorts) were also ancillary to Hellenic temples where, through the medium of esthetic Apollonian or ecstatic Dionysian ritual, priest and priestess offered religious as well as physical retreat and satisfaction to the avid participant. But the Greek genius for development and detail now added to the essential Ur-processes the following maneuvers, each included in one way or another in their medico-religious therapy:

FAITH IN SELF-HELP. On the physical side, calisthenics, athletics and other practices to develop the Body Beautiful and Triumphant. But physical strength was also to be multiplied manifold by Superior Knowledge, whether of the philosophical systems of the Ionic philosophers, the historical accounts of Thucydides, the cosmic harmonies of Pythagoras, the encyclopedic systematizations of Aristotle, or the supposed certainties of Platonic absolutism. Nor, for that matter, did the Greeks fail to admire and utilize the technologic-scientific application of Archimedes, who, twenty-two centuries ago, in an apotheosis of man's first Ur-defense, could proclaim "Give me but a place to stand, and with my levers I can move the world!" Greeks of the Athenian stripe were a confident breed, and thoroughly exploited the reassuring maxims "Knowledge is Power," and "Wisdom sets men free!"

TRUST IN FELLOW-MEN. This second Ur-fantasy was also intuitively utilized in the Asklepiad system in a number of ways divisible for purposes of discussion (though again indivisible in dynamic essence) as follows:

INTERPERSONAL. Depending on his conscious or unconscious needs, the patient could explore and satisfy vis-à-vis his physician-priest the following ("transference") expectations and attitudes:

(a) As a kindly and devoted parental or avuncular surrogate, who personally welcomed the troubled prodigal back to a haven of security and comfort. This was reinforced at the Sanatoria by intensive attention to bodily satisfactions through special diets (dietotherapy), baths (balneotherapy), massages (physiotherapy), and other services reminiscent of the attentions given a cherished infant (Gr. *therapeien*, service).

(b) As a learned and experienced guide and leader, whose counsels and systems for more restrained and balanced, and therefore healthier and happier, modes of life could be followed on rational and empirical grounds (e.g., as in the various Stoic schools).

(c) As a personally interested mentor, willing to listen to the supplicant's current difficulties ("present illness"), explore their relationship to the patient's past experiences (history†), derived meanings and values (semantics) and patterns of goal-directed action (operational analysis),

---

* From the Saxon root *hal*, which wondrously also covers all the Ur-faiths through its derivatives *hale* (whole), *hail* (friend) and *holy* (divine).

† The characteristically profound Greek concept of the term *history* was not a mere chronicle of events, but an interpretation of their *coherence* and *significance*.

so that the formulated "verbal" understandings so derived could then be applied to foster not only more satisfying but more lasting and useful adaptations (operational "insight"). Socrates required his students to work through their own verbal perplexities; Plato understood the conative nature of dreams and symbols; Aristophanes in his delightful comedy "The Clouds" pictured the distraught Strepsiades lying on a couch and trying to acquire understanding through fantasy and free association; and, as we have seen, Soranus recorded the cure of a case of "hysteria" by resolving an underlying sexual conflict in unequivocal action.

(d) Finally, the transference of passivity and trust could also take the forms of submission to the healer as physician, with avid acceptance of the efficacy of his quasi-scientific, quasi-mystical remedies. And the armamentarium available to the Hellenic *iatros* included not only the vast and mysterious pharmacopoeias of all the lands from Cathay to the Gates of Hercules, but also a variety of surgical and other manipulations, including the Egyptian practice of trephining the skull and incising the cortex (lobotomy) or, as described by Pliny the Elder, causing electric eels to discharge their current through the patient's skull. We read of Hippocrates' condemnations of the ignorance and superstition inherent in many "false remedies" but this alone proves how widely prescribed, then as now, they must have been.

GROUP RELATIONSHIPS.   In this category of therapy, too, the Greeks anticipated us by nearly two and a half millennia. Moreover, they apparently were wise enough to recognize—where we sometimes forget—that although reversion to various forms of passive interpersonal reliance may be necessary and occasionally desirable in the first stages of therapy, excessive dependence may encourage paralyzing regression, and must therefore be followed as soon as practicable by measures designed to foster personal redevelopment and social rehabilitation. These may at first require a protected environment where special techniques and expert supervision are available, but the objective continually must be to redeploy the patient's motivations, methods and skills for returning as rapidly as practicable to creative interpersonal living. According to medical historians (cf. Garrison, Zilboorg, Fulton, Riese, et al.) the following is only a partial list of the media for group communication and activity employed in classical therapy:

MUSIC, giving opportunity for feelings of conjoint rhythm and harmony, affective expression, group belongingness and other social consummatory experiences.

CALISTHENICS AND DANCING, with similar possibilities of group catharsis and communion.

COMPETITIVE ATHLETICS, with opportunities not only for the joy of action but through nondestructive competition for public recognition and reward.

DRAMATICS.   Here the esthetically sensitive psychiatrist (and there should be no other) may well ask: What writings better explore or epitomize basic human relationship than the plays of Euripides, Aeschylus or Aristophanes? And what productions can offer both participant or witness more varied identifications, vivid experiences or vicariously tragic or comic solutions of their own interpersonal problems? The Greeks cherished and utilized these dramas for their deep human empathies and meanings, endlessly varied their themes and were deeply involved as players, chorus or affectively moved audience.

INSTITUTIONAL SERVICE. This offered a transition from a passive dependence on the sanatorium to an eventual recognition of an obligation to return to a place in the community maintainable only through responsibility and effort for the common good.

THE UR-DEFENSES OF TRANSCENDENT MAGIC. In recognition of the importance of this last belief even the civilized Greeks demanded that Socrates pay the ultimate penalty for threatening the most cherished of all human defenses: an unreasoning trust in the existence of celestial Beings who, though all-wise and all-powerful, were nevertheless gullible enough to serve man in exchange for flattery, cajolery or, at most, a little bribery. To capitalize on this ultimate faith* the Asklepiad sanatoria, like many hospitals today, were ancillary to one or another religious cult and thereby added the following powerful factors to therapy:

A *"divinely revealed" doctrine* in which all believers could feel an exclusively self-elevating bond of fellowship.

A *reassuring ritual* which, through its origin in human needs and through millennia of empiric refinement, included such exquisitely gratifying procedures as:

The symbolic eating and drinking of the parent-god's body in the forms of mystically potentiating food and wine (as exemplified in the ancient worship of Melitta and Mithras).

The temple hymns, sung and played in the simple, repetitive, rhythmic cadences of a mother's lullaby—and often resulting in the hypnotic trances of the "temple sleep." This could be varied with Dionysian orgies to be doubly enjoyed, since they also honored one's sensually permissive and accommodating gods.

The "anointing" or "laying on of hands" to cure an injured bodily part—a direct reminiscence of soothing parental care of an injured child. And, if necessary, the temple could make available occasional or even permanent cloistered retreats or "sanctuaries" from earthly stresses and problems.

The corresponding emphasis on the spiritual, a concept as fundamental to life as is the neonate's first breath or *spiritus.* Every human is variously *inspired,* acquires an *esprit de corps,* becomes *dispirited,* and finally *expires* so that his immutable *spirit* can begin life anew. And here, too, the physician-priest functions in knowing the Spiritual World, or purveying professed contrition and remorse to the Spirits of our Fathers, and of requiring only a gratifyingly small penance with which to avoid the horrors of eternal punishment.

And finally, the priest mediates the supreme promise of all religious—or, for that matter, of all "scientific" systems: *the conquest, through life eternal, of the most grim and implacable enemy of human-kind: death itself.*

It is tempting to take dialectically opposite attitudes to the foregoing account of the evolution of the essentials of psychotherapy. One extreme would be to regard it as demonstrating that all was known and practiced to perfection in a Golden Age long past, and that we have simply deteriorated into greater confusion and awkwardness since then. Opposite views might be (a) to regard the descriptions above solely as pseudo-

* From a quite different perspective Rostand (in his *Can Man be Modified?*, 1959) comments: "Man cannot help regarding himself as something sacred . . . as the highest and most precious thing on the planet . . . as the 'unique being' . . . which perhaps has not its like in the whole vast universe."

historical fantasies analogous to wishful screen-memories, (b) to accept them only as approximations of wisdoms that were not really possessed at the time, much as the atomic theory was only vaguely anticipated by Democritus, or evolution by Anaximander, or (c) to assert that until recently men knew only "intuitively" what they were doing and applied it only sporadically and incompletely. Actually the last commentary would still be applicable to most of our psychotherapy, whereas the truth would lie somewhere closer to the first statement than to the strictures under (a) and (b). In fact, though admittedly there is no record that all the practices mentioned were carried on to full potentiality at Ur, Memphis, Cos, or any other ancient citadel of healing, it is not altogether misleading to point out that no method of therapy in the intervening ages has utilized any *essentially* new principles or combinations of techniques. Let us list a few of the seemingly diverse therapies that have remained effective through the ages because of this very fact.

Narcissistic self-assertions.   Since men continue to equate bodily strength with personal, sexual and social dominance, purveyors of perennial physical panaceas always have a dedicated following. Closely related are the body-worship cult so firmly entrenched under slogans such as "A strong mind in a strong body" that the most sedentary state hospital superintendent will automatically contend that his gymnasium is an essential part of his institution.

Also in the general category of narcissistic preoccupations, though less physically strenuous, are the various Orders of Adulation of the Supreme Self. These range from the blandly narcissistic "Every day I am getting better and better" of the late Emil Coué, through the pseudo-social, pseudo-religious pap peddled by perennial Self-Improvers, to the placid pomposities of phenomenology and existentialism reviewed in Chapter 6. And here, too, may be placed two other significant movements which have much in common, despite their contrasting panoplies; one is justly condemned as an ignorant fad, whereas the other, because of its professed aspirations toward objectivity, critical self-examinations and questionnaire research as to the results of treatment, has been avidly accepted by sincere therapists in "guidance clinics" and "counseling centers." The first is the "dianetics" of E. Ron Hubbard which operated on the belief that any person, under the direction of an "operator" with only a minimum of knowledge and a few hours of training can, in a session or two of recalling "engrams of association," not only "clear" his past, present and future of all obstacles and perplexities but emerge personally impregnable and capable of "operating" on others. The second system is the so-called "non-directive" or "client-centered therapy" of Carl Rogers, which, with initially similar assumptions as to therapeutic time and training required, also postulated that the client's "Self," if merely given an opportunity to "grow" through "Self-expression" in the presence of a "counselor" who acts only as a compliant observer, will spread its own "inner strengths" and likewise emerge transcendent and triumphant. Both of these understandably popular cults seductively term themselves "permissive," "warm," "self-determinative," "research-minded" and "scientific," and both, to be consistent, must deny communal fantasies and symbolic interpersonal relationships between patient and therapist. But since narcissism, however euphemistically formulated, here merges into a potent *folie à deux*, these and similar perennially recurrent movements may be placed in a transitional position between the frankly solipsistic orientations, and the interpersonal-manipulative therapies now to be considered.

Interpersonal therapies. These are, of course, infinite in variety, but a few leading examples may be mentioned under related dynamic categories as follows:

MATERNAL. Everyone who has once been a cherished child will thereafter welcome the ministrations of a kindly or powerful parental surrogate whether masseur, physiotherapist, priest, king, or physician. Greatrakes "stroked Diseases of the Flesh" out of supplicating thousands in post-Cromwellian times just as chiropractors do today; troubled human beings have always shown a proclivity for lying a-couched and being tended to tactually as well as verbally. And when even deeper regression is invited by soothingly reiterative inducements to "relax and sleep" under protective control, "relaxation therapists" exult in a mystic power and hypnotists tend to forget Bernheim's maxim: "It is a wise hypnotist who knows who is hypnotizing whom."

MEDICO-THAUMATURGIC. Here the psychiatrist can employ not only the physician's armamentarium against bodily pain and disease, but also specially developed methods for altering cerebral function either temporarily or lastingly by metabolic changes (CO_2, insulin), pharmacologic influences ("energizers," "ataraxics")[*], cerebral diaschisis (EST) or surgical incisions (lobotomy, thalamotomy). However, all of these inevitably carry or acquire a rich overlay of wishful belief, and when such fantasies of omniscience or of power over health, "mind" (*sanatos*) and life itself are too intimately joined by the psychiatrist, the quasi-delusional interchanges thus constituted may produce highly charged results, both favorable and unfavorable.

PSYCHOANALYSIS. Despite the rigidity of theory, teaching and technique insisted upon by some proponents who forget its dynamic evolution, psychoanalysis (cf. Chapters 3 and 7) can be regarded as a deeply searching and individual method of studying, formulating and altering human behavior. This may be true precisely because psychoanalysis constitutes an inclusive and effective combination of the universal narcissistic-supportive, interpersonal-transactive, and religio-philosophic media of therapy here being discussed. In effect, psychoanalysis develops these categories as follows:

From the personal standpoint, it affords a more detailed and dynamic reexamination and reevaluation of determinative life experiences, symbol formations and derived patterns of defense or goal-achievement.

---

[*] The insistent demand for "miracle drugs" to assuage psychosomatic sorrows was met successively in ancient times by extracts of precious stones, dragon's teeth, unicorn horn, or Galen's Samian clay; medievally, by powdered martyr's blood or the secret nostrums of university Professors of Physic, and more recently by overglorified antibiotics, hormones and "tranquilizers." As may also be expected, each new panacea is proclaimed and for a time defended by its devotees with a fervor formerly reserved for the manifestations of divine healing.

In parameters of interpersonal reexploration, it presents rich opportunities for controlled "transference"* and "counter-transference" interactions with the analyst as confessor, rival, expiator, erotic object, judge, pedagogue, protector, and in many other roles leading optimally to that of a maturely accepted friend.

Finally, group reorientative analytic experiences may become generalized and meaningful far beyond the therapist's office, and thus lead to more adaptive, stable and creative familial, occupational, religious and other social readjustments. True, psychoanalysis can also be prostituted into an escapist, sterile cult for both patient and analyst, but this is unfortunately true of all methods.

GROUP TECHNIQUES DERIVED FROM THE UR-FANTASY OF SOCIAL TRUST. Whether these are formally so designated or not, various methods of group psychotherapy (cf. the *Practice*, Part Three) can foster and guide an essential series of reexplorations through which the patient extends whatever insights and skills he has acquired to optimal familial, marital, occupational, and other social and cultural transactions. Without such final operational results all therapy, whatever the theoretical claims made for it, is only delusive or ephemeral.

METHODS UTILIZING THE FINAL UR-DEFENSE OF MAGICAL TRANSCENDENCE. In an article presenting an early analysis of the triune faiths of man (Int. J. Psychoanal., 1945) I predicted that during the postwar period of atomic fears and political, social and moral disorganization there would arise various world-wide movements among which the following would be most prominent:

---

* To supplement in this connection the discussion in Chapter 6, it may be noted that Freud originally used the term *transference* to connote the experientially derived attitudes which "from the beginning" color the patient's evaluation of the analyst, and which he "works through" in the therapeutic process. However, other writers (e.g., Sterba, Strachey, Glover, Klein, Alexander, Zetzel, et al.) have used the same word variously and variably to mean interpersonal projections developed either *in* or *out* of the analysis proper, either *confined* to the analyst or *generalized* to others, either *influenced* by or relatively *independent* of the therapist's methods or "counter-transference" and, most redundantly involved of all, "narcissistic," "ego-syntonic" or "Superego-cathected," in shifting *normal*, "normally neurotic" or "analytically-neurotic transference"* contexts. Another cult contends that what peculiarly distinguishes psychoanalysis from psychotherapy is the formation of an emotionally disruptive "transference neurosis" as the most necessary part of the treatment. Freud himself (cf. his *Autobiography* and *Analysis Terminable and Interminable*) strongly implied that the development of excessively regressive, aggressive, erotized or other neurotic transference relationships was an "artifact" of poor therapeutic technique, but then Freud, like other teachers before him, lost his influence long before he was canonized. Parenthetically, the peculiar doctrine that troubled patients can be helped by analytic therapy only if the latter makes them temporarily or even permanently more neurotic is whimsically reminiscent of Garrison's quotation of Teodorico Borgogni, who wrote six centuries ago:

"For it is not necessary . . . as many disciples teach and modern surgeons profess, that pus be generated in wounds. No error can be greater than this. Such a practice is indeed to hinder nature, to prolong the disease, and to prevent the conglutination and consolidation of the wound."

Needless to say, Teodorico was bitterly attacked for differing with the wisdom of current authorities and for his consequent ignorance of the best surgical technique of the day. For that matter, the desirability of "laudable pus" as a medium of healing was vigorously maintained long after Pasteur, Koch and Lister in their time also condemned it as an "artifact of poor technique."

Cults of the Glorified Self—in philosophy, ethics, art and psychology.

Formation of Cohesive Defensive-Aggressive Groups by supposedly strong mutual interests (such as occupation, age, race, nationality, language, etc.) with the corresponding adulation of glorified leaders by each such group. And less overtly but perhaps most deeply significant of all,

"The increased influence of organized mysticisms, especially expressed in the renewed appeal and power of various antirationalistic and religious institutions."

It is the relationship of this last prediction to psychotherapy with which we are here finally concerned. Despite the supposed "materialism" of the past two decades the Christian Science Church, as but one example, has grown tremendously in appeal and power precisely because it combines an astonishing number of the potent therapeutic techniques already discussed under each of the Ur-fantasies dealt with above. In effect, each Christian Scientist is aggrandized by assumed knowledge not only of the one true religion (Christianity) but of all relevant Science; each member is personally vouchsafed the metaphysical presence of a most energetic and provident Church mother—Mary Baker Eddy; the faith of each is daily renewed by her sacrosanct book—*Science and Health with Key to the Scriptures,* as exclusively and interminably quoted by "readers" in the church services; each member is offered warm acceptance and intimate communion with a remarkably cohesive group of fellow-believers; and each is granted influence over other mortals through a Power of Healing not only by direct contact but by the quasi-divine magic of "absent treatment." Such appeals are universal, and their potency is reflected in the fact that, however much we deplore its tragic consequences in individual cases, it is undeniable that Christian Science, with over 3000 highly active and proselytizing branches and societies in 46 countries, every year gives some measure of refuge and comfort to many more millions of people than will be directly helped by all psychiatrists in the next half century. Concurrently, "pastoral counseling" in other denominations has become increasingly prominent, will continue to grow in general acceptance and influence, and may also tend to become more narrowly cultist, dogmatic and mystic as man's vaunted sciences threaten to suffocate rather than succor him. Without belaboring the point, it becomes evident that the sophisticated therapist truly devoted to his calling will not only accept man's mystic yearnings as an essential determinant of human behavior, but will utilize them as among his most effective media of therapy.

Operational integration: summary and restatement

Clinically speaking, then, the essentials of psychotherapy are the following:

The maintenance of the scientific prestige, ethical integrity and social influence of the psychiatric and allied professions and of the individual therapist. Differences of honest opinion, as in any mystico-scientific field, are acceptable; extreme claims, public polemics and transparent exhibitionisms diminish our status and thereby our capacity to help.

The warm, unashamedly personal acceptance of each patient not as another "interesting case" in support of some preconceived theory, or as an object of inexorable analysis,* or even as grist for another therapeutic mill, but as a hurt, frightened and troubled human being seeking relief and guidance. These should be accorded him in the following ways:

The skillful utilization of every medical means available to relieve bodily pain and dysfunction, or to suspend undesirable activities (at a minimum risk of permanent addiction or defect) until better ones can be established.

The tactful and sympathetic exploration of the nature of the patient's motivations, the origins of his conscious and unconscious symbolic representations and value-systems, and the objectives of his characteristic patterns of behavior in relation to their interlocking advantages and disadvantages in the present and probable future. This exploration may be formal, minute and detailed (including "free associations," screen memories, dream material and so on), or it may be confined to a careful and perceptive analysis of interview, psychologic test, or other clinical data. In either case, the first objective will be *to help the patient recognize that his previous patterns of behavior were neither as necessary nor as advantageous as he had implicitly assumed them to be.* But to leave the patient here would be to place him in a new quandary: his former ways are no longer even delusionally effective, but he has not as yet learned new and better ones to take their place. It is therefore equally necessary *to utilize optimal transference situations and every other therapeutic opportunity to impart the second essential portion of the dual dicta of insight: namely that new patterns of conduct are really preferable*—not alone because they are legal, moral or "mature," but because in the long run they will result in greater over-all satisfactions for all concerned. Such reorientations, which must be achieved without letting the patient become too regressive and dependent in the "anaclitic" phases of transference, may be rendered more effective by combinations of the following techniques.

Reeducation of the patient by the therapist through reason, demonstration and implicit, or explicit, personal example.

Utilization of every available system of progressive social participation through enlightened self-interest, whether in directly supervised "milieu" or "group therapy" or as arranged with the patient's family, friends, employer or social group. Here, too, the deep influences of the patient's religious, political or other loyalties, instead of being attacked, may be used to their best advantage. Indeed, it is the eventual efficacy of all of these readjustments that determines whether or not the patient will be reaccepted as a happy and useful member of his society—and this in turn will spell the success or failure of the therapist.

---

* "We reject most emphatically the view that we should convert into our property the patient who puts himself into our hands in search of help, that we should carve his destiny for him, force our own ideals upon him, and with the arrogance of a Creator form him in our own image and see that it was good." (Freud, S.—*Turnings in the Ways of Psycho-Analytic Therapy*, Coll. P. 2: 398, 1918.)

References

Bonner, J. T.: Cells and Societies.
Feigl, H., and Bradbeck, M.: Readings in the Philosophy of Science.
Fromm- Reichmann, Frieda: Principles of Intensive Psychotherapy.
Fulton, J. F.: Medicine, Warfare and History.
Garrison, F. H.: History of Medicine.
Gerard, R. W., Kluckhohn, C., and Rapoport, A.: Biological and Cultural Evolution.
Gombrich, E. H.: The Story of Art.
Hoebel, E. A.: The Law of Primitive Man.
Jones, M.: The Therapeutic Community.
Linn, L.: A Handbook of Hospital Psychiatry.
Movius, H. L.: Archaeology and the Earliest Art.
Muller, H. J.: The Uses of the Past.
Riese, W.: An Outline of History of Ideas in Psychotherapy.
Roe, Anne, and Simpson, G. (Eds.): Behavior and Evolution.
Sarton, G.: A History of Science.
Simpson, G.: The Meaning of Evolution.
Zilboorg, G.: A History of Medical Psychology.

Appendices

Appendix 1

Ethology and biodynamics

THROUGHOUT this volume we have reviewed many experiments designed to clarify the dynamics of behavior, with special reference to psychiatrically significant principles of inducing or correcting deviations from the "norm." However, the study of the "spontaneous" behavior of organisms in their "natural" milieu—the science of ethology —though long neglected by psychiatrists, can also contribute data highly relevant to fundamental questions such as the following:

What relationship do the "instinctive," "innate" or "unconditioned" behavior patterns of animals have to pre-experiential "drives" and "unconscious" behavior potentials in man?

Can the order of the appearance of such patterns in young animals be correlated in any way with the postulated stages of "psychosexual development" in the child and adolescent? And are these phases related to the differential phylogenetic and ontogenetic development of the nervous system?

Are the ethologic concepts of "trigger stimuli" and "social releasers" relevant to the early channelizations or fixations of reaction patterns in the human infant? In view of the impersonality of such early automatic responses, is every subsequent relationship in the human primarily a reiteration, or at best a "transference" displacement or elaboration, of previous attachments and repulsions?

Of what significance are animal studies of modes of communication, courting customs, sexual patterns and group behavior?

Is there determinative or presumptive evidence for the postulate of "primal aggression" or of a "death instinct?" Or may the battles over territoriality, dominance and sexual possession in both animals and man be as readily formulated by Kropotkin's, Simpson's, Huxley's or, more recently, Montagu's concepts of a universal seeking for individual participation in an evolving social order? If so, is the ostensibly self-punitive or self-destructive behavior occasionally observed in animals based on deviant individual experiences without primal atavistic resonances? Or is the relatively rare occurrence of mass intraspecies self-immolation (e.g., by Norwegian lemmings) or warfare (e.g., in some varieties of ants as described by Schnierla) more in accord with Freud's gloomy concepts of man's inevitable fate as a victim of Thanatos?

In accordance with the best scientific tradition, we should welcome data from every available source that might help us answer such questions, and in this Appendix we shall sample the evidence from ethology.

Basic concepts

The following definitions may serve for a preliminary orientation:

Instinct, a term of protean meanings and therefore approved only after considerable debate by the International Ethologic Congress, has

as its operational referent any mode of behavior governed by hereditary patterns of function in the central nervous system and therefore
characterized by "spontaneity [but] *modifiability through learning*"
(Lorenz).

A *social releaser* is an external object or situation that, however fragmentary in itself, completes an operational *Gestalt* for the organism and
furnishes an "objective" or external goal to instinctive behavior. As an
example, if a red-spotted ball is exhibited above the horizontal plane
to a Siamese fighting fish, the total situation is apparently interpreted by
the fish as an encroachment on its territory and the ball is attacked as
a rival (Tinbergen); so also, the shadow of a toy plane which, moving
ahead, may look vaguely like the silhouette of a flying hawk will make
newborn chicks run for cover, whereas moving in the other direction it
apparently has the appearance of a harmless swan and is therefore
ignored.

Imprinting is a permanent modification of behavior by a *social
releaser;* e.g., Lorenz observed that if he himself squatted and quacked
a few times before a brood of newly-hatched ducklings, they would
thenceforth follow him and ignore the mother duck, whose "normal"
imprinting priority was thus usurped. The importance of *imprinting at
optimum early periods* was highlighted by Riesen, who observed that
if baby chimpanzees are blindfolded for six months after birth they are
apparently kept from taking advantage of that phase of cortical development best suited for the acquisition of visual perceptions; consequently,
when the blindfold is removed they can no longer "learn to see" or to
recognize objects, and may even make themselves physically amaurotic
by staring wide-eyed and uncomprehendingly at the sun.

Learning

"Protoplasmic" learning. Benson Ginsberg furnished appropriate temporal vistas for the concept of "learning" in the following
memorable passage:

"At the moment of fertilization [the organism] receives a distillate from
each of two samples of an unbroken series of evolutionary continuity. This
distillate is an organized collection of potentially immortal bio-molecules, none
of which has known death and each of which has undergone innumerable
replications and (presumably) mutations. In organization and structure, this
microscopic collection of matter in the zygote nucleus represents a sampling
from the accumulated experiences of countless ages of evolution. As such, it is
a finely adjusted mechanism, although its components probably represent a
unique qualitative combination that has never occurred before and will never
occur again."

Frank Brown, in discussing the basic rhythmic nature of animals and
plants and the covert influences that may affect them, bridges the gap
between releasers and learning as follows:

"Beans grown in constant darkness show no rhythmic sleep movements,
but a single brief light shock will start off a persisting 24-hour rhythm. . . .

Living things are sensitive to additional kinds of stimuli at energy levels so low that we have hitherto considered the living organism completely oblivious to them. These latter potentials may soon loom importantly in many areas of biology and medicine. . . ."

There is current controversy (Geller, Jensen, A. F. Mirsky, et al.) as to whether or not unicellular organisms can be "conditioned" to feeding and avoidance responses, but it seems certain that learning can occur in the most primitive neural organizations. As but one example, Bharucha-Reid noted that earthworms accustomed to a maze showed a greater facility in learning a subsequently required route to a food reward than those faced with the problem *de novo;* so also, Szymanski and others found little difficulty in training cockroaches, perhaps the most ancient of living insects, to reverse their "instinctive" escape patterns and seek light instead of darkness. Schnierla has shown that the ant, a much more adaptable insect, can be taught to solve mazes and remember the solutions without reinforcement for months. Indeed, self-maintenance, reproduction and *an innate capacity to retain learning* may be said to be the three essential characteristics of life.

"Instincts" and experience. Sauer, in an article entitled *Celestial Navigation in Birds,* thus eloquently puts the case for "pure instinct."

"When fall comes, the little garden warbler, weighing barely three quarters of an ounce, sets off one night on an unbelievable journey. All alone, never in the collective security of a flock, it wings its solitary way south-westward over Germany, France and Spain and then swings south to its distant goal in southern Africa. It flies on unerringly, covering a hundred miles or more in a single night, never once stopping in its course, certain of its goal. In the spring it takes off again and northward retraces its path to its nesting place in a German or Scandinavian thicket—there to give birth to a new generation of little warblers which will grow up, without being taught, with the self-same capacity to follow the same route across continents and oceans by the map of the stars."

Sauer demonstrated that his warblers navigated "instinctively" by adjusting their flight to the seasonal azimuths and declensions of the sun and the stars; however, no two warblers ever took exactly the same compass course in either spring or autumn; i.e., the behavior of his birds could not be proved to be totally independent of their postnatal experiences.

Neural correlations. Since injuries or stimulation of specific regions in the central nervous system can affect behavior profoundly, are instincts and their experiential channelizations neurologically localizable? As Neal Miller points out, hypothalamic lesions diminish hunger whereas electrostimulation of the septal region increases it; so also, stimulation of the medial forebrain bundle in rats causes penile erection and ejaculation. Wilder Penfield has reported that in some unanesthetized human subjects, stimulation of a single point in the temporal lobe or its adjoining "speech areas" can produce a vivid reliving of a specific past episode. On the other hand, Delgado, Roberts and others have confirmed our own findings (Masserman, 1939–43) that stimulation of the hypothalamus—a region previously supposed to be "the center of emotions"—cannot be conditioned at all to external experiences.* In intermediate regions, dorsomedial thalamic operations modify the expressions of rage and bilateral amygdaloidectomy profoundly alters sexual behavior (though differently in young and old animals), but the effects of these ablations, as we have shown, depend upon the individual development and previous experience of each animal and upon many concurrent circumstances such as the metabolic state of the animal, the "semantic set" of the milieu and, for that matter, covert and complex interactions with the examiner.

The situation is further complicated by the fact that there seem to be *inner* CNS summations, modifications and reversals of neural function. As but one example, Neal Miller noted that rats would press bars to stimulate electrodes inserted in the median forebrain bundle (sometimes at a tempo increasing to a quasi-orgastic peak) and then promptly rotate a wheel to turn the stimulus off; i.e., the same nerve center seemed to mediate increasingly "pleasant" and then suddenly "unpleasant" drive potentials. Further, as Brady et al. have shown, actual hunger or other physiologic needs will greatly modify the rate of lever-pressing for "cerebral self-stimulation." From such observations, David McK. Rioch concluded: "The feelings of 'euphoria' and 'dysphoria' are apparently related to adequacy of CNS functioning in the interaction of the organism with the environment, rather than to activity in any localized area." It remains problematic, then, whether in view of the rich templating of millions of years of organismic experience in the deoxyribonucleic helices in every gene, and the complex neural networks, environmental configurations and sensitive cybernetic feedbacks that continuously affect all behavior, simple conative entities called "drives" or "instincts" can justifiably be postulated. And since motivation, adaptation, maturation and retained learning thus become almost indistinguishably continuous, artificial distinctions between "conscious"† and "unconscious" or among "id," "ego" and "superego," etc., become even more heuristically questionable.

Innate learning.   Such considerations reopen the problem of the experimental transmission of learning. In 1928 Pavlov asserted unequivocally that rats taught to run a maze in his laboratory gave birth to rat pups that learned the same maze with greater ease, i.e., 300 lessons in the first generation as compared with only 10 lessons in the fourth. According to Razran, Pavlov himself later questioned these experimental

---

* Recently, Nakoa at Kyushu University reported success in conditioning hypothalamic responses to a buzzer, but his experimental technique was likely to produce total affective learning ancillary to the hypothalamic stimuli. J. Lilly agrees, but Pribram, Hunt, Delgado and others have confirmed our negative results.

† Tolman (chapter 22) writes: "And if psychology would only be content with the lower animals, and preferably with rats, and not try to mess around with human beings, this whole question of consciousness and of idea may well have been omitted. But human beings insist on being included in any psychological purview. And they insist that they are conscious and do have ideas—however improbable this latter may often appear . . . [page 205]. It is in the moment of changing behavior, in the moments of learning, that consciousness will appear."

results, but never denied his attraction to Lamarckism, and thus lent himself to eager identification with Communist ideology as having sanctioned the pseudoscientific ideas of later party stalwarts such as Michurin and Lysenko. But such thinking is not necessarily hemmed behind an Iron Curtain; in an article bravely entitled "Influence of pre-natal maternal anxiety on emotionality in young rats," W. R. Thompson of Canada describes how he shocked pregnant mother rats when they operated levers for food rewards and observed that their young were later deficient in food-seeking, in spontaneous activity and in learning to manipulate the levers. These effects, of course, were probably due merely to a metabolically impaired milieu in the troubled mother's uterine environment, but even so they highlight Stieglitz' maxim that organisms age—and in a sense "learn"—far more in the uterus than they do after birth. Primitive adaptations that occur so early that they may change hereditary predispositions other than through selective survival have also been noted by Beach: e.g., a certain female moth will always lay her eggs on hackberry leaves, but if her young are raised on apple leaves, some of them will lay on apple leaves. J. Sine reported an increasing tendency to gastric ulcer in succeeding generations of rats stressed by 48 hours of immobilization, and J. McConnell, in a most startling bit of evidence for hereditary learning, observed that if a flatworm conditioned to shrink from light is cut into 6 pieces, the worms that grow from these pieces and their subsequent artificial segmentations continue to shrink from light for several generations.

Can, then, our children be modified by our experiences more directly than strict Darwinism has allowed us to think? But be it noted that Darwin himself in his later writings, according to Darlington's incisive analysis, acknowledges "direction" as well as "selection" as a force in evolution.[*]

The value of movement. Ethologic observations challenge psychiatric prejudice against "acting out" as a form of learning or of solutions of inner dilemmas. Eckhard Hess has observed that, at an optimum time of 10 to 16 hours after hatching, wild mallard ducklings can be imprinted to follow a decoy *only if they are permitted to waddle after it;* Hess therefore concluded that "the strength of the imprinting appeared to be dependent not on the duration of the imprinting period but on the effort exerted by the duckling"—i.e., the youngster learns by doing. Nikolaas Tinbergen, in his classic observations, noted that a male stickleback fish threatened by a dummy rival so near the border of its territory that it is placed in obvious conflict as to whether to fight or run, must either divert its energies into the absurdly inappropriate busy-ness of building a nest, or else almost literally perish in a paretic impasse. In human education we have learned to teach scientific principles through

[*] One Darwinian sentiment merits direct quotation in this ethologic context: "The social instincts of men and the lower animals have no doubt been developed by nearly the same steps. It would be advisable, if found practicable, to use the same definition in both cases and to take, as the standard of morality, the general good of the community" (*Descent of Man,* p. 22).

learned skills,* in general adult life we pay lip service to the adage, "a sound mind in a healthy active body" (the Greek *sanitas* stood for indissoluble physical and psychic health), and in geriatrics we deplore physical inactivity as quickly leading to total desuetude. And yet, in some forms of psychotherapy, we forbid "acting out," pretend that life problems can be solved by supine conversation between two people respectively immobilized by chair and couch, and hope that somehow life will be improved without necessarily concomitant reexploration, relearnings and new achievements in, quite literally, the *act*-uality of living.

Early experiences. Equally significant are studies of the effects on adult behavior of induced variations of early experience in animals. P. Seitz has noted that rat pups raised in large litters hoarded food more strenuously and became subject to greater handicaps in adaptation than did those from smaller and better tended litters. This may include greater susceptibility to brain trauma: as an experimental example, S. Levine reported that normal rats showed few effects after septal lesions, whereas those that had been neglected in infancy developed patterns of persistent rage after the same operation. In a particularly striking pair of experiments, Thompson and Melzock observed that if puppies were raised with the best of metabolic care but in almost complete isolation they grew into adults subject to periods of glazed staring, apparently illusory startles, fears and rages, and peculiar attacks of epileptoid whirling; in contrast (Thompson and Heron), excessively protected and petted pups grew into insecure, helpless, overdependent and jealously demanding dogs—a not uncommon development in species other than the canine. Liddell reported that kids separated from the mother ewe for only a two hour period their first day after birth developed persistent difficulties in maternal and herd relationships and neurotic and psychosomatic handicaps of such severity that all died within six months. Others less seriously traumatized in infancy survived, but bore kids which they in turn neglected, and so perpetuated a "neurotic family history." Harlow's observations indicate that the trauma here demonstrated may stem not from "oral deprivations" in the usual psychoanalytic sense (all of the young animals in these studies were well nourished), but from the removal of opportunities for physical contact and cuddling *as initiated by the infant;* e.g., Harlow's baby macaques clearly cherished and avidly clung to artificial "mothers" made only of wire and terry cloth, and used them as an essential source of reassurance before undertaking new explorations. In this context, a new significance may be given to clinical cautions such as Bowlby's contention that if a child does not experience warm maternal care in the first years of life, he can never appreciate or seek friendly relationships with anyone thereafter and thereby becomes "autistic" and "schizophrenic."†

---

* The late Bela Mittelman emphasized the importance of the "motor urge" in exploratory orientations during early childhood, advocated free skeletal motility and regarded restraint as a neurotigenic determinant of later personality patterns.

† Compare Harlow's experimental data with another of Bowlby's clinical observations: "My impression in taking the histories of many disturbed children is that there

Regression. Relevant to such phenomena is the *fixation* of an activity that satisfies a current biologic need, or the *regression* under stress to patterns of behavior previously found to be satisfactory. Animals, like humans, may also persist in ("fixate" on) a behavior pattern apparently designed to compensate for an early frustration; for example, David Levy noted that pups adequately fed by tube or dropper, but thus kept from normal sucking experience, continued for years to nuzzle tassles, fingers or teat substitutes. As to regression, Levy, as already noted, also observed that a fully grown police dog which, as a puppy, had been indulgently nursed and pampered after breaking its leg, in late adulthood began limping again whenever its master played with a child or another dog, but frisked in four-footed glee when its security seemed restored.

Modes of communication. At all levels of life, there seems to be an unbroken line of intra- and interspecies communication from the relatively simple chemical or contact-signaling motions of infusoria to the complex communicative kinesics—of which the vocal cords are only the audible part—in man. The female swordtail (Morris) understands and responds very well to the courtship swimming patterns of the male. As to effective social propagandizing, few human speeches are as compelling as the hour-long dance, interpreted by von Fritsch and Lindauer, of a few scout bees who finally convince 50,000 hive mates that it is time to leave their brethren in an overcrowded nest and swarm to a new one.* In birds, kinesic and vocal forms of communication are more obviously present. Morris has written an exhaustive report on the versatility with which birds, by altering the arrangement of their body feathers, can signify the subtlest changes of mood in agreeable, thwarting or "neurosis-engendering" situations. On the auditory side may be cited an article by Frings and Jumber, who first recorded on tape the cry of distress and warning emitted by a starling held upside down and shaken, then amplified the sound to 30 decibels through the loud speaker of a mobile sound truck and in three nights were able to frighten away an estimated 10,000 to 12,000 starlings which had infested Millheim, Pennsylvania. Equally interesting was the fact that, possibly because of an odor left by the frightened starlings, few came to replace them.

Monkeys and apes are, of course, exceedingly responsive to both

---

is little if any relationship between form and degree of disturbance and whether or not the child has been breast-fed. The association which constantly impresses itself upon me is that between form and degree of disturbance and the extent to which the mother has permitted clinging and following, and all the behavior associated with them, or has refused them."

* Parenthetically, Lindauer, perhaps in delightful paraphrase of many a session of a Committee of the Whole, reports he once observed "a swarm that was unable to make up its mind. The choice had narrowed to two sites and the partisans [two delegations of bees that had returned to the nest after searching for new sites] kept up their competitive dance for 14 days with neither side giving in. Then they stopped and the groups proceeded to commit mass suicide. They built a new hive on the nearest available bush and froze to death the following winter."

kinesic and auditory communication,* and more sensitively dependent on individual training. For example, I. A. Mirsky observed that a monkey trained to depress a switch that prevented electroshock to itself would also do so when it observed a cagemate being shocked; again, a young rhesus in our laboratory would fetishistically fondle a rubber glove with which it had been nursed whenever it thought another monkey was being mistreated. Kathy Hayes taught a baby chimpanzee to say and referentially "mean" the word *cup*, to understand many nouns (e.g, *foot, mamma*) and verbs (e.g., *give, kiss*) and to obey—though with obvious surprise—a command combining three verbal categories (*"kiss your foot"*) the first time it was uttered.

John Paul Scott, in his *Animal Behavior* sums up comparative approaches to language functions as follows:†

> Students of human behavior are fond of pointing out that in at least one respect humanity is unique in the animal kingdom. Human beings have a highly developed system of verbal communication, and it is often argued that there is nothing else like it, and that its possession sets man distinctly apart from all other animals. However, the facts show that animal systems of communication possess in rudimentary form most of the basic characteristics of human language.
>
> In the first place, human communication is basically vocal, but there are numerous birds and mammals which also have some sort of vocal communication. Secondly, a great deal of information regarding the emotional state of the human speaker is conveyed not so much by his words as by his tones of voice. As far as we now know, the vocal communication of birds and mammals consists almost entirely of conveying feelings and emotions. Human language has been said to be unique in that it can be used to inform people about other

---

* Zuckerman (page 263) writes as follows about baboons in the London Zoo: "Many characteristic vocal sounds are associated with specific social activities of baboons . . . rhythmic lip, tongue and jaw movements . . . usually accompany friendly advances between two animals. In more direct sex activity this sound may give way to a rhythmic series of deep grunts similar to those with which the animals greet the sun. These grunts are commonly made in all states of well-being. One grunting seems to stimulate several others. Another characteristic cry of the baboon is the high-pitched screech of a young animal or a female, made either in a situation of obvious danger, or in sets, which to the human observer do not appear to contain any cause for fear. This cry usually attracts neighboring dominant baboons [who rush to protect the supplicant]. Sometimes adult males make a similar cry, but it is not so high-pitched and accompanies states of rage occasioned either by the attack of a more dominant animal, or by its own impotent attempts to attack a fellow. By attracting other animals, it may begin a new fight. This cry is altogether different from the far-carrying, deep-throated barks heard in the wild when the members of a troop of baboons are scattered, or when a possible enemy, for instance a man, is observed approaching. This cry, which in the wild probably effects the reunion of a scattered troop, is only rarely made in captivity. I once heard a female barking this deep call after the death and removal of her baby. It is always heard when babies are removed from the Hill [a free-roaming space] to a new cage and is then raised by many animals. For several weeks after the females were removed from the Hill to a new cage two hundred yards away they continued to call in this way and to be answered by the males whom they had left behind."

† Scott, J. P.: *Animal Behavior*, University of Chicago Press. Copyright 1958 by the University of Chicago.

objects and events outside the speaker; but this can be done also in the communication of bees. Human language can be used as an instrument to produce effects on other individuals, but so can the cries of other animals. A person confronted with a locked door calls to someone to open it, while his pet dog barks to produce the same effect. . . . Another outstanding characteristic of human language is that it can be converted into non-vocal symbols, such as written words, and thus can influence activities at far distant times and places. And yet many of the carnivorous animals, like wolves, mark certain posts and trees, and others that come along days later may react to them. . . .

In short, we may conclude that human language has evolved from capabilities which are present in a large variety of lower animals and that the chief differences lie not so much in possessing a different kind of basic ability as in the degree to which language has been developed and its importance in social organization.

Tool Using. The contention has often been advanced that animals differ from man in two major respects: (1) that they do not project, modify or enhance their power through tools, and (2) that they lack, or are not interested in, esthetic creativity. But ethologists can reply that the first of these shibboleths simply distinguishes those who refuse to believe that sand spiders use pebbles to tamp their tunnels, that Geospizas pick cactus spines with which to dig out their insect prey from the bark of trees, that monkeys can open cage locks with keys, and work for differently colored "coins" with which to secure grapes from vending machines (the "value" of the token, in terms of the number of grapes it can secure, determining the effort and ingenuity the monkey will put forth to earn it), or that chimpanzees can assemble complex levers and drive electric cars. A most interesting variant in the construction of a trap device is the modernized Iron Maiden technique used by the Arizona road-runner: as described by Dobie, this bird builds a corral of cactus leaves or prickly cholla joints around a sleeping rattlesnake, which then either starves to death or dies of multiple puncture wounds in attempting to leave its prison of daggers. In organisms with more highly potentiated nervous systems, exploration of the physical universe, presumably with a view to its control and manipulation—i.e., a technology—, may take precedence over all other motivations. Thus, in an article aptly entitled "Curiosity in monkeys" Butler reported that monkeys and apes—particularly young ones—readily leave food and other rewards to indulge in exploratory and "play activities" that consisted essentially in the development of increasing knowledge about, and control of, the physical milieu.

Art. Parallel to their pragmatic and research pursuits are animal aspirations to esthetics. In the field of architecture and domestic decoration only one of numerous examples need be cited. The bower birds of Australia and New Guinea, as reported by A. J. Marshall, build elaborately designed landscapes, tunnels and maypoles out of sticks, pebbles, seashells or other materials, paint them with berry juice or charcoal mixed with saliva, and decorate them with flowers in a manner that inspired the painter Sibol to pay sincere tribute to his avian fellow esthetes. In music, even birds must learn their songs. Baby orioles isolated by Scott did not spontaneously acquire the characteristic lay of the oriole; instead, if given the opportunity, they copied the melodic scores of other species. So also, sparrows incubated with canaries by Conradi tried to imitate the trills and chirps of canaries instead of developing their own sparrow calls.

Sexuality

Objectives.   At the unicellular level, H. S. Jennings observed that the members of a colony or *clone* of protozoa descended from the conjugation of a single parental pair divide asexually for several months and only then become sexual; in this way the *community* (cf. similar "superorganismic" concepts of human societies as formulated by Spencer, Toynbee, Gerard et al.) achieves a "maturity" not attained by earlier generations of individuals. However, despite the maturation of sexual capacities in most individuals of higher species, actual sex practices must, at least in some part, be learned. For example, male guppies will attempt to mate indiscriminately with all likely looking objects until they find only female guppies to be receptive (Noble); young doves (Craig), tomcats (Wortis) and apes must also pass "through a long series of fumbling approximations and adjustments that look remarkably like trial-and-error learning" (Maslow) before they achieve smooth and effective autoerotic, cross species, homosexual or heterosexual techniques. Submissive animals of either sex may assume "feminine" coital postures toward more dominant colony mates, but according to Lashley and others this may be more an invitation to friendship than a Freudian equation of inferiority with femininity.

Wooing and contrectation.   As to more elaborate developments we can do no better than quote some trenchant passages from Burton's evocative book on *Animal Courtship*.*

For humans, as for animals, symbolism and ceremony play a very large part. Moreover, both these things do, on occasion, look so very much alike in both the human and the animal spheres. There are in both the giving of gifts, the exhibitionism, the dressing-up, the bowing and curtsying, the communal interest in the proceedings, the rivalries, the jealousies, antagonisms, in fact the whole gamut; and all so very much according to tradition and custom (or, as we say for animal courtship, so stereotyped). If man has devised all these things for himself independently of what has been going on in the rest of the living world for a thousand million years or more, then the coincidence is most remarkable [page 14].
[Burton, page 50] A hen robin has been known to take a crumb from an observer's hand, fly with it to the cock, place it at his feet, open her mouth and quiver her wings [like a fledgling] until he picks it up and gives it to her. To stand on a saucer of food and to look to her mate to wait on her may be automatic behavior. If so, then a good deal of human behavior, which we fondly imagine to be the result of free-will, must also be automatic. [Page 122] The male empid spider [who is sometimes eaten by the female] is credited with a cunning trick for avoiding such an end. His wooing is preceded by a hunt to catch a fly . . . which he enshrouds in fine silk threads [and presents to

* With the kind permission of F. A. Praeger.

the female]. While she is unraveling the [victim] . . . mating takes place. But a male empid will sometimes take a small piece of stick, a petal . . . or any small object, enshroud it and present it to the female. Unpacking the parcel keeps her busy long enough for him to avoid the possibly fatal results of this approach. [Page 115] The premating behavior of animals high and low [brings] us as near to a rule as is possible in biology: that the male may do the courting but the female has the whip hand*. . . .

Uxorial relations.   Burton comments: "Male starlings often carry flowers into their nesting hole when the female is incubating. A herring gull will take a shell or sea-pink to his brooding mate." But as the species approaches man, the uxorial patterns seem to change in accordance with the description given by Yerkes for chimpanzees:

"The behavior of each mate [with regard to feeding and other privileges] seems to change in correlation with their sexual relationships, and the female comes to claim as if it were her right what previously she had allowed the male to take, while he as if in recognition of, or in exchange for, sexual accommodation during the mating period, defers to her and unprotestingly permits her to control the food-getting situation."

Conversely, a chimpanzee separated from its mate may refuse to eat (Kohler).

Parental behavior.   There are, of course, hormonal influences that govern patterns of nesting and nursing; for example, progesterin (and the availability of a secluded corner) promotes nest building in rats (Lorenz), whereas lactating cats given pituitary hormones that diminish mammary congestion will abandon their litters. On the other hand, parental patterns are released or enhanced only by appropriate stimuli: Leblond could elicit "maternal" behavior in adult mice of either sex by putting them in charge of litters, though young males and virgin females required close "concaveation" with baby mice for from one to four days before exhibiting responses of care and protection.

Parental conditioning.   Such observations, of course, bring up the further important question of what ethology can contribute to the clarification of child-parent relationships. To begin with, J. P. Scott calls attention to the fact that in animals as highly developed as canines, no conditioning can occur until the eyes and ears open at three weeks (after which they can be weaned without producing the after-suckling effect described by Levy) and that perhaps of all dogs only the cocker spaniel is "born socialized." In comparing his data with those on humans, Scott insists that, contrary to the concepts of Kleinian psychoanalytic theory, no conditioning of the human infant can occur until six weeks after birth—an observation in accord with René Spitz' finding that babies do not really differentiate faces until fully six months old. And yet very early fixations of affection can occur at considerably lower evolutionary (though perhaps comparatively older ontologic) levels; for example,

* Parenthetically, O. Heinroth also noted that a dominant gander may interfere in the public mating of couples in his pond, and observed, "To be scandalized by the sexual acts of others is often observed in the animal world." Lorenz, despite his qualms about "anthropomorphism," once commented to the author: "This is not jealousy, it is pure Puritanism."

Leonore Brandt's orphaned baby Diana monkey became exceedingly attached to her human foster mother, fed her cherished bananas, and pushed her out of congenitally feared open spaces into the protection of presumably safe trees. This is reminiscent of Lorenz' pet jackdaw who, after "adopting" Dr. Lorenz as a substitute fledgling, insisted on feeding him mashed meal worms through the ear canal—or the raven who warned him of the approach of an avian enemy with ravenesque swoops and tail flips while uttering, instead of the customary alerting *cawl,* the name given it by its Viennese friend in deference to his preference for the German language.

Aggression.   The following ethologic observations may be quoted on this subject:

[Burton, page 150] If a male stickleback in full breeding condition is imprisoned within a glass tube held horizontally, it will not display aggressively to a rival. As soon as the tube is held vertically, however, he will display violently . . . A corresponding situation is seen in the case of a human being, who finds it very difficult to be aggressive sitting down. And is not our first impulse, in calming someone who is becoming aggressive, to induce him to sit down?[*] [Page 63] This is not to say that wild animals do not throw their whole being into their [hostile] displays and sometimes go beyond the bounds of common animal decency, especially where two contestants are equally matched in prowess and determination; but really bloody fights are rare. [Page 75] Fundamentally, the loyalty has been primarily to the territory and only secondarily to the mate. The parallel is clear in business affairs. Wars are fought over territory; social revolutions arise from land-hungry masses; more marital difficulties spring from having to share space . . . than from any other single cause.

In discussing in ethologic terms the transition from sexual and familial rivalry to friendship, Lorenz writes:

The high survival value of . . . intraspecies fighting (spacing out of territory, defense of offspring, selection of the fittest, etc.) has long been securely established by ecologists. For species in which common parental care necessitates the staying-together of two individuals after copulation, and particularly in truly social species, it was necessary to evolve mechanisms which prevent the fighting between certain individuals without, however, otherwise impeding the important functions of intraspecies contention. The development of appeasing ceremonies ensued. The most important of these are those evolved by the ritualization of so-called re-directed activities, in which aggression primarily released by and directed at the mate or social partner, is side-tracked and directed at the hostile neighbor, or, in some cases, at a purely "symbolic" substitute object. In cases in which higher ritualization has set in, these behavior mechanisms, for example, the "triumph-ceremony" of geese, have obtained a high degree of autonomy and form a supremely strong bond between the individuals taking part in it.

Friendship.   Burton writes [p. 243] "A wounded elephant has several times been seen surrounded by the rest of the herd, who keep it upright and by the pressure of their bodies carry it to safety in the

---

[*] Cf. also our employment of "sedative" drug for "aggressive" (going some place) patients.

jungle . . ." [Katz, p. 205]: "Otters, too, will rescue a wounded comrade. Antelopes place sentinels for the herd, who remain on watch until relieved." Loveridge frequently observed a male baboon in flight returning in the face of danger to rescue a wounded fellow, or a female remaining behind to protect a dead colony-mate's body.* In cross-species friendships, Forel raised baby ants of three hostile species together, and observed that the adults coexisted amicably; according to Pattie, chicks raised in isolation with mice later preferred them to fowl company. Kuo, in summing up corresponding studies combining baby rats and kittens, reported that "kittens can be made to kill a rat, to love it, to hate it, to fear it or to play with it; it depends on the life history of the kitten." Other studies record harmonious companionships between a domestic dog and a vixen, a domestic bitch and a male fox—permanent and without any attempt at mating. Even more bizarre friendships developed between a goose and a goat, a goat and a llama, a cat and ducklings; badgers, foxes and rabbits which grew up together likewise showed a mutual tolerance (Burton, p. 253).

Utilitarian domestication. Schultz, quoted by Katz (page 22), observed that a certain species of ant "keeps beetles, whose secretions they like to the point of intoxication in which they may damage their nests and give their larvae to the beetles to eat, though at other times they will fight to the death for the same larvae." The cherished strains of yeast we keep in the vats of our breweries and distilleries lend their products to a more highly developed technology of production, sale and consumption—but the effects on human behavior are not altogether different.

Animal neuroses

This topic was discussed in detail in Chapters 7 through 12; however, we may here review representative studies by other workers that have confirmed or extended our findings.

Hillwold observed that hens frightened by a guinea pig at food-taking time became excited, "avoided the . . . haunted spot . . . because of a fear complex" and after five days of self-starvation had to be fed elsewhere to prevent death.

Further to illustrate the contingency of all "spontaneous" behavior, it has been observed that hens will eat almost twice as much from large or replenished mounds of grain as from small heaps, more from a soft, as compared to a hard surface, and more when other hens are present; i.e., "The same subjective state in animals as well as men can be the basis of widely different forms of behavior according to external circumstances" (Katz, page 169). Experimentally, rats will work far less ardently for

---

* In contrast, Zuckerman noted that baboons kept in captivity rather than in their natural habitat may act more like men in concentration camps, attack the weak, the ill and the aged, manhandle the females after sexual satiation, and otherwise act in a manner that would appear cruel and destructive to a human observer; however, Zuckerman added that under these circumstances baboons did not seem to recognize the death of adults of their own kind.

food if it is tinctured with quinine, if the lid to the food box is weighted, or if they merely anticipate the recurrence of a deterrent electroshock. Penguins deprived of eggs may attempt to hatch rounded pieces of ice (Levick), demonstrating how far awry in external expression even the relatively simple "brooding instinct" may go. Similarly, herring gulls will desert their own small unattractive eggs to set on larger, more attractively spotted china dummies.

Jacobsen and Skaarup repeated our experiments in cats and reported that they could induce neuroses so predictably that they used numerous animals in the statistical evaluation of tranquilizing drugs. P. Seitz likewise employed the technique of motivational conflicts as outlined in Chapter 11, and produced aberrations of behavior ranging from mild phobias to intractable catalepsy.

B. Rensch taught elephants to distinguish 100 different patterns of dots on cards that signified whether they would or would not be fed; when a card pattern was made equivocal the elephants attacked it and became dour and recalcitrant in their general behavior.

So also, ordinarily gentle Wendy, Yerkes' favorite chimpanzee, would turn her rage on Yerkes whenever the problems he set for her became too difficult; she would then become sullen, refractory and occupied with symbolically substitutive acts for long periods. Commented Yerkes: "Sometimes it seemed as if the subject were trying to save face or deceive itself by ignoring something which is potentially dangerous, as for example, the temptation to interfere with a companion by trying to take food out of turn."

J. Brady observed that if monkeys were required to press a lever every 20 seconds for six hours to prevent shock (i.e., become what Brady calls "executive monkeys"), they died in 23 days of massive duodenal hemorrhages; in contrast, control monkeys, who were actually shocked but who had no lever available and were therefore in no conflict about pressing it, showed no ill effects from their experience.

Bykov and his associates in Leningrad conditioned the movements and function of inner organs to external physical and, more significantly, social stimuli. Scull reports an extension of this work as follows:

One experiment involving the production of hypertension in primates is an amusing example of the ingeniousness of research done in Russia with use of an extension of Pavlovian technique. A male and a female ape are mated. Subsequently, the male is removed to an adjacent cage and a younger, more virile male is put in with the female. The first male is obliged to look on as his former mate enjoys the affections of the interloper. The "emotional" strain on the deprived male produces hypertension. A second experiment with primates involves mother and offspring. The mother is dressed in a blanket every time the child is placed with her for feeding. Soon the offspring associates "mothering" with the blanket and not the mother and is thus literally weaned away from the mother and "weaned to the blanket."

Curtis and Jean Pechtel in our laboratory have carefully studied the development of such fetishisms in young Rhesus monkeys, i.e., the permanent values attached to toys and other objects cherished in infancy and early childhood.

J. Conger, and Reynolds and Sommers repeated our alcohol experiments on rats and confirmed our findings that the drug both prevented and reduced the fear of a deterrent electric shock while affecting the more basic hunger drive to a far lesser extent.

Finally, Richter observed that wild Norway rats handicapped by having their whiskers clipped and then stressed by being made to swim in glass jars under circumstances that made the conflict seem "hopeless" died rapid "vagus deaths"; in contrast, Richter noted that "after elimination of the hopelessness, the rats do not die." Here, then, is an instance in which the stress conflict can lead to the ultimate psychosomatic disruption.

Etho-anthropologic significance

The preceding and countless other observations form the background for the increasing frequency of statements from eminent biologists such as the following:

Comparisons between *Homo sapiens* and other animals are legitimate contributions to comparative psychology, and comparisons between two or more non-human species are equally admissible. Like any other responsible scientist, the Comparative Psychologist is concerned with the understanding of his own species and with its welfare; but his primary aim is the exposition of general laws of behavior regardless of their immediate applicability to the problems of human existence.—F. A. Beach in *The Snark Was a Boojum.*

No absolute structural lines of demarcation can be drawn between the animal world and ourselves; and I may add that the attempt to draw a psychical distinction is equally futile, and that even the highest faculties of feeling and of intellect begin to germinate in lower forms of life.—T. H. Huxley in *Man's Place in Nature.*

Whatever may have been his views at the start of his career, a biologist comes to realize after years of close study that there is no fundamental difference between himself or the rest of mankind and the living world as a whole, plant or animal.—Burton, l.c., page 22.

For that which befalleth the sons of men befalleth beasts . . . as the one dieth so dieth the other; yea, they have all one breath; so that a man hath no preeminence above a beast.—*Ecclesiastes,* III, 19.

Most of us would by now be inclined to agree, and be no longer troubled by yet another shibboleth—that of "anthropomorphism." It can instead be asked: What attitude, "datum," perception, inference, conclusion—or, for that matter, wish or hope—is *not* anthropomorphic? Is there a more redundant word in any language or technical jargon including, as Max Planck has pointed out, the formulas of physics? Or, if it is contended that there must be an order *beyond* man, do we not also, as Heisenberg insists, "inform" that order and influence it by the very act of our observation? Here we may consult another slyly discerning metaphysician; comments Bertrand Russell in his *Outline of Philosophy:*

All animals that have been carefully observed have behaved so as to confirm the philosophy in which the observer believed before his observations began. Nay, more, they have all displayed the national characteristics of the observer. Animals studied by Americans rush about frantically with an incredible display of hustle and pep, and at last achieve the desired result by chance. Animals observed by Germans sit still and think and at last evolve the solution out of their inner consciousness.

Let us, then, speak freely among ourselves as human beings in human language, about human perceptions and human thought. There are no other media available to us—and we need no other for human understanding.

As stated in the introduction to this Appendix, these are but a few of the illuminations and stimulations to further work and thought that a study of ethology offers the psychiatrist. The following references will richly repay the student with many others.

References

Allee, W. C.: Cooperation among Animals. New York. Henry Schuman, 1951.

Beach, F. A.: The Snark Was a Boojum. Am. Psychologist, 5:11t, 1950.

Bharucha-Reid, R. P.: Latent learning in earthworms. Science, 123:243, 1955.

Bingham, H. C.: Sex development in apes. Comp. Psychol. Monogr., 5:1928.

Bonner, J. T.: Cells and Societies. Princeton. Princeton University Press, 1955.

Bowlby, J.: The nature of the child's tie to his mother. Internat. J. Psychoanal., 39:350, 1959.

Brady, J. V.: Ulcers in "executive" monkeys. Sci. Amer., 199:95, 1958.

Brown, F. A.: The rhythmic nature of animals and plants. Sci. Amer., 47:147, 1959.

Brunswick, E.: Perception and the Representative Design of Psychological Experiments. Berkeley. University of California Press, 1956.

Burton, M.: Animal Courtship. New York. F. A. Praeger, 1954.

Butler, R. A.: Curiosity in monkeys. Sci. Amer., 190:70, 1954.

Cobb, S.: Instincts. Am. J. Psychiat., 112:149, 1955.

Darlington, D. C.: The origin of Darwinism. Sci. Amer., 50:200, 1959.

Delgado, J. M. R., Rosvold, H. E., and Looney, E.: Evoking conditioned fear by electrical stimulation of subcortical structures in the monkey brain. J. Comp. & Physiol. Psychol., 49:373, 1956.

Dobie, J. R.: The roadrunner in fact and folklore. Arizona Highways, 34, 1948.

Forel, A.: The Social World of the Ants Compared to That of Man. New York. Boni, 1929.

Frings, H., and Jumber, J.: Preliminary studies on the use of a specific sound to repel starlings. Science, 119:318, 1954.

Ginsberg, B. E.: Genetics as a tool in the study of behavior. Perspectives in Biology. Seminar; personal communication.

Harlow, H. F.: Love in infant monkeys. Sci. Amer., 200:68, 1959.

Heinroth, Oscar: Beitrage zur Biologie. Int. Ornith. Kongs, 5, 1910.

Hellwold, H.: Untersuchungen über Triebstärken bei Tieren. Ztschr. Psychol., 123:38, 1931.

Hess, Eckhard: "Imprinting" in animals. Sci. Amer., 198:81, 1958.

Huxley, T. H.: Man's Place in Nature. London. Thomas, Ltd., 1898.

Jacobsen, E., and Skaarup, Y.: Experimental induction of conflict-behavior in cats: Its use in pharmacological investigations. Acta pharmacol. et toxicol., 11:117, 1955.

Katz, D.: Animals and Man. New York. Longmans Green and Co., 1937.

Kempf, E. J.: The social and sexual behavior of the infra-human primates and some comparable facts in human behavior. Psychoanal. Rev., 4:127, 1917.

King, J. A.: Parameters relevant to determining the effect of early experiences upon the adult behavior in animals. Psychol. Bull., 5:46, 1958.

Kuo, Z. Y.: Genesis of the cat's responses toward the rat. J. Comp. Psychol., 11:1, 1930.

Leblond, C. P.: Extra-hormonal factors in maternal behavior. Proc. Soc. Exper. Biol. & Med., 38:66, 1938.

Levik, G. M.: Antarctic Penguins. London. Trench Trubner, 1914.

Levy, D.: The relation of animal psychology to psychiatry. In Galdston, I., Ed.: Medicine and Science. International Universities Press, 1954.

Lindauer, M.: House hunt. Sci. Amer., *196:*70, 1958.
Loveridge, A.: Notes on East African mammals. J. E. Afr. N. H. Soc., *16,* 1938, *17,* 1939.
Marshall, A. J.: Bower birds. Sci. Amer., *194:*48, 1956.
Maslow, A. H.: Role of dominance in the social and sexual behavior of infra-human primates. J. genet. Psychol., *48:*261, 1936.
Miller, N. E.: Experiments in motivation. Science, *126:*1276, 1957.
Mirsky, A. F., and Katz, M. S.: Avoidance "conditioning" in paramecia. Science, *126:* 1276, 1957.
Mirsky, I. A., Miller, R. E., and Murphy, J. V.: The communication of effect in Rhesus monkeys. J. Am. Psychoanal. Assn., *6:*433, 1958.
Montagu, A. M. F.: Man—and human nature. Am. J. Psychiat., *112:*401, 1955.
Morgan, C. L.: Animal Life and Intelligence. London. Arnold, 1891.
Morris, D.: The courtship dance of the sword tail. Aquarest., March, 1955.
———: The feather posture of birds and the problem of the origin of social signals. Behavior, *9:*6, 1956.
Nakao, H.: Emotional behavior produced by hypothalamic stimulation. Am. J. Physiol., *194:*411, 1958.
Olds, J.: Self-stimulation of the brain. Science, *127:*315, 1958.
Oppenheimer, R.: Analogy in science. Am. Psychol., *11:*127, 1956.
Pattie, F. A.: The gregarious behavior of normal chicks and chicks hatched in isolation. J. Comp. Psychol., *21:*161, 1936.
Pavlov, I. P.: Lectures on Conditioned Reflexes. New York. International Publishers, 1928, p. 242.
Penfield, W.: The interpretive cortex. Science, *159:*1732, 1959.
Razran, G.: Pavlov and Lamarck. Science, *128:*758, 1958.
Rensch, B.: The intelligence of elephants. Sci. Amer., *196:*44, 1957.
Richter, C. P.: On the phenomenon of sudden death in animals and man. Psychosom. Med., *19:*191, 1957.
Rioch, D. McK.: Certain aspects of "conscious" phenomena and their neural correlates. Am. J. Psychiat., *111:*810, 1955.
Rosvold, H. E.: The effects of electroconvulsive shocks on gestation and maternal behavior: I. J. Comp. & Physiol. Psychol., *42:*118, 1949; II. ibid., *42:*207, 1949.
Russell, B.: An Outline of Philosophy. London. Allen and Unwin, 1927.
Sauer, H. G. F.: Celestial navigation in birds. Sci. Amer., *199:*42, 1958.
Schnierla, T. C.: Learning and orientation in ants. Comp. Psychol. Monogr., *6,* 1929.
Scott, J. P.: The process of socialization in higher animals. New York. Milbank Fund Publications, 1953.
Scott, W. E.: Data on song in birds. Science, *14:*522, 1901.
Seitz, P. F. D.: The effects of infantile experiences upon adult behavior in animal subjects. I. Effects of litter size during infancy upon adult behavior in the rat. Am. J. Psychiat., *110:*916, 1954.
Sibol, J.: The strangest birds in the world. Life, March 25, 1957, p. 88.
Szymanski, J. S.: Modification of the innate behavior of cockroaches. J. Animal Behavior, *2:*81, 1912.
Thompson, W. R.: Influence of prenatal maternal anxiety on emotionality in young rats. Science, *125:*698, 1957.
———, and Heron, W.: Protected pups, helpless dogs with a poor personality. Canad. J. Psychol. 8:17, 1954.
———, and Melzock, R.: "Whirling" behavior in dogs as related to early experience. Science, *123:*939, 1956.
Tolman, E. C.: Purposive Behavior in Animals and Man. New York. Century, 1932.
Vexhall, J. von: Unwelt und Innenwelt der Tiere. Berlin. Springer, 1920.
Warden, C. J., Jenkins, T. N., and Warner, L. H.: Introduction to Comparative Psychology. New York. Ronald Press, 1934.
Wiener, N.: Some maxims for biologists and psychologists. Dialectica, *4:*3, 1950.
Wiesner, B. P., and Sheard, N. M.: Maternal Behavior in the Rat. Edinburgh. Oliver and Boyd, 1933.
Yerkes, R. M.: Chimpanzees, a Laboratory Colony. New Haven. Yale University Press, 1943.
Zuckerman, S.: The Social Life of Monkeys and Apes. London. Kegan, Paul, Trench, Trubner & Co., 1932.

Illustrative motion picture films

THESE 16 mm. motion picture films on the neurophysiology of emotion, experimental neuroses, group relationships, and the effects of drugs and cerebral operations on behavior are obtainable from the Department of Neurology and Psychiatry, Northwestern University, Chicago, or the Psychological Cinema Register, State College, Pa.

Film 1. The dynamics of behavior and experimental neuroses

Total length, about 1650 feet, black and white. Four reels, each about 400 feet as follows:

Reel 1. **Methods.** The automatic "conditioning" apparatus and experimental techniques are illustrated. Cats are trained to respond to light or bell signals with specific feeding patterns. A motivational conflict between hunger and fear then induces food inhibitions, sensory hyperesthesias and specific phobias, motor disturbances, recurrent physiologic manifestations of anxiety and other "neurotic" behavior patterns in and out of the experimental situation (cf. Experiments 1 and 9).

Reel 2. **Controls and analysis.** The effects of various types of environmental frustration are contrasted with those produced by motivational conflict. Experimental increase of the intensity of the conflict or constriction of the reactive field exacerbates the neurotic behavior, whereas resolution of the impasse or escape from the situation alleviates many of the symptoms (Experiment 10).

Reel 3. **Experimental diminution of the neurotic behavior.** Four methods of "therapy" are illustrated in detail: (1) diminution of one of the conflictful drives, (2) retraining of the animal in the problem situation, (3) forced solution of the conflict by "environmental press" and (4) association with the normal behavior of a non-neurotic animal. Phenomena of subsequent immunity to the neurotic situation appear in the "cured" animals (Experiments 10 to 14).

Reel 4. **Spontaneity in behavior and neurosis.** Normal animals are trained to manipulate an electric switch to actuate their own feeding signals. Special experiments show both the dynamically adaptive and "gestalt" significance of the animal's behavior. Mechanical frustration of the response cycles induces substitutive or "symbolic" patterns, whereas an induced motivational conflict produces neurotic and regressive behavior. However, animals trained to exert partial control of the situation exhibit the capacity to "work through" the motivational problem to a resolution of their neurosis. Concluding subtitles summarize the significance of the experiments illustrated in Reels 1 to 4 in relation to dynamic psychology and psychiatry (Experiments 2 to 5).

The film is suitable for professional students and lay groups studying the dynamics of behavior, neurosis and "psychotherapy."

References: 7, 13, 14, 15, *16.**

Film 2. Dominance, neurosis and aggression

Black and white, two reels, about 375 feet each.

Reel 1. **Group relationships.** Cats trained in groups of four to compete for food after a conditional signal form a stable hierarchy in which the dominant individuals secure the food in succession without fighting. The intra-hierarchic relationships of each animal and the influences of competition, isolation, and frustration are illustrated in detail (Experiment 6).

Reel 2. **Neurosis and aggression.** Aggressive fighting appears in an animal either (a) when it is displaced by a more dominant animal or (b) when it is made experimentally neurotic by a motivational conflict; goal-orientated behavior is then deviated into aggressivity mainly directed against animals above it in the hierarchy. Amytal temporarily mitigates the neurosis and restores non-aggressive dominance. Concluding subtitles summarize the dynamic interrelationships of dominance, neurosis and aggression (Experiments 6 and 9).

This film is suitable for professional and lay students of psychology, psychiatry and sociology. References: 1, 7, 16, *18,* 20.

Film 3. The dynamics of competition

Black and white, about 350 feet.

Pairs of cats trained to manipulate a switch for food develop patterns of cooperation, conflict, dominance, and active or passive parasitism that parallel those in interhuman relationships (Experiments 6, 7 and 14).

This film is suitable for professional or lay students of dynamic and group psychology. References: 7, 16, 18, 19, *20.*

Film 4. The effects of morphine on behavior and neurosis

Black and white, about 400 feet.

In normal animals, morphine disintegrates complex behavioral adaptations into more primitive goal-directed patterns. Similarly, in animals made neurotic by a motivational conflict, morphine produces temporary abolition of the physiologic manifestations of anxiety, and of complex phobic, compulsive and regressive behavior, and thus affords temporary relief from the neurosis. The significance of these observations for opiate addiction is summarized (Experiment 17).

Suitable for professional students of psychology, pharmacology and psychiatry. References: 6, 10, 16, *17.*

* These references are to the bibliography listed at the end of this Appendix; the most directly relevant references are italicized.

Film 5. Neurosis and alcohol

Black and white, two reels, about 350 feet each.

Reel 1. **Alcohol and normal behavior.** Cats are trained to open a box for food, then to feed only after specific sensory signals and, finally, to manipulate a switch in various positions to actuate their own feeding signals. When alcohol is administered these patterns disappear in the order of recency and relative complexity of integration, until only the original, primitive feeding reactions remain (Experiment 16a).

Reel 2. **Alcohol and neurosis.** After recovery, the animals are subjected to a severe motivational conflict, and develop somatic manifestations of anxiety, inhibitions, phobias, motor disturbances, loss of dominance and other neurotic abnormalities. Alcohol again disintegrates these complex reactive patterns, alleviates the manifestations of anxiety, restores direct goal behavior and thereby temporarily relieves the neurosis. Some animals then prefer alcoholic to non-alcoholic drinks until their addiction is cured by the relief of the underlying neurosis (Experiment 16b and c).

Suitable for professional and lay groups interested in the dynamics of behavior, neurosis and alcoholism. References: 7, 8, 9, *16, 21, 22*.

Film 6. The role of the hypothalamus in behavior and neurosis

Black and white, two reels, about 350 feet each.

Reel 1. An aseptic Horsley-Clarke technique for inserting electrodes into the hypothalamus of cats and the automatic "conditioning" apparatus are illustrated. Stimulation of the hypothalamus in recovery animals induces dramatic motor and sympathetic manifestations of "sham rage," but the behavior is stereotyped, unadaptive and stimulus-bound (cf. Chapter 8).

Reel 2. Environmental stimuli associated as many as 480 times with "sham rage" reactions could not be conditioned to induce true affective states. In contrast, recovery animals continue feeding or other adaptive behavior during hypothalamic stimulation, and show normal fear and rage despite extensive hypothalamic lesions. Cardiac and vasomotor accompaniments of hypothalamic "conditioning" cannot be produced in anesthetized animals (technique and tracings illustrated). It is therefore concluded that the hypothalamus may integrate the efferent pathways of affective expression, but does not serve as a source of "drive" or as a "center of emotion" (cf. p. 17 f.).

Suitable for professional students of psychology and neurophysiology. References: 7, 10, 11, *12*, 13, 16.

Film 7. The effects of electrical stimulation and destruction of the hypothalamus

Black and white, about 475 feet.

Reel 1. **Stimulation experiments.** The Horsley-Clarke stereotactic technique for inserting needle electrodes into the hypothalamus of the cat is demonstrated, and the methods of experimentation in acute and recovery preparations are illustrated. Hypothalamic stimulation produces tachycardia, vascular hypertension, mydriasis, piloerection, vocalizations, clawing and running movements, and other sympathetic and motor responses; in recovery preparations these constitute typical "sham rage" or pseudo-affective behavior (p. 17 f.).

Reel 2. **Destruction experiments.** Bilateral destruction of the hypothalamus causes stupor and catalepsy, with subsequent diminution and disintegration of emotional mimetic responses; however, adequate stimulation in recovery animals shows that these are not abolished. Perihypothalamic stimulation produces partial effects which are diminished by intravenous Amytal but not by the direct injection of the drug (p. 17 f.).

Suitable for professional students of the neurophysiology of emotion. References: 1, 2, 4, *11*, 12, 16.

Film 8. The effects of various drugs on the emotional mimetic reactions of the hypothalamus and cerebral cortex

Black and white, five parts, total about 450 feet.

Part 1. **Differential effects of alcohol.** Faradic stimulation of the hypothalamus in a waking cat through an implanted needle electrode induces effects similar to those in rage and fear, whereas stimulation of the right sigmoid cortex produces only motor and postural responses. The intravenous administration of 2 to 10 cc./K. of ethyl alcohol causes ataxia and stupor, diminishes the reactivity of the cortex, but does not materially alter the motor and sympathetic responses of the hypothalamus. The experiments indicate that intoxicant doses of alcohol impair the function of the cerebral cortex to a greater degree than those of lower emotional mimetic centers (cf. Experiment 16).

Part 2. **Dilute alcohol.** Recovery cats are prepared with needle electrodes placed respectively in the left anterior sigmoid cortex and in the hypothalamus. Faradic stimulation of the cortex produces characteristic sniffing, licking and chewing responses which are increased by the direct injection of 0.1 cc. of 0.05 per cent ethyl alcohol or by the intraperitoneal administration of 0.5 to 1.0 cc./K. of alcohol in Ringer's solution. Electrical stimulation of the hypothalamus induces the characteristic sympathetic and motor effects of "sham rage," which are slightly increased by the direct or systemic administration of alcohol in small doses. Simultaneous electrical stimulation of both the cortex and hypothalamus increases the characteristic responses from each region and this mutual facilitating effect is more marked after the administration of small doses of alcohol. It is concluded that sub-intoxicant doses of alcohol have a mildly stimulant effect on both the cortex and hypothalamus (cf. Experiment 16).

Part 3. **Effects of Metrazol.** The injection of 0.1 cc. of a 10 per cent solution of Metrazol into the hypothalamus of a recovery preparation induces a syndrome of sympathetic and motor reactions resembling a frenzy of "sham" fear or rage. The effects reach peak intensity in about ten minutes and then rapidly abate to complete recovery.

Part 4. **Morphine.** The intraperitoneal injection of 40 to 230 mg. of morphine sulfate into a recovery preparation causes ataxia and excitement, but does not change the reactions of the hypothalamus or cortex to direct electrical stimulation. Direct injections of 1.0 per cent morphine into the brain produce no significant effects.

Part 5. **Sodium Amytal.** This drug diminishes the emotional mimetic reactions of the hypothalamus when administered intravenously but not when injected directly into the hypothalamus.

Concluding subtitles summarize the effects of various other analeptic and sedative drugs on the cortex and hypothalamus.

Suitable only for professional students of neurophysiology and pharmacology. References: 1, 3, 5, 6, 8, 9, *10*, 12, 16, 17, 21.

Film 9. The hypothalamus and the heart

Kodachrome, 60 feet.

This film illustrates the reactions of the exposed heart of the cat to weak (parasympathetic) and strong (predominantly orthosympathetic) stimulation of the hypothalamus.

Suitable for students of physiology. References: 1, *16*.

Film 10. Alcohol as a preventive of experimental neuroses

Black and white; about 400 feet.

Cats induced to drink alcohol to the point of mild intoxication during an experimental conflict show few or no neurotic residua (compare Films 1 and 5). As a further control, the same animals, if subjected to corresponding motivational stresses while not under the influence of alcohol, develop persistent neurotic symptoms (cf. Experiment 16b).

Prepared in collaboration with Mary Grier Jacques. Suitable for lay and professional groups. References: 16, 21, 22, 23.

Film 11. Effects of cerebral electric shock on experimental neuroses

Black and white; about 400 feet.

Electroshock treatments disrupt the complex symptomatic patterns of experimental neuroses in cats and partially restore simpler, more directly goal-directed behavior. However, highly developed perceptual, integrative and adaptive capacities are also impaired, and various neurotic reactions to the shock experiences may develop (cf. Experiment 17 ff.).

Prepared in collaboration with Mary Grier Jacques. Suitable for students of comparative neurology and psychiatry. References: 16, 24.

Film 12. Experimental neuroses in monkeys

Monkeys subected to experimental conflicts between learned feeding patterns and innate aversions to an artificial rubber snake developed persistent phobias and compulsions, marked social and sexual aberrations and regressions, "hysterical" paraplegias, severe gastrointestinal dysfunctions or other somatic disorders and hallucinatory-delusional behavior e.g., eating imaginary food pellets while avoiding real ones. The film illustrates the interplay of constitutional and experiential factors as determinants of conduct.

Prepared in collaboration with Curtis Pechtel. Suitable for students of psychology and psychiatry. Reference: 25.

References*

1. Effects of Sodium Amytal and other drugs on the reactivity of the hypothalamus of the cat. Arch. Neurol. & Psychiat., *37*:617–628, 1937.
2. Destruction of the hypothalamus in cats. Effects on activity of the central nervous system and its reaction to Sodium Amytal. Arch. Neurol. & Psychiat., *39*:1250–1271, 1938.
3. The effect of strychnine sulphate on the emotional mimetic functions of the hypothalamus of the cat (with assistance of E. W. Haertig). J. Pharm. & Exp. Therap., *64*:335–354, 1938.
4. The influence of hypothalamic stimulation on intestinal activity (with E. W. Haertig). J. Neurophysiol., *1*:350–356, 1938.
5. Action of Metrazol (pentamethylenetetrazol) on the hypothalamus of the cat (with assistance of E. W. Haertig). Arch. Neurol. & Psychiat., *41*:504–510, 1939.
6. Effects of morphine sulphate on hypothalamus of the cat. Proc. Soc. Exp. Biol. & Med., *42*:315–317, 1939.
7. An automatic apparatus for the central conditioning of small animals. J. Comp. Psychol., *28*:201–205, 1939.
8. Effects of ethyl alcohol on the cerebral cortex and the hypothalamus of the cat (with Leon Jacobson). Arch. Neurol. & Psychiat., *43*:334–340, 1940.
9. Stimulant effects of ethyl alcohol in cortico-hypothalamic functions (with assistance of John Beal and Rosaltha Sanders). J. Pharm. & Exp. Therap., *70*:450–453, 1940.
10. Effects of analeptic drugs on the hypothalamus of the cat. Res. Publ. Ass. Nerv. & Ment. Dis., *20*:625, 634, 1940.
11. Hypothalamic lesions and pneumonia in cats. With notes on behavior changes (with E. W. Haertig). J. Neurophysiol., *3*:293–299, 1940.
12. Is the hypothalamus a center of emotion? Psychosomat. Med., *3*:3–25, 1941.
13. The hypothalamus and psychiatry. Am. J. Psychiat., *98*:635–637, 1942.
14. Psychobiologic dynamisms in behavior. Psychiatry, *5*:341–347, 1942.
15. Experimental neuroses and psychotherapy. Arch. Neurol. & Psychiat., *49*:43–48, 1943.
16. Behavior and Neurosis. Chicago, University of Chicago Press. 270 pp., 30 half tones, 1943.
17. The effects of morphine on learned adaptive responses and experimental neuroses in cats (with Dr. A. Wikler). Arch. Neurol. & Psychiat., *50*:401–404, 1943.
18. Dominance, neurosis and aggression. Psychosom. Med., *6*:7–16, 1944.
19. Counting behavior in cats. J. Comp. Psychol., *30*:87–88, 1944.
20. Experimental neuroses and group dominance. Am. J. Orthopsychiat., *14*:636–643, 1944.
21. Neurosis and alcohol. Am. J. Psychiat., *101*:389–395, 1944.
22. The influence of alcohol on experimental neuroses in cats (with K. S. Yum). Psychosom. Med., *8*:36–52, 1946.
23. Alcohol as a preventive of neurosis (with Mary Grier Jacques). Quart. J. Study Alc., *6*:281–299, 1945.
24. The effects of cerebral electroshock on experimental neuroses (with Mary G. Jacques). Am. J. Psychiat., *104*:92, 1947.
25. Neuroses in monkeys (with C. Pechtel). Ann. N. Y. Acad. Sci., *55*:253, 1953.

* Publications by the author and his associates which provide supplementary reading for the films listed above.

Illustrative psychoanalysis
of a neurotic personality

THIS CASE history is included to illustrate the techniques and interpretations employed in a formal psychoanalysis, the nature of the symbolisms, association and transference relationships elicited during the analytic process, and the therapeutic dynamisms utilized in the intrapersonal and social readjustments of the patient.

Case 40. Neurotic personality with gastrointestinal "psychosomatic" symptoms

PRESENTING PROBLEM. The patient, a thirty-five-year-old, unmarried girl with a diminutive, boyish appearance and a diffident, overingratiating manner, stated that she came for psychoanalysis primarily because she had been troubled for the preceding five years by nausea or actual vomiting whenever she attempted to dine in the presence of a man and, more recently, even when she merely thought of such a situation. The patient with some difficulty had been able to continue her work as a stenographer, but to circumvent her symptoms she found it necessary during the last four years to avoid the company of men altogether, to forego almost all cultural and recreational pursuits, and to live in self-imposed isolation with her widowed mother as her only close companion. The patient also complained of recurrent "chills," headaches and attacks of diarrhea but regarded these and other symptoms as of relatively minor importance. Nevertheless, in view of the failure of past medical treatment, her many harassing personality limitations and the deepening discouragement in regard to her occupational, marital and social prospects, she had decided to try analysis as a last therapeutic resort.

ANAMNESIS. The patient was born as the youngest of three sisters into a middle class family in an eastern European city. When she was two years old her father departed for America. She was left in the care of her doting mother, a forceful, independent, ambitious, but emotionally unstable individual, who apparently at first indulged her youngest daughter greatly; in any case, the patient believed that the first few years of her life in Europe had been exceedingly happy. However, she soon learned that the family was really being supported by a paternal uncle, from whom she was taught to expect—and sometimes even to beg—not only her little luxuries but also the very clothes and food she required. It is significant that only two conflictful oral memories persisted from this period: in both instances "elderly men offered food" and then attempted to approach her sexually, and on both occasions she had been "too frightened to tell mother."

When the patient was five years old the family left Europe and rejoined the father in America. On the initiative of her ambitious mother, the patient was then placed on a regimen of training that, it was hoped, would make her a famous violin virtuoso. She took readily to this plan, practiced arduously and began to delight in exhibiting herself in many little recitals arranged by her mother. Up to about the age of her menarche she took pride in helping with the housework and seemed especially interested in the preparation of food for the family. She was frankly ashamed of her father, who had never acquired what she considered an adequate American culture and whose work as a tailor she regarded as a handicap to her anticipated social position as a musical prodigy. However, when at about fourteen the mediocrity of her talent became apparent even to her mother, the intensive musical training was discontinued. At this time the patient became consciously aware that the mother had shifted her favor to the eldest sister because the latter had, on her own merits, achieved greater social and occupational success. In reaction to the withdrawal of her mother's support, the patient became outwardly more aggressive to her mother and sisters and for a time even took her father's part in the many domestic quarrels. During this period, significantly, she began to prefer boyish clothes, adopted various athletic pursuits and became a disciplinary problem at school, which she left at the age of fifteen. She then secured a series of positions which she held with fair success until the time of her analysis, although beneath a facade of independence and self-sufficiency she continued to be shy and hypersensitive, highly limited in her social contacts and interests and almost exclusively immersed in the minutiae of the household and family relationships.

In tracing through the origins of her somatic symptoms during the initial anamnestic interviews, the patient recollected that her first attack of nausea had occurred at the age of twelve when a boy whom she admired had offered her a piece of cake at a party. After this episode, eating in the presence of men often induced vague abdominal discomfort or mild nausea and diarrhea—reactions which became definitely worse after the death of her father when she was eighteen. In relation to such memories, however, she emphatically denied that she had acquired any sexual knowledge or had experienced even a single erotic fantasy until her menarche at sixteen, at which time her mother "explained" sexual intercourse to her in a depreciatory manner and stringently warned her against the "animal intents" and seductive activities of men.

PRESENTING ILLNESS. The patient's symptoms took their present form at the age of twenty-five under the following circumstances. During her first prolonged separation from her mother, she was visiting the summer home of her middle sister and was there introduced to her first prospective suitor. At first she disliked the man but then began to feel a guilty erotic attraction towards him. One evening, after dinner with him during which the patient had felt peculiarly tense and uncomfortable, she permitted some sexual play, but when he began to caress her breasts, she began to experience unusually severe nausea and abdominal discomfort. She immediately informed the man that she never wished to see him again and the next day, in compliance with a sudden compelling desire, she returned to her mother's home. She remained relatively symptom free for a period, but only by the device of avoiding almost all heterosexual contacts. At the age of thirty, nevertheless, she "fell in love" with the son of her employer but again found herself able to accept his attentions only through the strict observance of certain conditions: sex play had to be non-stimulating, her breasts could not be touched and, most imperative of all, the man was not permitted to mention food or drink in her presence, let alone invite her to indulge in them; otherwise she would develop severe nausea and sometimes vomit.

Such ritualistic defenses sufficed for several months, but later became much more elaborate. She soon found it necessary to forbid her fiancé even to telephone her while she was having a meal at home lest intense nausea, emesis or diarrhea ensue. Vomiting became frequent despite all precautions, a persistent anorexia set in and her symptoms became so severe that in a few months she lost thirty-two pounds without, however, corresponding loss of strength or energy. Her family naturally regarded her condition as of serious physical import, urged her to quit her job and finally induced her to enter a well-known diagnostic clinic. Thorough physical, laboratory and roentgenologic examinations showed completely normal findings, a diagnosis of "anorexia nervosa" was made and the patient was discharged by the internist with the admonition to lead a "more active and normal life."

Significantly, the patient informed her mother that the doctor had obviously meant to specify heterosexual relationships, but that she would virtuously refuse to follow any such recommendation no matter what the penalty in ill health might be. The unexpected result of these protestations was that her mother took the patient's misinterpretations of her medical advice at their face value, disregarded her professed moral scruples and insisted that the patient begin having intercourse with her fiancé immediately, on pain of being disowned by the family; in fact, the mother actively arranged the details of moving the patient into an apartment for the greater convenience of the couple. During the seven months that this "therapeutic" liason lasted the patient's symptoms improved somewhat and she regained considerable weight, although she remained sexually inhibited, was excessively dependent upon and demanding of her lover, and continued to find it difficult to eat in his presence. Moreover, when he finally deserted her to marry another girl whose deficiencies in physical charm were overbalanced by the attractions of greater emotional maturity and considerable wealth, the patient's anorexia, vomiting and diarrhea promptly reappeared and once again became severe and disabling. Pleading her lack of control of these symptoms, she then gave up all further attempts at sexual or other emancipation and returned to live with her mother. For a time she seemed comparatively content, but since her social isolation and various disabilities eventually became burdensome both to herself and her family, she yielded finally to their repeated urgings and applied for analysis.

Physical, laboratory and x-ray examinations preceding the analysis again revealed essentially normal findings. The patient's intelligence quotient on the second Stanford Revision of the Binet-Simon scale was 134. It is of interest that her responses to the Fantasy Test,[*] given for the purpose of a preliminary psychodynamic survey, accurately anticipated the essential determinants of some of the patient's main unconscious reactions as later revealed in the analysis. Thus, in association to a stimulus picture of a monstrous eerie dragon issuing from a cave in a mystic canyon, she produced a very unusual fantasy in which she identified herself with this threatening phallic or clitoral symbol, yet anxiously represented it (herself by projection) as a depreciated, helpless, oral incorporative creature (a caterpillar) which, after a brief contact with the dangers and anxieties of the outside world, gladly regresses to the security of the mother's womb:

"Here's a little caterpillar that wanted to seek his fortune and he left his nice, cozy, warm, little home for the great, big world. (I don't know what else to say. Wait till I embellish this a little.) Somehow or other he was beset by dangers wherever he went, rocky paths to cross, dangerous enemies to pass, no food in sight and so he finally stopped and pondered: 'This great, big world I was trying to find doesn't seem to be remarkable after all. Maybe I should have thought twice instead of giving up that nice, comfortable, cozy little place I left and maybe it wouldn't be too late to turn back now.' And so dear children, even though you don't see him returning, that's what he did and he's content to stay where he is, the big outside world no longer having any fascination for him."

[*] Cf. Murray (1938), Masserman and Balken (1939).

COURSE OF THE ANALYSIS. The patient's initial transference was one of a self-conscious, puerile flirtatiousness in which significant oral components and naive regressive fantasies were early expressed. Typical associations in the first three hours were the following:

"This . . . is like a first date, because I get the same sort of sick nauseated feeling . . . Mother certainly has a queer daughter . . . Once when I was four years old and sick she brought me a doll . . . I'm not so sure of things when I'm out with a man . . . I won't keep this up if it makes me feel nauseated . . . Why did even thinking of B (patient's lover) make me sick to my stomach? . . . I hope I'll be able to come tomorrow."

True to these indications and despite simple, reassuring interpretations that she might be tempted again to react with vomiting as an escape from uneasiness over erotic or hostile feelings mobilized in the analytic situation, the patient spent the week-end after her tenth analytic hour vomiting almost continuously and insisting to her family that this proved the analysis to be not only useless but probably actually harmful. However, the patient's mother, apparently again sensing the patient's intense unconscious guilt and her need for explicit maternal reassurance, strongly urged resumption of the treatment. The patient therefore returned and for some twenty hours thereafter defended herself against her highly ambivalent genital and oral transference by picturing the analyst as a haughty, cold, unapproachable individual, or an unprincipled seducer sure to be thwarted by her strong moral resistance, or else—even more damningly—as an unsympathetic confidante who did not give her adequate support and solace. Closely connected with such attitudes were early oral fantasies which indicated, with the naiveté of initial analytic material, the patient's desire that the analyst present her with a male organ with which to please and win her mother. In fact, the only defense she summoned was to regard the oral incorporation of the phallus—which she fancied her mother wanted her to have—as unpleasant and *nauseating*, as illustrated by the following dream sequence:

Dream: "I reached for a hat . . . It went over a partition but a man gave it back to me. I wore it and brought my mother and sister some cookies which I hoped would please them. Then mother gave me a frankfurter and I ate it, but I said it tasted terrible, like pork."
Associations: "(Hat) Men's hats. A new hat makes me feel self-confident. (Man) You. I came back to the analysis to please mother. (Frankfurter) My mother and sister always joke about their being penises: I like to eat them, but this morning the thought made me sick. (Pork) I don't let myself eat it, but mother always fed us well with other things."

As may be expected, she did not at this time develop further these early indications of deep oral conflicts, but instead erected a categorical defense to the effect that, instead of being a weak, dependent child who must please her mother in order to secure food and protection, she was really an able, self-sufficient and even potent individual who, incidentally, needed no analytic or other treatment. However, when she ventured the ultimate bravado of dreaming that her father and mother were dead, and that she was a famous violin virtuoso with the rest of the world at her feet, her reactive anxiety was so great that she recollected a firm resolution of childhood to *swallow poison* if ever she were bereaved of her parents. Aggressive material also appeared in more frankly anal forms of attack:

"I want to be very destructive—tear things up and throw them out of the window . . . Your couch cover is filthy . . . I hate all teachers . . . Once in high school class I let wind from my rectum and it made a terrible noise. I was so embarrassed I quit school and never went back—I decided to study music instead."

In further masochistic reaction against hostile jealousies directed mainly towards the analyst as a father figure, the patient brought the following dream:

"A man sang love songs in German to a woman who was with him on a balcony. I said I understood German too, so he came down and beat me."
Associations: Dad used to sing love songs to mother. Germans are terribly cruel—they kill people. (Balcony) Our home bedroom.

These and other associations indicated that the dream expressed competitive identification with the mother but that, in reaction, the primal scene was conceived so sadistically that the patient's gratification was far outweighed by an overwhelming fear of the adult female role. Analysis of this fantasy also led to a franker expression of reactive castrative impulses towards father figures (as expressed in increasingly critical remarks about her boss, the analyst and other men) accompanied, as usual, by a retreat in fantasy to the welcoming safety of the mother. This was typified a few days later in another dream:

"Men lay in hospital cots all bandaged up like with mumps . . . I dreamed of my Dad, who's dead . . . Then there was an avalanche and I was in danger, but finally I was at home with my mother all cozy and warm."
Associations: (Hospital cots) My father died there. (Mumps) Makes men sterile. (Avalanche) Danger. (Cozy with mother) Warm, clean house on Friday night and the wonderful meal mother used to feed us.

In connection with other covert avowals of aggressions against the father and retreat to the mother the patient remembered a fantasy which had recurred frequently between the ages of about eight and sixteen: namely, that she was not her "father's real daughter; he only found me in my mother's garden." However, when the significance of such fantasies of virgin birth with regard to her early rejections of her father was explored, she defended herself for a period against recollecting predominantly oral hostilities towards him by maintaining that in her girlhood it had actually been her "happy task" *to bring him his meals,* especially [sic] during the frequent parental quarrels.

Positive Oedipus memories also appeared, but with so little guilt as to make it obvious that these recollections of genital attraction toward the father were really defenses against hostile rivalries with him. For instance, as early as the first month of her analysis the patient brought a (screen?) memory that one day, at about the age of ten, she had actually encouraged her mother to leave home after a quarrel, and that night had "innocently" entered her father's bed "to make up for mother"—although this, she hastily added, had only made his grief all the greater. Nevertheless, as the reasons for her actual renunciation of men and the regressive flight to the mother were further analyzed, the patient was led to face her jealousies of the father not only on a superficial genital, but also on more significant pregenital levels. The characteristic features of the patient's oral conflict then appeared more clearly: whereas she could admit her ostensibly erotic temptations towards her father or his surrogates with little difficulty (she dreamed frankly of marrying her cousin "which would be as bad as marrying my father"), she nevertheless wished to renounce her oral aggressive wishes to "incorporate" her father as a mother substitute and at the same time "eliminate" him as an envied, thwarting rival. Consecutive fragments of her defensive associations at this stage are almost self-explanatory:

"I fear marriage because I can't cook like my sisters and it wouldn't be right to let my husband feed *me* . . . Often when I sat down to a meal, if the phone rang for a date I wouldn't be able to eat any more. I remember my father urged me to eat on fast days, but I just couldn't because I'd get nauseated. When B (former lover) kissed me after a meal I vomited all that night . . . Once when I was fourteen mother went away and Dad cooked my meal . . . I vomited all that night too . . . I also avoid marriage because my teeth bleed at night and that would be embarrassing. (An indication that assumption of an adult feminine role would evoke oral biting aggressions and would also symbolize self-castration.)

Yet more directly symbolic of her orally cathected guilts was the fact that the patient cancelled several analytic hours in order to be treated for a *"painful mouth and throat"* although no organic basis for these paresthesias was ever found by a competent oral surgeon. From a psychosomatic standpoint it was also interesting that periods of reactive aggression towards the analyst, conceived as a rejecting parent figure, were characteristically accompanied by urges to vomit, defecate or urinate during the hour, whereas genital urges (which were less guilt-charged and which the patient characterized lightly as "hot ideas") were reacted to only by minor bodily "chills" and subjective tremors. In this connection she clearly recalled that she had habitually slept with her mother until she came to America and that she had then greatly resented the fact that her father then joined them in bed. Despite her father's presence, she had insisted on continuing to share their bed until she was eight years old, and even then had energetically resisted being sent to sleep with her sister because at that time she "wanted to keep on being warm and cozy with Mother and Dad." Moreover, the substrate of this material in deep oral attachment to her mother and jealousies against the first father imago in her life (her uncle) soon appeared in other associations:

"My uncle in W—, where I lived until I was four, didn't like me and was mean to me because I took up mother's time—but mother said I should be nice to him because he was the bread-giver; once she even refused to feed me until he could bring us more food . . . I think my boss should leave me his money, because Dad never provided enough for us."

At this time the patient also began to deal with the specific nature of her incorporative desires toward men: namely, to acquire their penises as a symbol of the masculinity prized in them by her mother, thereby eliminate them as competitors, and at the same time displace them homosexually in her mother's affections. Such desires were soon indicated with increasing clarity in a multitude of dreams and associations. For instance, in the 78th hour the patient reported the dream:

"I aroused my sister R. sexually and didn't know whether to be glad or contemptuous."

In this dream the sister was definitely associated with the mother and the patient granted herself the power (phallus) to arouse a mother figure sexually, yet wished to depreciate that same power because of the accompanying guilt over its acquisition.* Early (screen?) memories also came to the fore:

"In W— when I was in a hospital a nurse passed by with a tray of buns that I wanted. I then asked the doctor to get me one and he promised, but instead he stuck a needle in my stomach and it hurt."

* The corollary or obverse interpretation of this bisexual dream, namely, that the patient reversed the sexual roles and depreciated femininity, is equally characteristic of the patient's regressive rejection of all sexuality.

Similarly, the object she desired to incorporate from her father appeared in the next dream, in which, after a reiteration of her anxious rejection of the female role and a denial that she had ever been robbed of a fantasied penis, she allayed her anxiety by self-reassurance that she knew how to handle masculine appurtenances even though she did not openly despoil their envied owners—the analyst ("Buddha with the pencil") and the little boy with the spear:

"A man who was with my father wanted to sleep with me, but I refused because people were looking. Then I thought a burglar had gone through my clothes and taken something, but found he hadn't. I then helped my nephew to select a tie that I liked and saw a Buddha with a pencil attached that I wanted. Then I was showing a little boy how to hold a spear and be a knight!" (Tie, pencil and spear were all almost directly associated with penis symbols.)

While this material was being worked through the patient showed considerable clinical improvement: she no longer spent nearly all her free time with her family; she permitted herself a greater number of social and recreational outlets in mixed company and she even dined out on one occasion with an elderly male acquaintance. To test her newly found freedom (and also, apparently, in a more or less conscious effort to please the analyst to whom she had a concurrently strong maternal transference), she even ventured at this meal to eat strawberries despite her conviction, born of invariable experience, that she would break out in hives if she did so. To her own surprise, however, she felt no nausea at the meal and suffered no ill effects afterward.

But, of course, many unconscious conflicts remained to be analyzed. For one, the patient continued to reject femininity in favor of deeply guarded fantasies that despite her own guilt-charged rejection of the wish for the oral acquisition of the phallus, she had somehow acquired a symbolic penis which was of value in cementing her exclusive solidarity with her mother and which therefore had to be cherished and defended from all threats of castration. An amusing instance of this, related to many dreams and fantasies in which burglars had unsuccessfully attempted to search and rob her clothes or her room, was the following: one day, the patient playfully began to count the cylindrical buttons on her dress to the accompaniment of the familiar childhood chant of "Doctor, lawyer, merchant, chief." Suddenly she stopped in manifest consternation: the word "thief" had come out on the button over her genitals! During this period she also professed great concern that her breasts "were so very small," whereas her nose "was so very large"*—both ideas having the import of a denial of matronly or feminine qualities and a wishful preoccupation with masculine ones. In the same significant connection, she frequently reminisced that her mother had always admired her "boyish figure." In this period also she became interested in various girl friends whom she suspected of being homosexual, was jealous that R. ("the most mannish" of her sisters) was living with her mother and stated wishfully that the latter was "disappointed because I can't get a [sic] raise and take care of her myself." However, a beginning resolution of both her homosexual and heterosexual oral conflicts, arising from a

---

* These preoccupations with her bodily form at times approached the intensity of a "dominant idea" (Benedek) that not only must she abjure adult feminine activities but she also must not look like a woman. While this idea was never stated explicitly, the analytic material indicated that syntonic obsessions of this nature may have contributed to the overdetermination of her vomiting and diarrhea, inasmuch as these symptoms tended to keep her thin, sallow and heterosexually unattractive and thereby protected her from situations in which her oral aggression and reactive fear of men would be mobilized.

partially relenting maternal identification, appeared in the 168th hour in the following dream:

"Mother offered me a sausage, and I again spit it out saying, 'I don't eat pork!' Then my mother said I could have men if I liked."*

Associations: (Sausage) penis. (Have men) you buying me a meal.

After this initial working through of guilt over phallic incorporative fantasies, the patient could for the first time pleasurably visualize the analyst buying her food; moreover, in the next hour the defenses were sufficiently penetrated to permit the patient to have the sudden fantasy of *eating the analyst's penis*—a desire which, of course, had not been interpreted in specific terms previously. Similarly, feelings of nausea in subsequent hours were often associated with explicit ideas of having eaten and then vomited the analyst's or some other man's penis. In this connection the patient also mobilized material relative to her rejection of femininity and the fantasied identification with men in order to displace the father in the mother's favor. For instance, the patient remembered that whereas she had had no compunctions about entering the bathroom while her father was naked (as though she also were a man), she "had always been ashamed" to expose her breasts or pubic region to her mother "because I always felt there was something wrong with my shape"; likewise, menstruation always made her feel "hurt" or deficient (castrated) in some way. Similar material led to the formulation of the patient's castration anxiety on the basis of a feared retaliation for the aggressive oral incorporation of the father's penis —an act which must therefore be partially expiated in compulsive vomiting. For instance, the patient felt *very nauseated* and almost vomited on reading that Ethiopian slave boys were castrated and that *savages ate testicles to become more masculine.* An even more direct reference to the oral method of incorporating the phallus was revealed in a dream to the effect that her cousin's penis was filled with peas (as though it were edible) and that then her own vagina began growing them—to which she associated the memory that once, after eating pea soup prepared by her father, she had become nauseated and had vomited severely. At this point the patient was finally able to formulate an explicit and basic fantasy previously deeply hidden:

"Any man is really more like food . . . I feel like a cannibal when I eat with one . . . I get nauseated and vomit . . . The same thing happens when I see babies feeding at the breast . . . I never could stand that sight; I can't even yet."

From this and similar material the patient then formulated another previously inexpressible fantasy arising from fear of retaliation for her oral aggressions toward men: if she permitted herself to be "feminine" and had sexual relations with a man, *somehow she would be physically hurt by him.* She then elaborated this apprehension by assertions that her mother "had suffered and lost her health [sic] through sexual intercourse"; by specific phobias of menstrual blood, dentists, operations, etc., by an anxious play on the analyst's name as meaning "knife-man" and by a peculiarly displaced obsession that "If I parted my hair in the middle, i.e., (exposed my vagina for intercourse) I would become bald (castrated)!" During this period the patient also felt compelled to urinate forcefully both before and after each hour, as though this characteristically aggressive and boyish activity had a definitely reassuring

---

* Material relevant to this dream indicated that at a deeper level the patient also desired to castrate her thwarting, aggressive, phallic mother, and, in reaction, dreamed of the latter's forgiveness and indulgence.

value for her.* Moreover, for the first time she could remember what she had really been acutely aware of throughout early childhood, namely, that both her parents had been greatly disappointed that the patient, their last child, had not been born a boy. Her conciliatory longing for her father and her jealous oral castrative reactions toward him were then simultaneously expressed in a duplex dream:

> 1. "A man had a dog I wanted to pet."
> 2. "I had a little dog that I cherished, and I protected him from a bigger dog. A Negro couple were going to bed and I felt alone. A man came along and I avoided him. But my mother and sister petted the bigger dog and I was mad."
> *Associations:* (Dog) Penis. (Pet the dog) I would like to own a big dog. (Big dog) It threatened my dog. (Negro couple) My father and mother have crinkly hair (depreciated parents). (Mother and sister played with bigger dog) I felt jealous and wanted to chase him away but I was afraid.

In response to the appropriate interpretations of such dreams and their related material, the patient then produced a wealth of deeper fantasies relative to her wish to acquire the penis by oral incorporation. For instance, an anxious dream about herself as "a little boy becoming a little girl" (refeminized by the analysis) was followed by a reassuring one in which the patient concealed her genitals in a public bath, and was then *willingly fed by a man with* "almonds" (association: "nuts, testicles") "*and chocolate*" ("penis—feces—bad taste in my mouth like before I vomit"). Likewise, her desire to use the orally acquired penis to seduce her idealized mother away from the father was epitomized in a dream of limpid cogency:

> "Ginger Rogers and Tyrone Power were making love, and I was in the way. There was some danger, but I went to a room in my mother's house and got some chocolate and nuts (rebirth as a male). I gave these to Ginger Rogers, and she was pleased. She paid no more attention to Tyrone Power and he disappeared."

To this dream the patient again associated that when she had slept in her parents' bed she had felt particularly displaced and jealous *when her father fondled her mother's breasts* (oral jealousy). Chocolate was again associated to penis and feces (depreciated phallus) and "nuts" frankly represented testicles. Moreover, not long thereafter the partial renunciation of this same desire to incorporate a phallus even to please her mother was indicated in the third and final dream of the "frankfurter" series:

> "My mother once again gave me a cut-up frankfurter that looked good to eat, but this time my father was there and I gave it to him because I felt it belonged to him."

Concurrently, the anal components of her aggressive and incorporative fantasies about her father also appeared more openly: for instance, the patient played with the phrase "eliminating father" and reported that whereas she now no longer vomited, thoughts of sexual intercourse still occasionally induced diarrhea. To this she associated a childhood concept that intercourse was performed per rectum, in connection with persistent fantasies that her feces at the same time eliminated and substituted for an anally incorporated penis—an organ which, in specific relation to her father's phallus, was always conceived as "dirty" and "soiling." Strong feelings of disgust with all mucous and "slimy" things were also specifically associated with a revulsion to obsessive thoughts

---

* Cf. M. Gerard, F. Alexander and C. Van der Heide on the symbolism of urination as a penis fantasy in girls.

of fellatio and with a fantasy the patient had had of swallowing semen during possible oral contacts with the father's penis while she was sleeping in the parental bed.

With the defensively "undoing" and restorative aspects of the patient's vomiting and diarrhea thus disclosed, the analysis could then also attack the overdeterminations and positive cathexes of her various neurotic behavior patterns. These were, in brief, the symbolic significance of the vomiting and diarrhea as disguised expression of oral and anal aggressions and as reactions to coprophilic impulses, the pseudo-masochistic gratification and various secondary gains (sympathy, indulgence, protection, etc.) the patient derived from her illness, and, finally, its unconscious use in frustrating the analyst while the patient acted out fantasies of infantile narcissistic omnipotence in the tolerant and receptive analytic situation. Eventually, the following clinical improvements became well established: the patient of her own volition moved away from her family and began successfully to pursue extrafamilial friendships and musical, social and recreational interests. The vomiting ceased, the diarrhea became infrequent and mild, and the other minor symptoms disappeared. The patient found little or no difficulty in associating with men, sought and experienced satisfactory sexual relationships, and began cultivating suitors with a view to eventual marriage and the establishment of a home. A follow-up interview four years after the termination of her analysis revealed that she had not yet attained the latter two objectives, but that in all other respects she considered herself relatively happy and well.

DYNAMIC FORMULATION. In fairness to any attempt to formulate analytic material it may be conceded at the outset that no simple running account of the emotional development and vicissitudes of any individual can give really adequate consideration to the multiplex interplay and changing vector balance of the relatively simple dynamisms operative even in early childhood, let alone their multitudinous and conflictful elaboration in later life. (Chapters 3 to 6.) In the present case, nevertheless, the analysis seemed to justify a fairly specific reconstruction of the nature and development of at least the main conative trends and their counterposed defenses, not only because these appeared with relative clarity in the analytic material, but also because the patient was permitted by circumstances to "act out" many of her childhood neurotic patterns in her daily life until the time of her analysis. The dynamic origins of her outstanding personality deviations and neurotic symptoms may therefore be reconstructed as follows.

The patient's primary "oral" attachment to her mother, represented in the infantile formula "to be loved is to be fed" and by the *Ursymbol* of sole possession of the maternal breast, was early intensified and fixated as her main libidinal drive by a number of intercurrent factors: her puny, delicate physique, her indulgences by her mother as the youngest child, her jealous rivalry with her elder sisters, the early departure of her father from the family, and the subsequent insecurity and poverty of her childhood. This passive overdependence on the mother, however, was threatened when she learned that the providing member of her immediate circle was really a paternal uncle who fed and clothed the entire family. Obviously, this posed what may be termed the patient's first major problem: how to divide her allegiance between this intrusive male and her mother without incurring the latter's jealousy and prejudicing her primary desire for the unassailable security of the suckling. The child's problem was further aggravated by the fact that the uncle obviously resented her presence in the mother's home. To the first three years of the patient's life, then, belong the pregenital screen memories of running to her mother with feelings of guilt when men tempted her *by offering her food* and the fantasy of summoning "a nurse carrying buns" (symbolically breasts) in preference to a "doctor who might hurt her." To the latter part of this period, moreover, may belong the patient's earliest wishes actually to acquire a penis and thus, by becoming the little boy her mother expressly desired, to secure for herself the latter's exclusive support and protection. However, these early conflicts gave rise to relatively little anxiety, inasmuch as the patient appears to have left Europe at the age of five in a fairly secure oral receptive relationship with her mother. Unfortunately, when the family rejoined the father in America her position was more gravely threatened, which led to a series of emotional reactions and counter-cathexes that determined the patient's subsequent character neurosis and furnished the basic dynamisms of her "psychosomatic dysfunctions" and personality patterns. Thus, the patient's continuous desire for oral dependence on her mother, coupled with her need to remain physically close to the latter even in the parental bed, made the patient for a number of years an actual witness of the primal scene, the most harrowing and "disgusting" detail of which she characteristically remembers as her father's fondling of the mother's breasts. On the other hand, the patient's misunderstood persistence as an obtrusive third party in the marital relationship apparently also aroused the mother's suspicion and jealousy, with the result that the latter reacted not only by showing preference for the patient's eldest sister (the most "masculine" of the daughters) but also by punishing the patient in a number of highly traumatic ways—including a reiteration of her disappointment that the patient had not been born a boy. In this manner, the mother in turn became for a time no longer a protective and all-providing figure, but an unreliable, rejecting, fickle person who, until she was won back, would not provide complete security. Concurrently, the patient's anxieties were accentuated by the emerging genital components of her Oedipal impulses which, strengthened but at the same time rendered extremely guilt-charged by her nightly physical contacts with the father in the presence of the mother, themselves increased her guilt and fear and therefore pressed for adequate adaptations. The urgent problem faced by the patient at this juncture was, then: how to resolve this now complex and highly conflictful emotional situation and escape the dangers that seemed to threaten on every side?

The patient's initial attempt at solving her dilemma seems to have been simply to shunt the energy of her genital desires back to the *oral* sphere, transfer her dependent attachment from the temporarily unreliable mother to her kindlier father, and substitute in her typically passive receptive fashion the desire to feed from him (possibly, in an early fantasy of anatomical displacement, from his dischaging penis) in lieu of the withdrawn maternal breast that had now been preempted by the father. In accordance with the lag in her libidinal development and the persistence of strong oral urges, this relationship at first constituted what might, in psychoanalytic language, be termed an "oral Oedipus"—namely, the emergence for a period of predominantly oral receptive desires directed to the father with concomitant fear of retribution by the mother. At the same time the mother was wishfully conceived to be jealous of the loss of the patient's dependent devotion, as indicated by the patient's self-reassuring statements of her mother's pleasure when the patient resisted other oral temptation. Nevertheless, the positive genital Oedipus fantasies, continually stimulated by physical heterosexual contacts, could not long remain completely repressed, so that she began to wish more or less consciously to be not only the paternal suckling, but also to displace her mother as the father's mistress. This genital Oedipal phase was then related to the transient fantasies, predominantly prepubertal, of displacing the mother in the father's bed.

This, however, was likewise an untenable situation, since the patient, still passive and insecure, and now conceiving herself helplessly adrift from her accustomed receptive relationship to her mother, found no really safe refuge in the father, whom she soon perceived to be vacillating, powerless, and as subservient to the mother as she herself was. There remained then only one alternative for the patient's weak, uncertain ego: a repression of the hostile part of her ambivalence and a final strategic retreat to an oral passive relationship to the only strong personality in the family, the mother, who must therefore again be won at all costs. But now certain modifications even in this libidinal relationship were necessary, inasmuch as the patient's oral desires, in response to repeated frustration, had changed vectorially from a merely passive receptivity to an actively attacking incorporation, as expressed in the unconscious fantasy that *if her mother no longer willingly gives her the breast or the father his phallus, she must aggressively take them for herself.* Moreover, the second portion of this fantasy—the symbolic desire for her father's penis—was now overdetermined by her wish to displace the father in an exclusive homosexual relationship with her mother—a relationship designed to supplement and strengthen the primary oral dependent one. It was in this manner, then, that her main conflicts assumed their final form, since primitive cannibalistic fantasies such as the oral incorporation of breast and penis were so charged with guilt that not only repression but nearly every other defense from denial to sublimation needed to be summoned to assure the indirect discharge of their cathected energy. She therefore began to be governed both alloplastically and autoplastically by a number of interrelated dynamic syllogisms which, as stated, were reflected not only in her symptoms but also in her distinctive character traits and reality maladjustments up to the time of her analysis. Some of these syllogisms, for the sake of simplicity of presentation, may be formulated separately as follows:

I. REGRESSION. Since all levels of libidinal satisfaction above that of primal oral attachment to the mother appeared to be beset by dangers and anxieties, the patient renounced nearly all her ambitiously aggressive and genital strivings and devoted her life to resuming and making secure the only comparatively safe relationship she had ever known—a passive, infantile dependence on the mother.

a. *Genital Renunciation.* The patient surrendered her transient Oedipal wish to preempt the father from the mother. In fact, she foreswore all outward semblance of genital or other possessive desires for all men and indulged in such relationships only if and when they were permitted or demanded by the mother. At all other times, the patient by an unconscious compulsion made herself in both appearance and behavior actually unattractive to men.

b. *Pregenital Patterns.* 1. Anal-Sadistic Depreciation and Aggression. The patient obsessively conceived of all genitality as obscene (forbidden) or dirty (aggressive and depreciated). In this sense she regarded everything her father touched as contaminated, as shown in many compulsions and fantasies, particularly in relation to his discharging penis. In the same manner she conceived of sexual intercourse as a frightening anal attack, and equated the phallus with a column of feces which she could then not only herself possess, but also eliminate aggressively by diarrhea whenever threatened with the passive role in heterosexuality. Beneath these concepts, however, was an important element of quasi-"masochistic" gratification in her vomiting and other symptoms and in the few traumatic genital contacts that, with the mother's express consent, she had permitted herself.

2. Defense of Secondary Narcissism. In deference to the mother's expressed desires, the patient made a pretense of apparent emancipation

from her, but only in ways that served really to cement their relationships. For instance, she studied music and played it showily as the mother desired, yet never sufficiently well to become proficient or financially independent. Similarly, she held a job and made just sufficient money to help support the mother—but never enough to justify living apart from her.

II. "PENIS WISH." Still other defenses against anxiety were necessary, since the mother once undeniably had discarded the patient in favor of the father's phallus and thus had severely traumatized the patient's narcissism. To emasculate and displace the father and at the same time regain the mother she therefore erected and cherished a fantasy that she also had a penis, acquired by oral incorporation from the father; however, to preserve this fantasy that she had masculine attributes, she *had to conceal her femininity.* She therefore professed pride in the smallness of her breasts and the "boyish figure" she hoped her mother admired, yet she always avoided letting the latter see her naked and penis-less. She played tomboy until her menarche (which was delayed until sixteen), and even in her adolescence walked into her father's bath as though on equal terms with him. Later, she raged against menstruation and feared dentists, operations, and all other castrative threats, however indirect their connotation.

III. "PSYCHOSOMATIC" DYSFUNCTIONS. Finally, by an appearance of self-punishment and specific restitutions she could allay the obsessive guilt over desires that had led to the fantasy of the oral (or anal) incorporation of the penis.

a. *Talion Fear.* Because she hated the father for displacing her with the mother and thus thwarting her both orally and genitally, and because she therefore wished to castrate him, she became fearful of physical retribution in kind by all men and manifested this fear by chills, palpitation, and various neuromuscular disturbances in their presence.

b. *Fantasy of Oral Rejection and Restitution.* More specifically in relation to the main determinant of the vomiting, if she dared actually to take food in the presence of a man and thus repeated the symbolic act of oral castration of the father, she immediately experienced disgust and eliminated the phallus (more deeply, the breast—cf. nausea at the sight of infants feeding) by vomiting and diarrhea. This she did not only to deny deep cannibalistic desires but also *to restore* what once in fantasy she had actually wished to incorporate.

Such, then, were the main vortices of libidinal conflict in the patient's character and organ neuroses. Unfortunately, the defects of such analytic formulations are readily apparent: they are necessarily abbreviated and oversimplified; they assume a specificity of libidinal expressions and defenses not completely substantiated by the sketchy account of the analysis; they artificially telescope into "crucial" episodes of the patient's life various actions and reactions that were probably worked through over long periods, and, finally, they represent under separate rubrics various economically indissoluble dynamisms that really bore to each other an ever varying relationship in determining the patient's internal and external adjustments. Only two considerations extenuate these difficulties: first, that the "logic of the unconscious" (Alexander) and the "language of the body" (Dunbar) are in reality relatively direct and elemental; second, that even in the description of complex intra-psychic reactions the limitations of language unfortunately demand that only one topic be dealt with at any one time. It is hoped, nevertheless, that despite these limitations this case analysis has indicated the nature and derivations of the patient's unconscious, complex, but pervasive conflicts and their influence on her personality development, clinical symptomatology and therapeutic course.

Discussion

"Psychosomatic" diagnosis. From the medical standpoint, the question naturally arises: was the "diagnosis" of anorexia nervosa "correctly" made in this patient? The answer obviously depends on how rigidly delimited this syndrome is considered to be.* At the time of her admission to the medical clinic five years before analysis the severe anorexia, marked weight loss, cachexia with characteristically unimpaired energy and activity, intractable vomiting after food intake and absence of any positive indication of organic disease were almost pathognomonic of the syndrome of "anorexia nervosa" as originally described by Gull, although it must be remembered that other less determinative criteria, such as loss of hair and amenorrhea, were not present. However, with particular respect to the menstrual function, it could easily be conceived that had the patient's rejection of this aspect of femininity and her castration fears been even greater than they were at the time, her menstruation, instead of becoming merely scanty and painful, might have been suppressed as completely as it had been previous to the age of sixteen; had this happened, the temptation on the part of a medical observer to diagnose her case on a purely "endocrine" basis might have become overwhelming. Conversely, her symptomatic improvement after her previous hospitalization at the medical clinic, and her nearly complete recovery after psychoanalytic treatment, do not prove the absence of "psychosomatic" endocrine involvement, since the unconsciously reassuring psychotherapy she received from her medical physicians and her mother at the time of her former treatment, combined with the special environmental arrangements made for her (removal from the home, expressly permitted heterosexual outlets, etc.), temporarily relieved some of her pressing anxieties and internal physiologic tensions and so aided in restoring a possibly disturbed endocrine balance. Nevertheless, it should be made clear that the psychoanalytic findings in this patient are not necessarily applicable to every case of "anorexia nervosa," since the term has a broad medical rather than a specific psychosomatic connotation.

Psychoanalytic and psychosomatic formulations. As early as 1892, Freud, in a paper with Breuer, mentioned "chronic vomiting and anorexia carried to the point of refusal of food" as being of psychic origin, and stated that "a painful affect, which originally excited while eating but was suppressed, produces nausea and vomiting, and this con-

* The general nonspecificity of medical-psychiatric "diagnoses" has already been considered (Chapter 1) and is discussed in detail in Parts 1 and 2 of the *Practice*.

tinues for months as hysterical vomiting . . . which accompanies a feeling of moral disgust." Freud, in his *Interpretation of Dreams* (1900), also speaks of a patient who had chronic vomiting both in fulfillment of, and self-punishment for, a fantasy of being continually pregnant by many men. The possible roots of oral conflicts are then further traced in Freud's *Three Contributions to the Theory of Sexuality* (1905), as follows:

"One of the first . . . pregenital sexual organization is the oral, or, if one will, the cannibalistic. Here the sexual activity is not yet separated from the taking of nourishment* and the contrasts within it are not yet differentiated. The object of the one activity is also that of the other; the sexual aim then consists in the incorporation of the object into one's own body, the prototype of identification, which later plays such an important psychic role."

In 1911, Ernest Jones developed another thesis with regard to neurotic vomiting, namely, that the symptom expressed a rejection of an incorporated penis, conceived as an incestuous pregnancy. In effect, Jones agreed with Melanie Klein that little girls "enjoy taking the penis into the body . . . to make a child from it." Similarly, Ferenczi attributed the vomiting of hyperemesis gravidarum to an attempt on the part of the patient simultaneously "to deny the genital localization" of the pregnancy and to give up "the phantasied 'stomach-child.'" Ferenczi also recognized that vomiting may be a reaction to coprophagic fantasies, as expressed in the case cited by the expulsive oral rejection of the dirty, distasteful penis.† While similar associations in the patient might have

---

* In this connection, Starke speaks of the withdrawal of the mother's breast as the "primal castration."

† In such fantasies the equation mother=penis is often also depreciatingly and aggressively expanded to penis=feces (Abraham), so that primary oral incorporative fantasies are reacted to with nausea, disgust and vomiting.

The primitive "psychosomatic" reaction of removing dangerous incorporated substances through diarrhea and vomiting has been called by Rado the "riddance principle" and is described by him as follows: "Control of pain is directed toward eliminating the source of suffering, if necessary even by the sacrifice of a part of one's own body. Such conduct reveals a principle ingrained in the organization of all animals, including man. In the phylogenetic scale of increasing differentiation and complexity of organization there gradually become apparent many reflexes designed to eliminate pain-causing agents from the surface or inside the body. The scratch reflex, the shedding of tears, sneezing, coughing, spitting, vomiting, colonic bowel movement are but a few well-known instances of this principle of pain control in our bodily organization. This principle I have called the 'riddance principle' and its physiological embodiments the 'riddance reflexes.'"

Following the experimental demonstration by Cannon of the intimate interrelationships of emotional states and gastric motility, it has also been shown clinically that gastric peristalsis increases during hunger (Cannon and Washburn) and either ceases or is reversed during strong emotions and especially in disgust (Schindler). However, as Alexander states in his *Medical Value of Psychoanalysis*: "Even psychogenic vomiting itself may not always express anything psychological, for example, disgust, although conditions in the stomach which led to vomiting may have been called forth by psychological factors." For a brief review of the psychosomatic aspects of vomiting, cf. "Emotions and Bodily Changes," Dunbar, pp. 311–315.

been traced to deeply repressed fantasies of impregnation by the father's incorporated phallus, it must be stated that further material explicitly relevant to this complex did not appear in the analysis.

Abraham, in his study of *The Development of the Libido* (cf. Appendix 4), dealt with the unconscious desires of the melancholic patient for the oral incorporation of the lost and ambivalently loved object and stated that the refusal of food in depressive states could be traced to the corresponding cannibalistic guilt. That this fantasy was operative in the patient here described was indicated by her prolonged refusal of food and frequent vomiting during the several months of depression after the death of her father. It is significant, however, that mere anorexia was apparently insufficient to expiate the guilt attached to her previous incorporative fantasies towards the lost father, so that vomiting as a symbolic restitution was also economically necessary.

More directly germane to the psychoanalytic aspects of the present study is a series of papers published in 1934 on *The Influence of Psychologic Factors upon Gastro-Intestinal Disturbances* by several members of the Chicago Psychoanalytic Institute. In his introductory section to this symposium, Alexander pointed out that in patients with gastric neuroses characteristic attitudes of "parasitic receptiveness" are thwarted by internal or external circumstances and therefore become colored by oral aggressivity and strong narcissistic protests over feelings of inferiority. As a result, unconsciously weak, orally dependent patients adopt a defensive facade of great personal self-sufficiency, an exaggerated attitude of helpfulness toward others and a superficial optimism that they in turn will always be provided for—traits characteristic of the patient, whose analysis was presented above. In the same symposium, Catherine Bacon described a woman with a gastric neurosis who was a frequent witness of the primal scene in her childhood, had intense rivalry with a sister, marked ambivalence to her thwarting mother and strong early heterosexual inhibitions. Bacon's analysand resembled the present patient in other ways: she associated genital sexuality with eating and "when her oral desires were thwarted by external frustration, she went into a rage the content of which was a desire to attack the penis of the thwarting object and incorporate it."

A corresponding case of a forty-one-year-old woman who suffered from a recurrent duodenal ulcer was reported by George Wilson,[*] who found that his patient had a "retaliation fear because of the castration wish. . . . The oral dependent attitude toward the mother was transferred to a wish to incorporate the penis orally . . . due not only to resentment and fear but also to the wish to own something, the possession of which pleased the mother. . . . She wanted to possess a penis with which she can please the mother as the father does and in consequence continue to

---

[*] That corresponding unconscious mechanisms (compulsive disgorgements and restitution of gastric contents) are operative in male patients with gastric neuroses is indicated by the analyses of patients reported by Harry Levey and by Maurice Levine. In Levine's patient the relationship of vomiting and diarrhea to the neurotic character structure is especially well indicated.

receive from her."* One other comparison is noteworthy: in both patients, pregenital conflicts were manifested mainly in gastrointestinal dysfunctions, whereas genital ones were expressed symbolically in the neuro-muscular system. To illustrate: Wilson's patient, while working through the reawakened guilt over incestuous relations with her brother, suffered from various muscular pains and disturbances of locomotion; whereas the patient described in this Appendix reacted to heterosexual fantasies with characteristic paresthesias (vaginal itching; pilomotor "chills," etc.) and sensations of generalized muscular tremors.

The various psychogenic roots of the patient's diarrhea have not been treated as fully in this discussion as have those of the dysgeusia, nausea and vomiting, but the subject of colonic dysfunction has received extensive theoretical consideration in the psychoanalytic literature, particularly by Abraham, Jones and by the members of the Chicago Institute. More specifically from a clinical standpoint, Alexander cites the case of a female patient in whom "the diarrhea, apart from the meaning of restitution, had also the narcissistic significance of masculine activity and expressed the masculine strivings of the patient." Similarly, Wilson found that in women with colitic diarrhea the symptoms signified a rejection of femininity, in that the female role was conceived to be either parasitically oral-receptive or else too aggressively castrative in significance. Freud (1910) postulates that on a deeper level the diarrhea may also represent the anal elimination of an incestuous pregnancy. However, in the present patient the diarrhea which developed in reaction to fantasied or actual threats of heterosexuality had the significance not only of a conciliatory gift to the mother and a guilty elimination or restitution of the penis *per anum* as well as *per os,* but at other times also represented a jealous and sadistic attack on the analyst or other parent imago for fantasied thwarting in the oral or genital spheres. A corresponding explanation for the patient's urinary urgency as symbolic of masculine aggressivity may be found in Freud's *Interpretation of Dreams* (p. 512). From an economic standpoint, therefore, the patient's various symptoms— vomiting, diarrhea and urinary urgency—served as channels for an autoplastic discharge through the eliminative functions of various guilt-ridden aggressive or erotic impulses which the patient, because of covert fear, was inhibited from expressing in alloplastic social behavior.

Summary

The analysis of a patient with character difficulties, neurotic vomiting and diarrhea and the syndrome of anorexia nervosa is outlined. The organic dysfunctions are shown to be somatic manifestations of a highly complex personality disorder arising from severe early emotional con-

---

* Felix Deutsch attributes the rejection of food in two cases of "anorexia nervosa" that he analyzed to early concern on the part of the mother as to the patient's food intake and "stabilization of phantasies around the gastrointestinal tract" after "maternal rejection." While, as Deutsch contends, this would lead to the "choice" of the gastrointestinal tract to express the patient's neurosis, the psychodynamism described does not seem sufficiently clear to be regarded as *pathognomonic* of anorexia nervosa.

flicts, especially in the oral sphere. The most important specific psycho-dynamism of the vomiting appears to be a symbolic rejection and restitution of the father's phallus, orally incorporated in an attempt to render exclusive her basic passive dependence on the mother; however, the symptom also expresses an aggressive attack on the thwarting parents, masochistic expiation and other psychic overdeterminants. These and other psychosomatic reactions are related to the present psychoanalytic concepts of various gastrointestinal neuroses.

References

Abraham, K.: Contributions to the Theory of Anal Character. In: Selected Papers. London. Hogarth Press. 1927, p. 299.

———: The Influence of Oral Erotism on Character Formation. Ibid., p. 393.

———: A Short Study of the Development of the Libido. Ibid., p. 418.

Alexander, F.: The Medical Value of Psychoanalysis. New York. W. W. Norton & Co. 1936, p. 197.

———: Gastro-Intestinal Neuroses. In Portis, S.: Diseases of the Digestive System. Philadelphia. Lea & Febiger. 1941.

Breuer, J., and Freud, S.: On the Psychical Mechanism of Hysterical Phenomena. Coll. Papers, I, p. 25.

Cannon, W. B.: The influence of emotional states on the functions of the alimentary canal. Am. J. M. Sc., 137:480, 1909.

——— and Washburn: Alimentary peristalsis. Am. J. Physiol., 9:114, 1902.

Deutsch, F.: Choice of organ in organ neurosis. Int. J. Psychoanalysis, 20:252, 1939.

Dunbar, H. F.: Emotions and Bodily Changes. 4th Ed. New York. Columbia University Press, 1954.

Freud, S.: Interpretations of Dreams. In: the Basic Writings of Sigmund Freud. New York. The Modern Library, 1938, p. 512.

———: Three Contributions to the Theory of Sexuality. New York. Nervous and Mental Disease Publishing Co., 1910.

Gull, W. W.: Anorexia nervosa. Lancet, 2:171, 1868.

Jones, E.: Papers on Psychoanalysis. Baltimore. William Wood and Co. 1938.

Klein, Melanie: The Psychoanalysis of Children. London. Hogarth Press. 1932, pp. 269 ff.

Rado, S.: Developments in the psychoanalytic conception and treatment of the neuroses. Psychoanal. Quart., 8:427, 1938.

Wilson, G.: The transition from organ neurosis to conversion hysteria. Int. J. Psychoanalysis, 19:1, 1938.

Psychoanalytic
formulations of the psychoses

With critical references to mania and melancholia

A discussion of the modern psychoanalytic concepts of the development of the libido and its relationship to the psychoses may perhaps best begin with a survey of the earlier contributions to the field. Leaving aside the prophetic flashes that a careful exegesis of Freud's earlier writings would reveal, we may therefore start our review with Abraham's earliest articles on manic-depressive psychosis in 1911, Freud's analysis of Mourning and Melancholia in 1916, Abraham's reformulation of the fundamental issues in 1924, and the subsequent contributions by Rado, Helene Deutsch, Fenichel, and others.

Psychoanalytic formulations

Karl Abraham, in his first article on the subject in 1911, attempts to fit specific "intrapsychic mechanisms" to a rigid Kraepelinian nosology and accepts almost without reservation the necessarily cyclical nature of "manic-depressive psychosis." He categorically differentiates the psychodynamics of this disorder from the more rapid oscillations of "ambivalence" in the obsessive-compulsive neuroses, and states that the rapport of the manic-depressive patient is "like that of a five-year-old," presumably regressed to the oral incorporative stage. And yet, Abraham attempts to apply to manic-depressive reactions a number of the more fundamental psychodynamic concepts that had been advanced by Freud during the preceding ten years. Paraphrasing the Schreber case (Freud, *Collected Papers*), Abraham states that the depressed patient feels universally hated because he himself feels incapable of loving anyone, but that in this very self abasement the melancholic obtains not only "masochistic gratification" but also an indirect sadistic revenge on those who must care for him. In contrast to the melancholic, the manic is happy because "Ego inhibitions" are suspended, "Id gratifications" are immediate, rapport with the environment is complete and there is thereby, "as in normal wit," a great saving of intrapsychic tensions, rendering the freed energy available for external activity. An anticipation of a more quantitative and economic theory of psychic functions is also implicit in Abraham's statement that in melancholia so much libido is "narcissistically bound by the Ego" that very little is available for external object-cathexes; in this sense, the patient's delusions of loss of external possessions have a very real psychodynamic basis. Finally, Abraham expresses his belief that the identification with the lost love object occurs through a phantasy of actual oral incorporation, the guilt of which is then symbolically atoned for by a refusal of food, compulsive self-starvation, and other psychosomatic disturbances characteristic of melancholia.

Freud in his "Mourning and Melancholia," published six years later, points out that in both states there is the same psychic pain (and Freud uses the specific term *Schmerz* rather than the neutral *Unlust*) and the same temporary inability to acquire a new love object arising from a parallel libidinous withdrawal in both conditions. Freud contends, however, that in mourning, the transference of the libido to the love object is less narcissistic and ambivalent, so that when the libidinous investment is released at the loss of the object and is then "reincorporated into the Ego," the work of mourning need consist only in dispelling predominantly pleasant memories "until the Ego is once again free." In contrast, the Ego of the melancholic is intensely ambivalent to the reincorporated love object, the choice of which, according to Rank, had in the first place been highly narcissistic. As a consequence, whereas the return of so large an investment of secondary libido to the melancholic is manifest in feelings of increased self-importance even in abasement (cf. Chapter 5), the Ego "must now also turn upon itself the hatreds and aggressions previously unconsciously felt for the lost object," and must therefore go through a period of self-castigation and suffering. In fact, if this secondary self-hatred is sufficiently great, suicidal impulses appear and self-destructive acts become possible. The immediate conditions for the development of melancholia, then, are (1) a strongly narcissistic object cathexis, (2) ambivalent feelings toward this object, and (3) the loss of the object, leading to (4) its symbolic reincorporation. Throughout this discussion Freud significantly places great emphasis not only on the nature of the "psychic forces" brought into play but also upon their quantities, directions and economic balance. On the other hand, he makes characteristic allowances for physiological and toxic factors, in statements such as:

[It is questionable] "whether an impoverishment of ego-libido directly due to toxins would not result in certain forms of melancholia"

and again

"In melancholia . . . the relationship to the object is (one of) ambivalence. This later is either *constitutional*, i.e., it is an element of every love-relationship of the particular Ego, or else it proceeds from . . . a threat of losing the object."

Abraham's final contribution (in 1924) to the subject of melancholia may now be summarized as follows: In Part I, he contends that melancholia and obsessive-compulsive neurosis are indeed closely related in their phasic character, in the depth of ambivalence present in each, and in their common roots in the "anal state of libidinal organization." They differ fundamentally, however, in that the melancholic breaks off external object-relations and regresses to the "expulsive phase" of anality, whereas the obsessive-compulsive retains his external object cathexes and regresses no deeper than the "retentive" anal libidinal phase. The obsessive-compulsive therefore maintains a position safely above the dividing line between these two stages of anality—a dividing line which constitutes the all-important "boundary" between neuroses and psychoses.

In Parts II and III of his paper Abraham elaborates this thesis by stating that despite the tendency to the anal expulsion of love objects, the melancholic "reintrojects" them in order to reverse or at least mitigate the narcissistic trauma at their loss. This introjection takes the form of a scoptophilic phantasy of actual oral reincorporation of the ejected object, which is usually the mother or a mother-substitute. This leads to cannibalistic breast fetishes and apparently to a further regression to the ambivalent or biting stage of oral libidinal organization—a stage fortunately still above the unambivalent, object-less, narcissistic oblivion to which the schizophrenic regresses. The schizophrenic, then, is indifferent to deprivation, whereas the melancholic, since he still has some externalized libido, complains of the loss of his love object. Abraham then sums up his analysis of the stages of libidinal development in the following paragraph:

> "Within the first, the oral period, the child exchanges its preambivalent libidinal attitude, which is free from conflict, for one which is ambivalent and predominantly hostile toward the object. Within the second, the anal-sadistic period, the transition from the earlier to the later stage means that the individual has begun to spare his object from destruction. Finally, within the third, the genital period, he overcomes his ambivalent attitude and his libido attains to its full capacity both from a sexual and a social point of view."

In Part IV of his article Abraham expands Freud's list of the four prerequisites in melancholia into the following five: (1) a "constitutional tendency to oral-erotism," (2) fixation of the libido at the oral aggressive level, (3) successive disappointments in love, causing repeated narcissistic traumata, (4) an especially severe disappointment in the mother before the resolution of the Oedipus complex, and (5) a repetition of this primary disappointment in later life, precipitating a melancholia. In melancholia, then, to use the language of Abraham, the love-object is ano-sadistically expelled like feces, orally reincorporated by a cannibalistic phantasy, sado-masochistically tormented as part of the Ego, and finally, after mutual rapprochement between the incorporated object and the rest of the Ego, once more restored to the world by anal expulsion. Abraham calls this expulsive-incorporative-digestive-expulsive sequence "a process of psychological metabolism" of the object by the melancholic Ego. Moreover, Abraham believes it important to distinguish two forms of introjection of the lost love object: (1) as a parent-figure which reinforces the patient's Superego in castigating the patient's Ego, and (2) as an object incorporated into part of the Ego, but which is then both loved and attacked by another part of the same Ego. We shall later consider the theoretical paradoxes that arise in Abraham's formulations of the dynamisms of melancholia.

Mania. In mania, Abraham holds that after the final reexpulsion of the love object the process of "psychological metabolism" is greatly expedited, so that the manic, in fantasy, "devours everything, but expels it immediately." In manic-depressive states, therefore, there is repeated incorporation and expulsion of the love object, usually the mother, whereas the obsessive neurotic struggles to avoid the "symbolic killing and eating of the father" and the subsequent necessity of melancholic expiation of this primal and inadmissible crime.

In the final sections of his article Abraham makes a few recommendations as to the psychoanalytic treatment of manic-depressive states; namely, that treatment be begun during recovery from a depression, and that attempts be made (a) to do away with the regression, and (b) to reestablish adult genitality, since the attainment of even the phallic phase will at least change the psychosis to a neurosis. Finally, Abraham relates his analysis of the three phases of libidinal fixation with the sequence of ontogenetic and embryologic development of mouth, anus and genitals.

Critique. It is, of course, difficult either to follow or to agree with such early analytic formulations, although one's critical faculties are sometimes numbed by the earnestness and authoritative dogmatism of their exposition. Some errors in logic are self-evident; e.g., in drawing support from ethnic material for the ambivalent "anal-retentive" and "anal-expulsive" symbolism of money in melancholia and its relationship to an earlier "oral ambivalence" toward the mother, Abraham cites the case of a tribe who used sea-shells for purposes of property and exchange. The shells, because of their opposing bright and dirty sides, "clearly represented" the mother, but this symbolism "was so close to being conscious" that the tribe could bear to use shells that came only from long distances. Even granting the possible existence of such unconscious dynamisms and the validity of the recourse to ethnic evidence in the analysis of behavior patterns, one is nevertheless tempted to ask: how in the name of financial as well as emotional economics can a tribe use as money shells that could be gathered in unlimited numbers at the front door of any hut? And do not such single-valued reconstructions minimize the narcissistic, self-adorning significance of money that has made shells, wampum, pretty stones, silver and gold the measures of object-value (i.e., "narcissistic cathexis") since earliest times? Granted, then, that money may have a strong "anal" significance, e.g., through our infantile "pride" in our first product—the stool, yet it may be seen that a conflict involving the significance of money may have its roots in every so-called phase of "libidinal" organization—narcissistic, oral, anal and—by Abraham's own earlier construction—even genital. Ideas of poverty and deprivation in the depressions, therefore, are not proof of the relationship of this psychosis to the specifically "anal" conflicts, since other dynamisms are quite evidently involved.

More cogent from a theoretic standpoint is the difficulty one experiences in following Abraham's derivation of his proposed "phases" of libidinal development in their relationships to specific neurotic or psychotic reactions. When Abraham describes the quasi-compulsive self-abasement and self-punishment of the guilty melancholic, and the euphoric libidinal release of the manic when expiation is done, his syllogisms are at least understandable. But when Abraham leaves the field of the dynamic and economic interplay of adaptive patterns and attempts not only to structuralize his concepts but also to assign them to various so-called "levels of libidinal expression," his exposition becomes either obscure or inconsistent. As one example, Abraham reasons that there must be two anal-sadistic phases—the retentive and the aggressive—and that the dividing line between the two constitutes the all-important distinction between obsessive-compulsive neuroses and depression. Yet later in his exposition Abraham moves the depressions down still another theoretical peg to the third or "oral biting stage" and fills the vacancy in phase number four, the anal expulsive, with the paranoid psychoses. The question naturally arises: would it not really be more illuminating to forego such tenuous dichotomies and tabular niceties, permit the psychodynamic formula "I cannot love—I hate and therefore am hated" to serve as one of the essential emotional syllogisms in both paranoia and melancholia—and then perhaps distinguish between the two on the basis of the type of defensive reaction, such as the relative amount of projection of aggressive impulses, or of identification with the lost object? Similarly, Abraham runs into even greater complications with his somewhat rigidly structuralized concepts of personality organization. The melancholic, he is "forced to conclude," may incorporate the lost love object in three ways: into his Ego, into his Superego, or into both—but whatever its fate, the intrapersonalized love object both loves and condemns one section of the Ego and is at the same time both loved and condemned by it. We are thus left with the picture of an Ego (which, we remember, first built for itself a Superego out of identification with certain aspects of the love object) splitting and then reincorporating that same love object in a newly doubled form. Mercilessly sacrificed, it seems, is the clarity of a dynamic and economic analysis of psychotic reactions for the sake of a "depth-psychology" of involved, paradoxical and unnecessarily mystic abstractions.

Perhaps at this point one might also begin to wish for a more adequate definition of the various terms which Abraham uses to denote the process of "intrapersonalization" of the "lost love object." Early in his exposition, Abraham uses the term "identification," obviously one that could well imply a change in the personality of the subject to conform with a quality of the lost loved one. However, Abraham next adopts Ferenczi's term "introjection" and illustrates this process first, with the case of a woman who called herself "thief" like her dead father; next, with the instance of an analysand who in a dream seemed to represent his dead wife by a symbol of raw meat, and finally with a personal anecdote that after the death of his gray-haired father Abraham's own hair turned gray for several months. It is obvious that the first example as briefly outlined is one of identification rather than necessarily "introjection," that only in the second of these examples is there any reference to a possible "oral" inclusion of the lost object, whereas in the third citation Abraham claims a direct specificity of organ activity (hair turning white) that must be considered highly questionable on physiologic grounds. Moreover, Abraham next cites the case of a young man with "strongly ambivalent" feelings toward his mother, who after her death stated that from then on "I carried mother in me." Yet, despite this phantasy of actual "incorporation"—Abraham's third term—of an object with a highly ambivalent cathexis, this patient did *not* develop melancholia but, instead—again to use Abraham's description "he became blissful!"

Similar considerations apply to Abraham's formulation of mania. In this state, according to Abraham, the Ego turns to the outer world after throwing off the yoke of the Superego—which, as in the melancholic, represents the doubly-introjected parent. In this sense, mania might be considered as a socially difficult but nevertheless comparatively pleasurable and desirable state of personality harmony—a sort of internal celebration at the termination of expiatory stress and suffering. In contradistinction to this concept, in many instances of mania the "Ego" does not turn to "reality" in any holiday spirit of release; instead the patient seems to do so only because he is driven by anxiety into a frantic and futile grasping after every fleeting bit of external distraction. Manics such as these cannot be said to be truly euphoric, but rather present an alloplastic acting-out comparable to the restless hyperactivity sometimes seen in an analytic patient—not when he has actually worked through an emotional problem—but when he is faced with what appears to be an insoluble anxiety. In this connection also, it is interesting to record that often when the superficial productivity of an apparently elated manic is inhibited by the intravenous administration of Sodium Amytal, the mask of euphoria drops, the facies, activity, ideation and speech become frankly depressive, and the self-castigations and nihilistic preoccupations of the melancholic are then easily elicited (cf. Case 20). While, therefore, there undoubtedly are cases of what might be called euphoric mania, one must distinguish from these cases those of defensive or anxiety driven pseudo-mania just outlined.

There remains to be considered briefly only a few contributions subsequent to Freud's and Abraham's formulations. Rado, in "Das Problem der Melancholie" (1927), attempted to solve the question of the introjection of the love object into both the Ego and the Superego by the contention that, whereas the original Superego had been built up by the introjections of the prohibiting aspects of the love object, the depressive, whose narcissism has been starved for love, reincorporates the lost love object not only to condemn it in himself, but also to "woo it" and finally, through suffering and atonement, obtain from it the love he craves. The formula would then be, "I both hate and love you, but since I suffer so, you must only love and not hate me." However, once this sadistic portion of the ambivalence is expiated and the introjected object finally won to the Ego, a manic celebration ensues. Rado, in another paper (on drug addiction, 1926), likened depression to a continuation of the infant's hunger, and mania to a state of satiation.

Helene Deutsch in the final chapter in her book, "The Psychoanalysis of the Neuroses," describes the case of an elderly spinster who developed a severe melancholia. The patient had spent almost a life-time of self-sacrificing and unappreciated devotion to a younger sister, to whom the patient wishfully attributed various high qualities that she herself really possessed. Beneath this over-reactive attachment, however, there lay a strong unconscious ambivalence springing from the fact that the sister had in her infancy displaced the patient in their mother's favor. After many years of selfish acceptance of all the patient had to offer, the sister suddenly married and left the patient with hardly a word of gratitude. The patient at first withstood this defection and even remained loyal to her ungrateful sibling, but when after some time the patient's pet dog also disappeared, she suddenly felt altogether deserted, unloved and helpless. She then entered into an agitated depression characterized by limitless self-reproaches and obsessive apprehensions that she herself would soon be cast out on the street unclothed, there to be deserted and left to perish miserably. Helene Deutsch analyzes these phantasies as being covert expressions of aggressive wishes really directed to the ungrateful sister whom the patient has now incorporated into her suffering Ego. At a deeper level the sister is also the patient's mother-surrogate and in the capacity of a reinforced Superego is also castigating the patient's Ego for her own previous hatreds of the mother. Helene Deutsch thus develops Abraham's formulations, both as to the introjective mechanisms in melancholia, and in the imbalances of the personality structure that result. Curiously, like Abraham, she does not comment explicitly on the evident homosexuality of this heterosexually inhibited, elderly spinster who, despite her manifestly paternalistic overattachment to her sister, had withstood her departure well enough until the final symbolic threat of the loss of her dog. Since Helene Deutsch evidently could not present or discuss the case material in full, it must be surmised that these more nearly genital conflicts were, in her opinion, only overdeterminative and not basic in the patient's psychosis; nevertheless, we may still suspect in this pedagogic type of case presentation a tendency toward an oversimplified traditionalism of formulation in accordance with the orthodox analytic concepts of Abraham.

In his chapter on manic-depressive reactions, Fenichel makes a statement sufficiently trenchant to be used as a text for a discussion of certain fundamental issues in psychoanalytic theory (cf. Chapter 7). To quote: "The Ego of the depressed patient is at odds with its Superego, as the neurotic's Ego is with its Id, and that of the schizophrenic with reality." Fenichel then goes on to develop Rado's concept of the relation of oral hunger to depression, and of mania to the state of satiation after a so-called "alimentary orgasm." Depression and mania thus alternate on the same biological grounds as do their physiological prototypes. Nevertheless, Fenichel contends that normal mourning and both neurotic and psychotic depressions differ not in the nature of the fundamental mechanisms, but only in the quantity of the libido involved.

Finally, in a reflective article entitled "Internalized Objects," Marjory Brierly proposes that our own individual and characteristic uses of the unconscious mechanisms of "introjection" and "projection" lead us either to accept too readily, or to reject too critically, these very same theoretical concepts. (Parenthetically, this is a typical example of circular logic, i.e., Brierly attempts to prove the existence of such mechanisms by saying we fail to recognize them because we unconsciously have them—thereby already assuming their existence.) According to Brierly, people with a character preference for the mechanism of projection "lay stress on the relations of the internal world to external reality and are not content to consider it (the internal world) in isolation." In the healthy, she continues, the "internalized objects" do not lead a recognizably distinct existence, but are integrated into a unitary Ego which does not disintegrate when subjected to only moderate conflict. Nevertheless, this very Ego, according to the concepts of Glover and Melanie Klein, is built up from a primary nucleus by successive accretions of many "internalized" objects. In depression, this Ego-synthesis is reversed and some of these assimilated objects once again come to be regarded as bad and foreign. According to the implications of this concept, then, there are no new introjections of love objects in depression (as contended in the view previously outlined) but simply disintegrations of older fusions of the objects already within the Ego.

Summary

We may, then, conclude this review of the psychoanalytic formulations of "libido-development" in relation to the psychoses* as follows:

1. There is little heuristic value in erecting a specific hierarchy of the neuroses and psychoses as correlated to a multiple-stage account of the development and vicissitudes of the libido. Instead, it can be contended on both theoretic and clinical grounds (a) that the so-called libidinal stages of development have a temporal existence only in so far as the growing infant becomes physiologically capable of expressing them (cf. Chapter 3), and (b) that in later life the "psychological" counterparts of these libidinal organ-cathexes overlap and intermingle in total adaptation.

2. Melancholia itself is not a unitary type of behavior pattern to be differentiated qualitatively from "normal mourning" or the so-called reactive or neurotic depressions. Instead, we must regard the dynamisms of all such reactions as interrelated and distinguishable from the "normal" hypothymias only by the intensity and fixity of the underlying conflicts and compensatory maneuvers.

3. In effect, then, we may permit stereotyped mechanistic formulations of various indefinable psychiatric entities to recede into the background, and interest ourselves instead with a more dynamic analysis of the qualitative nature, the polarity of vector direction and the quantitative balance of the transactional patterns as they appear in our patients from day to day. Each of our patients will then present for our study not a series of oversimplified and transient diagnoses but a richness and

---

* For a more specific discussion of psychoanalytic formulations with regard to other types of psychotic reactions, see: Frieda Fromm-Reichmann, Federn, Sullivan and Zilboorg (schizophrenia); Nunberg (catatonia); Freud (the Schreber case) and Schilder (paranoia); and W. Menninger, and Ferenczi and Holos (paresis). The subject is considered in greater detail in Part Three of the *Practice*.

interplay of intrapersonal dynamisms, with perhaps the characteristic predominance of a few—but never only one—of the almost infinite variety and intensity of all the adaptive normal, "neurotic" or "psychotic" patterns possible in human behavior.

References

Abraham, Karl: In Selected Papers. Woolf, 1930; Manic-Depressive Psychoses. 1911; Melancholia and the Development of the Libido. 1924.

Brierly, M.: Internalized objects. Int. J. Psychoanysis, *11*, July-Oct., 1939.

Deutsch, Helene: The Psychoanalysis of the Neuroses. London. Hogarth Press, 1932.

Fenichel, O.: Outline of Clinical Psychoanalysis. New York. W. W. Norton & Co., 1934.

Ferenczi, S.: Thalassa: a Theory of Genitality. Albany. Psychoanal. Quart Press. 1938.

Ferenczi, S., and Holos, S.: Psychoanalysis and the Psychic Disorder of General Paresis. Washington. Nerv. & Ment. Dis. Monogr. 1925.

Freud, S.: Mourning and Melancholia. Coll. Papers, Vol. 2. New York. International Psychoanalytic Press, 1924.

Menninger, W. C.: Juvenile Paresis. Baltimore. Williams and Wilkins Co., 1936.

Nunberg, H.: Allgemeine Neurosenlehre auf psychoanalytischer Grundlage. Bern. Hans Huber, 1931.

Rado, S.: Das Problem der Melancholie. Int. J. Psychoanalysis, 9:420, 1928.

Schilder, P.: Introduction to a Psychoanalytic Psychiatry. Nerv. & Ment. Dis. Monogr. no. 50, 1928.

Zilboorg, G.: Ambulatory Schizophrenia. Psychiatry, 3:123, 1940.

Bibliography

This bibliography of some fifty score titles will, it is hoped, make it possible for the student to cull an initial reference list for special reading or research in the various branches of biodynamics and ancillary fields of study. Clinical reports have been included only when they are of direct theoretic significance; other references in all branches of psychiatric diagnosis, prognosis and therapy will be found on pp. 713–760 of *The Practice of Dynamic Psychiatry*.

Abraham, K.: Selected Papers. New York. Viking Press. 1927.

Abrahamson, D.: Crime and the Human Mind. New York. Columbia University Press. 1944.

Abramson, H. A., Ed.: Neuropharmacology. New York. Josiah Macy, Jr., Foundation. 1955 & 1957.

Abt, L. E., and Bellak, L., Eds.: Projective Psychology. New York. Alfred A. Knopf. 1950.

Ackerley, S.: Instinctive, emotional and mental changes following prefrontal lobe extirpation. Am. J. Psychiat. 92:717, 1935.

Ackerman, N. W., in Slavson, S. R., Ed.: The Practice of Group Therapy. New York. International Universities Press. 1947.

Adler, A.: A Study of Organ Inferiority. Nervous and Mental Disease Monograph Series, No. 24. New York. 1917.

Adler, A.: The Practice and Theory of Individual Psychology. New York. Harcourt, Brace & Co. 1924.

Adrian, E. D.: The Basis of Sensation. New York. W. W. Norton & Co. 1928.

Adrian, E. D.: Presidential Address to the British Association for the Advancement of Science. Science 120:444, 1954.

Aichhorn, A.: Wayward Youth. New York. Viking Press. 1935.

Aldrich, C. A., and Aldrich, M. A.: Babies Are Human Beings. New York. The Macmillan Co. 1938.

Aldrich, C. K.: Psychiatry for the Family Physician. New York. McGraw-Hill Book Co. 1955.

Alexander, F.: Psychoanalysis of the Total Personality. New York. Nervous and Mental Disease Monograph Series, No. 52, 1930.

Alexander, F.: The Medical Value of Psychoanalysis. New York. W. W. Norton Co. 1936.

Alexander, F.: Addenda to The Medical Value of Psychoanalysis. Psychoanalyt. Quart. 5:548, 1936.

Alexander, F., et al.: Culture and personality: a round table discussion. Am. J. Orthopsychiat. 8:602, 1938.

Alexander, F.: Psychological aspects of medicine. Psychosom. Med. 1:7, 1939.

Alexander, F.: Fundamentals of Psychoanalysis. New York. W. W. Norton & Co. 1948.

Alexander, F.: Psychosomatic Medicine. New York. W. W. Norton & Co. 1950.

Alexander, F.: Psychoanalysis and psychotherapy. J. Am. Psychoanalyt. A. 2:685, 1954.

Alexander, F., Bacon, C., Wilson, G. W., Levy, H. B., and Levine, M.: The influence of psychological factors upon gastro-intestinal disturbances: A symposium. Psychoanalyt. Quart. 3:501, 1934.

Alexander, F., French, T. M., and others: Psychoanalytic Therapy: Principles and Application. New York. The Ronald Press. 1946.

Alexander, F., and Healy, W.: The Roots of Crime. New York. Alfred A. Knopf. 1935.

Alexander, F., and Ross, Helen, Eds.: Dynamic Psychiatry. Chicago. University of Chicago Press. 1952.

Alexander, F., and Staub, H.: The Criminal, the Judge and the Public. New York. The Macmillan Co. 1951.

Alexander, L.: Treatment of Mental Disorder. Philadelphia. W. B. Saunders Co. 1953.

Alexander, L.: Objective Approaches to Treatment in Psychiatry. Springfield, Ill. Charles C Thomas. 1958.

Allee, W. C.: The Social Life of Animals. New York. W. W. Norton & Co. 1938.

Allee, W. C.: Social biology of subhuman groups. Sociometry 8:21, 1945.

Allee, W. C.: Cooperation among Animals. New York. Henry Schuman. 1951.

Allen, F.: Psychotherapy with Children. New York. W. W. Norton & Co. 1942.

Allport, F. H.: Theories of Perception and the Concept of Structure. New York. John Wiley & Sons, Inc. 1955.

Allport, G. W.: Personality: A Psychological Interpretation. New York. Henry Holt & Co. 1937.

Allport, G. W., and Odbert, H. S.: Trait-names: a psycholexical study. Psychol. Monog. 47:1, No. 211, 1936.

Allport, G. W., and Vernon, P. E.: Studies in Expressive Movement. New York. The Macmillan Co. 1932.

Alpers, B. J.: Personality and emotional disorders associated with hypothalamic lesions. Res. Publ. Ass. Nerv. & Ment. Dis. 20:725, 1948; also Psychosom. Med. 2:286, 1940.

Altschule, M. D.: Roots of Modern Psychiatry. New York and London. Grune and Stratton. 1957.

Ambrumova, A. G.: The problem of so-called "familial" schizophrenia. (First Moscow Medical Institute, order of Lenin.) Zh. Nevropat. 57:1101–1105 (Sept.), 1957.

American Psychiatric Association: One Hundred Years of American Psychiatry. New York. Columbia University Press. 1944.

American Psychiatric Association: Psychiatry and Medical Education. Washington, D. C. 1952.

Anastasi, A., and Foley, J.: Survey of the literature on artistic behavior in the abnormal. IV. Experimental investigations. J. Gen. Psychol. 25:187, 1941.

Anderson, D.: Alcohol and public opinion. Quart. J. Stud. Alcohol 3:376, 1943.

Anderson, G. C.: The Founding of the Academy of Religion and Mental Health. Address. Princeton. Oct. 19, 1956.

Anderson, H. H., and Anderson, G. L.: An Introduction to Projective Techniques and Other Devices for Understanding the Dynamics of Human Behavior. New York. Prentice-Hall. 1951.

Anderson, J. E., Ed.: Psychological Aspects of Aging. Washington, D. C. American Psychological Association. 1956.

Anderson, V. V.: Psychiatry in Industry. New York. Harper & Bros. 1934.

Angell, N.: The James-Lange theory. Psychol. Rev. 23:259, 1918.

Angier, R.: The conflict theory of emotion. Am. J. Psychiat. 39:390, 1957.

Angyal, A.: Foundations for a Science of Personality. New York. Commonwealth Fund. 1941.

Anonymous: The Well of Loneliness. New York. Philosophical Library. 1940.

Anshen, Ruth N., Ed.: The Family: Its Function and Destiny. New York. Harper & Bros. 1949.

Appel, K. E.: Psychoanalysis: reflections on varying concepts. Am. J. Psychiat. 112:711, 1956.

Appel, K. E., and Strecker, E. A.: Practical Examination of Personality and Behavior Disorders. New York. The Macmillan Co. 1936.

Arader, H. F.: A system for testing and increasing the intelligibility of technical reports. Science *121*:537, 1955.

Arieti, S.: Interpretation of Schizophrenia. New York. Robert Brunner. 1955.

Arieti, S., Ed.: American Handbook of Psychiatry. New York. Basic Books. 1959.

Aristotle: Basic Works. Richard McKeon, Ed. New York. Random House. 1941.

Ashby, W. R.: Design for a Brain. New York. John Wiley & Sons. 1952.

Ashby, W. R.: An Introduction to Cybernetics. London. Chapman & Hall. 1956.

Association for Research in Nervous and Mental Disease: Psychiatric Treatment. Baltimore. Williams and Wilkins Co. 1953.

Azima, H.: Sleep treatment of mental disorders. Dis. Nerv. System *19*:523, 1958.

Azima, H., Azima, C., and Ferns, S.: Studies on perceptual isolation. Dis. Nerv. System, Monograph Supplement, July, 1957.

Bacon, F.: Advancement of Learning (1605), in Selected Writings. New York. Modern Library. Random House. 1905.

Bailey, H.: The Physiology of Thought. New York. William-Frederick Press, 1949.

Bailey, P.: Intracranial Tumors. 2nd ed. Springfield, Ill. Charles C Thomas. 1948.

Bailey, P.: Janet and Freud. A.M.A. Arch. Neurol. and Psychiat. *76*:76, 1956.

Bailey, P.: The great psychiatric revolution. Am. J. Psychiat. *113*:387, 1956.

Bailey, P.: Modern attitudes toward the relationship of the brain and mind. A.M.A. Arch. Neurol. & Psychiat. *2*:361, 1960.

Bailey, P., and Von Bonin, G.: The Isocortex of Man. University of Illinois Press. 1951.

Baird, J. N.: Memory, imagination, learning and the higher intellectual processes. Psychol. Bull. *9*:321, 1912; *14*:303, 1917.

Baker, H. J.: Introduction to Exceptional Children. New York. The Macmillan Company. 1944.

Balint, A.: Identification. Internat. J. Psycho-Analysis *24*:97, 1943.

Balken, Eva R.: A delineation of schizophrenic language and thought in a test of imagination. J. Psychol. *16*:239, 1943.

Barber, T. X.: "Hypnosis," analgesia and the placebo effect. J.A.M.A. *172*:680, 1960.

Bard, P.: Neural mechanisms in emotional and sexual behavior. Psychosom. Med. *4*:171, 1942.

Barker, R., et al., Eds.: Child Behavior and Development. New York. McGraw-Hill Book Co. 1943.

Barnes, H. E.: A survey of the contributions of Gustave LeBon to social psychology. Am. J. Psychol. *31*:333, 1920.

Barnett, L.: The Universe and Dr. Einstein. New York. Mentor. 1954.

Basowitz, H., Persky, H., Korchin, S. J., and Grinker, R. R.: Anxiety and Stress. New York. McGraw-Hill Book Co. 1955.

Bateson, G.: Naven. Stanford. Stanford University Press. 1958.

Bateson, G., and Mead, Margaret: Balinese Culture. New York. William Morrow & Co. 1942.

Beach, F. A.: Central nervous mechanisms involved in the reproductive behaviour of vertebrates. Psychol. Bull. *39*:200, 1942.

Beach, F. A.: The snark was a boojum. Am. J. Psychol. *5*:115, 1950.

Beach, F. A., and Jaynes, J.: Effects of early experience upon the behavior of animals. Psychol. Bull. *51*:239, 1954.

Bechterew, V. M.: General Principles of Human Reflexology. New York. International Publishers. 1932.

Beck, S. J.: Introduction to the Rorschach Method. American Orthopsychiatric Association. 1937.

Beecher, H. K.: The powerful placebo. J.A.M.A. *159*:1602, 1955.

Beers, C.: A Mind That Found Itself. 7th Ed. New York. Doubleday & Co. 1948.

Behanan, K. T.: Yoga—A Scientific Evaluation. New York. The Macmillan Co. 1937.

Belknap, I.: Human Problems of a State Mental Hospital. New York. McGraw-Hill Book Co. 1956.

Bell, E.: The basis of military psychiatry. Dis. Nerv. System *19:*283, 1958.

Bellak, L.: Dementia Praecox. New York. Grune and Stratton. 1948.

Bellak, L.: Manic Depressive Psychosis and Allied Conditions. New York. Grune and Stratton. 1952.

Bellak, L.: An experimental exploration of the psychoanalytic process. Psychoanalyt. Quart. *25:*385–414, 1956.

Bellak, L.: Schizophrenia. New York. Logos Press. 1958.

Bender, J. F.: Ourway Ecretsay Anguageslay. New York Times Magazine Section, Dec. 31, 1944.

Bender, Lauretta: Child Psychiatric Techniques—Diagnostic and Therapeutic Approach to Normal and Abnormal Development through Patterned, Expressive and Group Behavior. Springfield, Illinois. Charles C Thomas. 1952.

Benedek, Therese: Insight and Personality Adjustment. New York. The Ronald Press. 1946.

Benedek, Therese: Psychosexual Functions in Women. New York. The Ronald Press. 1952.

Benedek, Therese, and Rubinstein, B.: The correlations between ovarian activity and psychodynamic processes. Psychosom. Med. *1:*245, 461, 1939.

Benedict, Ruth: Culture and the abnormal. J. General Psychol. *10:*49, 1934.

Benedict, Ruth: Patterns of Culture. New York. Mentor. 1953.

Benedict, Ruth, and Weltfish, G.: The Races of Mankind. New York. Columbia University Public Affairs Pamphlet, No. 85, 1943.

Bennett, A. E.: Alcohol addiction: problems in treatment. California Med. *85:*235, 1956.

Bennett, A. E., Hargrove, E. A., and Engle, Bernice: The Practice of Psychiatry in General Hospitals. Berkeley and Los Angeles. University of California Press. 1956.

Bennett, A. E., Keegan, J. J., and Wilbur, C. B.: Prefrontal lobotomy in chronic schizophrenia. J.A.M.A. *123:*809, 1943.

Bentham, Jeremy: The Works of Jeremy Bentham. Edinburgh. Wm. Tait. 1843. 11 Vols.

Bercel, N. A.: The web spinning of spiders. A.M.A. Arch. Gen. Psychiat. *2:*189, 1960.

Bercel, N. A., Travis, L. E., Olinger, L. B., and Dreikurs, E.: Model psychoses induced by LSD-25 in normals. Arch. Neurol. & Psychiat. *75:*588, 1956.

Beres, D.: The contributions of psychoanalysis to the biography of the artist. Internat. J. Psychoanalysis *40:*84, 1959.

Bergson, H.: Mind Energy. New York. Henry Holt & Co. 1920.

Bernal, J. D.: Science in History. London. Watts. 1959.

Bernheim, H.: Suggestive Therapeutics. Westport, Conn. Associated Booksellers. 1957.

Berry, Mildred F., and Eisonson, J.: Principles and Practices of Therapy. New York. Appleton-Century-Crofts, Inc. 1956.

Bertalanffy, L. von: An essay on the relativity of categories. Phil. Sc. *22:*243, 1955.

Bettelheim, B.: Individual and mass behavior in extreme situations. J. Abnorm. & Social Psychol. *38:*417, 1943.

Bettelheim, B.: Love Is Not Enough. Glencoe, Ill. Free Press. 1950.

Beyle, Marie-Henri (Stendhal): The Red and the Black. New York. Liveright Publishers. 1937.

Bharucha-Reid, R. P.: Latent learning in earthworms. Science *123:*222, 1956.

Bibring, E.: The development and problems of the theory of the instincts. Internat. J. Psychoanalysis *22:*2, 1941.

Bieber, I.: A critique of the libido-theory. Am. J. Psychoanalysis *18:*52, 1958.

Bingham, H. C.: Sex development in apes. Comp. Psychol. Monographs. *5:*1928.

Binswanger, L. M.: Ausgewahlte Vorträge und Aufsätze. Bern. Franche & Co. 1947.

Binswanger, L. M.: Existential analysis, psychiatry, schizophrenia. J. Exist. Psychiat. *1:*157, 1960.

Birdwhistell, R. L.: Contribution of linguistics. *In* Auerbach, A., Ed.: Schizophrenia. New York. Ronald Press. 1959.

Bleuler, E.: Textbook of Psychiatry. Translated by A. A. Brill. New York. The Macmillan Co. 1924.

Bleuler, E.: Dementia Praecox or, The Group of Schizophrenias. New York. International Universities Press. 1950.

Bleuler, M.: Schizophrenia: A review of the work of Prof. Eugene Bleuler. Arch. Neurol. & Psychiat. *26:*610, 1931.

Bleuler, M.: Endocrinologische Psychiatrie. Stuttgart. George Thiem. 1954.

Bliss, E. L., Clark, L. D., and West, L. J.: Studies of sleep deprivation—relationship to schizophrenia. Arch. Neurol. & Psychiat. *81:*348, 1959.

Bluemel, C. S.: War, Politics and Insanity. Denver. The World Press. 1948.

Blum, G. S.: Psychoanalytic Theories of Personality. New York. McGraw-Hill Book Co. 1953.

Blumer, H.: Movies and Conduct. New York. The Macmillan Co. 1933.

Bonaparte, Marie, Ed.: Origins of Psychoanalysis. (Freud's letters to Fleiss.) New York. Basic Books. 1957.

Bonime, W.: The psychic energy of Freud and Jung. Am. J. Psychiat. *112:*372, 1955.

Bonner, C., and Kent, G.: Overlapping symptoms in catatonic and manic excitement. Am. J. Psychiat. *92:*1311, 1936.

Bonner, J. T.: Cells and Societies. Princeton University Press. 1955.

Bonner, J. T.: Differentiation in social amebae. Scientific American *201:*152, 1959.

Boring, E. G.: A History of Experimental Psychology. New York. The Century Co. 1929.

Bose, G.: The duration of coitus. Internat. J. Psychoanalysis *18:*335, 1937.

Boss, M.: Meaning and Content of Sexual Perversions. New York. Grune and Stratton, 1949.

Boulenger, E. G.: Apes and Monkeys. New York. R. M. McBride & Co. 1937.

Bovet, L.: Psychiatric Aspects of Juvenile Delinquency. Geneva. WHO. 1951.

Bowlby, J.: Maternal Care and Mental Health. Geneva. WHO. 1951.

Bowlby, J.: The nature of the child's tie to his mother. Internat. J. Psychoanalysis *39:*350, 1959.

Bowling, L.: The molecular basis of genetics. Am. J. Psychiat. *113:*492, 1956.

Bowman, K. M.: Art of insane patients. Life *5:*No. 17 (Oct. 24), 1938.

Bowman, K. M.: Alcoholism. Am. J. Psychiat. *114:*621, 1957.

Bowman, K. M., and Jellinek, E. M.: Alcoholic mental disorders. Quart. J. Stud. Alcohol *2:*312, 1941.

Boynes, H. G.: The Mythology of the Soul. New York. Harcourt, Brace & Co. 1940.

Braatøy, T.: The Fundamentals of Psychoanalytic Technique. New York. John Wiley & Sons. 1954.

Brady, J. V.: The experimental analysis of emotional behavior. Proc. XIV. Internat. Congress Psychology. Amsterdam. North Holland Publishing Co. 1955.

Brady, J. V.: Ulcers in "executive" monkeys. Scientific American *199:*95, 1958.

Brady, J. V., Boren, J. J., and Conrad, D.: The effect of food and water deprivation upon intracranial self stimulation. J. Comp. & Physiol. Psychol. *50:*2, 1957.

Brady, J. V., Porter, R. A., Conrad, D. G., and Mason, J. W.: Avoidance behavior and the development of gastroduodenal ulcers. Am. J. Exp. Behavior *1:*69, 1958.

Brady, M.: Quoted by Calder, K. T.: J. Am. Psychoanalyt. A. *6:*552, 1958.

Brain, W. R.: Diseases of the Nervous System. 4th Ed. New York. Oxford University Press. 1951.

Brandt, L.: Operation Diana. Child-Family Digest *15:*19, 1956.

Branham, V. C., and Kutash, S. B., Eds.: Encyclopedia of Criminology. New York. Philosophical Library. 1949.

Brenman, Margaret, and Gill, M. N.: Hypnotherapy. New York. International Universities Press. 1947.

Brenner, C.: Facts, coincidence and the psi hypothesis. Internat. J. Psychoanalysis *38:*51, 1957.

Breuer, J., and Freud, S.: Studies in Hysteria. New York. Nervous and Mental Disease Publishing Co. 1936.

Bridgeman, P. W.: Probability, logic and ESP. Science *123:*15, 1956.

Brill, A. A.: Freud's Contribution to Psychiatry. New York. W. W. Norton & Co. 1944.

Brill, A. A., Ed.: The Basic Writings of Sigmund Freud. New York. The Modern Library. 1938.

Brill, N. A., et al.: Factors in ECT. Am. J. Psychiat. *113:*999, 1956.

Brinton, C.: The Shaping of the Modern Mind. New York. Mentor. 1953.

British Medical Journal: Menstruation and acute psychiatric illness. *1:*148, 1959.
Brock, S.: Basis of Clinical Neurology. 3rd Ed. Baltimore. Williams and Wilkins Co. 1953.
Brody, Sylvia: Patterns of Mothering. New York. International Universities Press. 1956.
Brosin, H. W.: The primary process and psychoses. Science *2:*62, 1957.
Brown, F. A.: The rhythmic nature of animals and plants. Scientific American *47:*147, 1959.
Brown, J. F.: The Psychodynamics of Abnormal Behavior. New York. McGraw-Hill Book Co. 1940.
Brunswick, E.: Perception and the Representative Design of Psychological Experiments. Berkeley. University of California Press. 1956.
Buber, M.: I and Thou. New York. Charles Scribner & Sons. 1937.
Buber, M.: Distance and relations. Psychiatry *20:*97, 1941.
Buber, M.: Between Man and Man. New York. The Macmillan Co. 1948.
Buchner, F.: Personality and Nature—Modern Medicine. New York. Grune and Stratton. 1958.
Burckhardt, J. C.: Civilization of the Renaissance in Italy. 3rd Ed. New York. Phaidon. 1951.
Bursten, B., and Delgado, J.: Positive reinforcement induced by intracerebral stimulation in the monkey. J. Comp. & Physiol. Psychol. *51:*6, 1958.
Burton, M.: Animal Courtship. New York. F. A. Praeger. 1954.
Burton, Robert: The Anatomy of Melancholy. New York. Empire State Book Co. 1924.
Butler, R. A.: Curiosity in monkeys. Scientific American *190:*70, 1954.

Cameron, D. E.: Objective and Experimental Psychiatry. New York. The Macmillan Co. 1941.
Cameron, D. E.: General Psychotherapy. New York. Grune and Stratton. 1950.
Cameron, D. E.: Repetition of verbal signals in therapy. *In* Masserman, J. H., Ed.: Current Psychiatric Therapies. New York. Grune and Stratton. 1961.
Cameron, N. A., and Cameron, Margaret Anne: Behavior Pathology. Boston. Houghton Mifflin Co. 1951.
Campbell, D. T.: Adaptive behavior from random reference. Behav. Scien. *1:*105, 1956.
Cannon, W. B.: Bodily Changes in Pain, Hunger, Fear and Rage. 2nd Ed. New York. The Appleton Co. 1929.
Cannon, W. B.: The Wisdom of the Body. 2nd Ed. New York. W. W. Norton & Co. 1939.
Cannon, W. B.: The Way of an Investigator. New York. W. W. Norton & Co. 1945.
Cantril, H., Ed.: Tensions That Cause Wars. Urbana. University of Illinois Press. 1950.
Cantril, H.: Perception and interpersonal relations. Am. J. Psychiat. *114:*119, 1957.
Carral, J. B.: The Study of Language. Cambridge. Harvard University Press. 1953.
Carrie, Joan: ABC of Jung's Psychology. London. Kegan, Paul, Trench, Trubner. 1928.
Cartwright, D., and Zander, A.: Group Dynamics. Evanston. Row, Peterson and Co. 1953.
Cassirer, E.: Determinism and Indeterminism in Modern Physics. New Haven. Yale University Press. 1945.
Cattell, J. P.: Psychopharmacological agents: a selective survey. Am. J. Psychiat. *116:*182, 1954.
Cattrell, L.: The Anvil of Civilization. New York. Mentor. 1957.
Chapman, L., Henkle, L. E., and Wolff, H. G.: Organic effects of stress. Am. J. Psychiat. *117:*193, 1960.
Chase, S.: Roads to Agreement. New York. Harper & Bros. 1951.
Cherry, C.: Human Communication. Cambridge, Mass. Technology Press. New York. John Wiley & Son. 1957.
Childe, V. G.: What Happened in History. New York. Mentor. 1946.
Childe, V. G.: Man Makes Himself. New York. Mentor. 1955.

Cleckley, H. M.: The Mask of Sanity. 3rd Ed. St. Louis. C. V. Mosby Co. 1955.
Cobb, S.: Borderlands of Psychiatry. Cambridge. Harvard University Press. 1944.
Cobb, S.: Emotions and Clinical Medicine. New York. W. W. Norton & Co. 1950.
Cobb, S., Ed.: Biology of Mental Health and Disease. New York. Paul B. Hoeber, 1952.
Cobb, S.: Instincts. Am. J. Psychiat. *112:*149, 1955.
Cohen, J.: Subjective probability. Scientific American *197:*128, 1957.
Colby, K. M.: Primer for Psychotherapists. New York. The Ronald Press. 1951.
Cole, Nyla J., Roger, B. A., Gortatowski, M. I., and Branch, C. H. Hardin: Studies of behavior and the metabolism of indole derivatives in schizophrenia. Am. J. Psychiat. *117:*393, 1960.
Cole, N. J., et al.: Mental illness: A survey assessment of community rates, attitudes, and adjustments. A.M.A. Arch. Neurol. & Psychiat. 77:393, 1957.
Coleman, J. C.: Abnormal Psychology and Modern Life. Chicago. Scott, Foresman & Co. 1950.
Comte, I.: Cours de Philosophie Positive. London. John Chapman. 1853.
Conger, J. V.: The effects of alcohol on conflict behavior in the albino rat. Quart. J. Stud. Alcohol *12:*1, 1951.
Conradi, E.: Song and call-notes of English sparrows when reared by canaries. Am. J. Psychol. *16:*190, 1905.
Cooper, I. S., et al.: Surgical Therapy of Extrapyramidal Disorders. Baltimore. Williams and Wilkins Co. 1956.
Cooper, I. S., and Bravo, G.: Five year study of basal ganglia operations. Neurology *8:*701, 1958.
Craig, W.: Male doves reared in isolation. J. Animal Behavior *4:*121, 1914.
Crofts, L. W., Schnierla, T. C., Robinson, Elsa, and Gilbert, R. W.: Recent Experiments in Psychology. New York. McGraw-Hill Book Co. 1950.
Crombie, A. C.: Descartes. Scientific American *201:*160, 1959.
Curran, F. J.: Convergent and divergent views in the problem of religious confession. Bull. Isaac Ray Library *2:*135, 1954.
Cushing, J. G. N.: Committee Report. Bull. Am. Psychoanal. Assoc. *8:*44, 1952.

Dahl, R. A.: Clergy and Physician. Quart. Bull. Northwestern Univ. M. School *3:*88, 1958.
Darlington, C. D.: The origin of Darwinism. Scientific American *200:*60, 1959.
Darrach, H.: Up Horoscope. Life, *48:*97, 1960.
Davidson, Audrey, and Fay, Judith: Phantasy in Childhood. New York. Philosophical Library. 1953.
Davidson, H. A.: Forensic Psychiatry. New York. Ronald Press. 1952.
Davies, J. D.: Phrenology: Fad and Science. New Haven. Yale University Press. 1955.
Davis, J. E.: Principles and Practice of Rehabilitation. New York. A. S. Barnes & Co. 1943.
Davis, S. W.: Stress in combat. Scientific American *194:*31, 1956.
Dean, S. R.: Reappraisal of psychoanalysis. Am. J. Psychiat. *113:*936, 1957.
DeJong, H. H.: Experimental Catatonia. Baltimore. Williams & Wilkins Co. 1945.
DeJong, R. N.: The Neurologic Examination. 2nd Ed. New York. Paul B. Hoeber. 1960.
Delgado, J. M. R.: Cerebral structures involved in transmission and elaboration of noxious stimulation. J. Neurophysiol. *18:*261, 1955.
Delgado, J. M. R.: Electronic command of movement and behavior. New York Acad. Sci. *21:*689, 1959.
Delgado, J. M. R.: Emotional behavior in animals and humans. Physiol. Res. Reports, *12:*259, 1960.
Delgado, J. M. R., Roberts, W. W., and Mettler, N. R.: Learning motivated by electrical stimulation of the brain. Am. J. Physiol. *179:*587, 1954.
Delgado, J. M. R., Rosvold, H. E., and Looney, E.: Evoking conditioned fear by electrical stimulation of subcortical structures in the monkey brain. J. Comp. Physiol. & Psychol. *49:*373, 1956.

Dennis, W., et al.: Current Trends in Psychological Theory. Pittsburgh, Pa. University of Pittsburgh Press. 1951.

DePoncins, G.: Kabloona. New York. Reynal & Hitchcock. 1941.

Deutsch, A., Ed.: Sex Habits of American Men. New York. Prentice-Hall, Inc. 1948.

Deutsch, A.: The Mentally Ill in America. 2nd Ed. New York. Columbia University Press. 1949.

Deutsch, F. and Murphy, W. R.: The associative anamnesis. Psychiat. Quart. 8:354, 1939.

Deutsch, Helene: Psychology of Women. New York. Grune and Stratton. 1944–45. 2 vols.

Dewey, J.: Human Nature and Conduct. New York. Modern Library. 1922.

Diserens, C. M., and Fine, H.: A Psychology of Music. Cincinnati. College of Music. 1939.

Dobie, J. R.: The roadrunner in fact and folklore. Arizona Highways *34*, 1948.

Dollard, J., and Miller, N. E.: Personality and Psychotherapy. New York. McGraw-Hill Book Co. 1950.

Dorcus, R. M., and Shaffer, G. W.: Textbook of Abnormal Psychology. Baltimore. Williams & Wilkins Co. 1945.

Downs, R. B.: Books That Changed the World. New York. Mentor. 1956.

Dubois, F. S.: Rehabilitation and occupational therapy. Am. J. Psychiat. *114*:632, 1957.

Ducasse, C. J.: A Philosophical Scrutiny of Religion. New York. Ronald Press. 1952.

Dunbar, Helen Flanders: Psychosomatic Diagnosis. New York. Paul B. Hoeber. 1943.

Dunbar, Helen Flanders: Emotions and Bodily Changes. 4th Ed. New York. Columbia University Press. 1954.

Dunbar, Helen Flanders: Homeostasis during puberty. Am. J. Psychiat. *114*:673, 1958.

Earle, W.: Jaspers and Existential Analysis. J. Exist. Psychiat. *1*:166, 1960.

Eaton, J. W., and Weil, R. J.: Culture and Mental Disorders. Glencoe, Ill. Free Press. 1955.

Ebaugh, F. C., and Barnes, R. H.: Psychiatric education. Am. J. Psychiat. *115*:650, 1959.

Edwards, A. L.: Experimental Design in Psychological Research. New York. Rinehart & Co. 1950.

Edwards, A. L.: Statistical Methods for the Behavioral Sciences. New York. Rinehart & Co. 1954.

Ehrenwald, J.: Telepathy and Medical Psychology. New York. W. W. Norton & Co. 1948.

Ehrenwald, J., Ed.: From Medicine Man to Freud. New York. Dell Publishing Co. 1956.

Ehrenwald, J.: Non-Euclidian models of personality. Internat. J. Parapsychol. *1*:54, 1959.

Einstein, A., and Infeld, L.: The Evolution of Physics. New York. Simon & Schuster, 1938.

Eisenbud, J.: On the use of the psi hypotheses in psychoanalysis. Internat. J. Psychoanalysis *36*:370, 1955.

Ellenburger, H.: The ancestry of dynamic psychiatry. Bull. Menninger Clin. *20*:288, 1956.

Ellery, R. S.: Psychiatric Aspects of Modern Warfare. Melbourne. Reed and Harris. 1945.

Elliott, Mabel A., and Merrill, F. E.: Social Disorganization. 3rd Ed. New York. Harper & Bros. 1950.

English, O. S.: Personality Manifestations in Psychosomatic Illness. Philadelphia. Edw. Stern & Co. 1953.

English, O. S., and Finch, S. M.: Introduction to Psychiatry. New York. W. W. Norton & Co. 1957.

English, O. S., and Pearson, G. H. J.: The Emotional Problems of Living. New York. W. W. Norton & Co. 1955.

Erikson, E. H.: Childhood and Society. New York. W. W. Norton & Co. 1950.
Erikson, E. H.: The problem of ego identity. J. Am. Psychoanalyt. A. 4:56, 1956.
Ernst, M. L., and Loth, D. D.: American Sexual Behavior and the Kinsey Report. New York. Greystone Press. 1948.
Ey, H.: The reality of mental disease and the disease of reality. Compr. Psych. 1:2, 1960.

Fairbairn, R. D.: On the nature and aims of psychoanalytical treatment. Internat. J. Psychoanalysis 39:74, 1959.
Farrar, B. A.: Psychological theory and the belief in God. Internat. J. Psychoanalysis 36:187, 1954.
Farrar, C. B.: Psychotherapy. Am. J. Psychiat. 113:865, 1951.
Feidler, F. A.: A comparison of therapeutic relationships in psychoanalytic, nondirective, and Adlerian theory. Consult. Psychol. 14:436, 1955.
Feigl, H.: Existential hypothesis. Phil. Sc. 17:35, 1951.
Feigl, H., and Bradbeck, M.: Readings in the Philosophy of Science. New York. Appleton-Century-Crofts. 1953.
Fein, Rashi: Joint Commission on Mental Illness and Health. Monograph Series No. 2. New York. Basic Books. 1958.
Fenichel, O.: The Psychoanalytic Theory of Neuroses. New York. W. W. Norton & Co. 1945.
Ferenczi, S.: Sex in Psychoanalysis. New York. Basic Books. 1950.
Fielding, W. J.: Strange Customs of Courtship and Marriage. New York. New Home Library. 1942.
Fielding, X.: The ghosts of Frangastello. Listener 49:187, 1953.
Fischer, C.: Studies of induced dream symbols. Proc. Am. Psychoanalyt. Soc., May 1957.
Fischer, S.: Principles of General Psychopathology. New York. Philosophical Library. 1950.
Fish, Barbara: Involvement of the central nervous system in infants with schizophrenia. Arch. Neurol. 2:115, 1960.
Flaubert, G.: Madame Bovary. New York. Random House. 1957.
Fletcher, J.: Morals and Medicine. Princeton. Princeton University Press. 1954.
Flower, V. C.: An Approach to the Psychology of Religion. In Roback, A. A., Ed.: Present Day Psychology. New York. Philosophical Library. 1955.
Flugel, J. C.: A Hundred Years of Psychology. 1833–1933. New York. The Macmillan Co. 1934.
Flugel, J. C.: The Psychoanalytic Study of the Family. 6th Ed. Westport, Conn. Associated Booksellers. 1950.
Fodor, N., and Gaynor, F., Eds.: Freud: Dictionary of Psychoanalysis. New York. Philosophical Library. 1950.
Foerster, H. von, Ed.: Cybernetics. New York. Josiah Macy, Jr., Foundation. 1952.
Ford, C. S., and Beach, F. A.: Patterns of Sexual Behavior. New York. Harper & Bros. 1951.
Forel, A.: The Social World of the Ants as Compared to That of Man. New York. Boni. 1929.
Forel, C.: The Sexual Question. New York. Physicians and Surgeons Book Co. 1926.
Frank, J.: Why patients leave psychotherapy. Arch. Neurol. & Psychiat. 77:283, 1957.
Frank, J., et al.: The dynamics of the psychotherapeutic relationship. Psychiatry 22:17, 1959.
Frank, J. D., et al.: Patients' expectancies and relearning of factors in determining improvement in psychotherapy. Am. J. Psychiat. 115:961, 1959.
Frazer, J. G.: The Golden Bough—A Study in Magic and Religion. New York. The Macmillan Co. 1940.
Freedman, L., and Hollingshead, A.: Neurosis and social class. Am. J. Psychiat. 113:769, 1959.
Freeman, F. S.: Individual Differences. New York. Henry Holt & Co. 1936.

Freeman, F. S.: Theory and Practice of Psychological Testing. New York. Henry Holt & Co. 1955.

Freud, Anna: Introduction to the Technic of Child Analysis. New York. Nervous and Mental Disease Publishing Co. 1928.

Freud, Anna: The Ego and the Mechanisms of Defense. New York. International Universities Press. 1946.

Freud, Anna, and Burlingham, Dorothy T.: War and Children. New York. International Universities Press. 1944.

Freud, Anna, Hartmann, H., and Kris, E., Eds.: The Psychoanalytic Study of the Child. New York. International Universities Press. Vol. 1, 1945. Vol. 2, 1946.

Freud, S.: The Psychopathology of Everyday Life. New York. The Macmillan Co. 1917.

Freud, S.: Totem and Taboo. New York. Dodd, Mead. 1918.

Freud, S.: Group Psychology and the Analysis of the Ego. London. International Psychoanalytic Press. 1922.

Freud, S.: The Future of an Illusion. New York. Liveright. 1928.

Freud, S.: Three Contributions to the Theory of Sex. 4th Ed. Baltimore. Williams and Wilkins. 1930.

Freud, S.: The Interpretation of Dreams. Rev. ed. New York. The Macmillan Co. 1933.

Freud, S.: New Introductory Lectures on Psychoanalysis. New York. W. W. Norton & Co. 1933.

Freud, S.: The Problem of Anxiety. New York. W. W. Norton & Co. 1936.

Freud, S.: Postscript to a Discussion on Lay Analysis. Collected Papers. 1937.

Freud, S.: Moses and Monotheism. London. Hogarth Press. 1939.

Freud, S.: A General Introduction to Psychoanalysis. New York. Garden City Publishing Co. 1943.

Freud, S.: Leonardo da Vinci. New York. Random House. 1947.

Freud, S.: Outline of Psychoanalysis. New York. W. W. Norton & Co. 1949.

Freud, S.: The Question of Lay Analysis. New York. W. W. Norton & Co. 1950.

Freud, S.: An Autobiographical Study. London. Hogarth Press. 1950.

Freud, S.: The Origins of Psychoanalysis: Letters to Wilhelm Fleiss, 1887–1902. New York. Basic Books. 1954.

Freud, S.: Civilization and Its Discontents. London. Hogarth Press. 1955.

Freud, S.: Collected Papers. Ed. by James Strachey. New York. Basic Books. 1959.

Fridon, Audie: Sex Happiness. New York. J. F. V. Rensselaer. 1938.

Frings, H., and Frings, Mabel: The language of crows. Scientific American *201*:119, 1959.

Frings, H., and Jumber, J.: Preliminary studies on the use of a specific sound to repel starlings. Science *119*:318, 1954.

Frohman, C., et al.: Evidence of a plasma factor in schizophrenia. Arch. Physiol. 2:255. 1960.

Frolov, I.: Pavlov and His School: The Theory of Conditioned Reflexes. New York. Oxford University Press. 1937.

Fromm, E.: Escape from Freedom. New York. Farrar and Rinehart. 1941.

Fromm, E. The Forgotten Language. New York. Rinehart & Co. 1951.

Fromm, E.: Sigmund Freud's Mission. New York. Harper & Bros. 1959.

Fromm-Reichmann, Frieda: Principles of Intensive Psychotherapy. Chicago. University of Chicago Press. 1950.

Fromm-Reichmann, Frieda: Psychotherapy of schizophrenia. Am. J. Psychiat. *111*:410, 1955.

Fromm-Reichmann, Frieda: Loneliness. Psychiatry *22*:1–15, 1959.

Fromm-Reichmann, Frieda, and Moreno, J., Eds.: Progress in Psychotherapy. New York. Grune & Stratton. 1956.

Fuller, J. L.: Nature and Nurture: A Modern Synthesis. New York. Doubleday & Co. 1954.

Fulton, J. F.: Physiology of the Nervous System. 3rd Ed. New York. Oxford University Press. 1949.

Fulton, J. F.: Frontal Lobotomy and Affective Behavior: A Neurophysiological Analysis. New York. W. W. Norton & Co. 1951.

Fuster, J. M.: Effects of stimulation of brain stem on tachistoscopic perception. Science *127*:150, 1958.

Galdston, I., Ed.: Medicine and Science Lectures to the Laity. XVI. New York Academy of Medicine. New York. International Universities Press. 1954.

Galdston, I.: Freud and semantic medicine. Bull. Hist. Med. *30:*489, 1956.

Galdston, I., Ed.: On the Utility of Medical History. New York. International University Press. 1957.

Gallinek, A.: Fear and anxiety in the course of electrotherapy. Am. J. Psychiat. *113:*428, 1956.

Gantt, W. H.: The Origin and Development of Behavior Disorders in Dogs. New York. Psychosomatic Monographs. 1942.

Gardiner, M.: Facts and Fallacies in the Name of Science. New York. Dover Publications. 1957.

Gardner, G. E.: Child psychiatry and the general practitioner. J.A.M.A. *163:*105, 1957.

Geffe, P. R.: Letter. Scientific American *195:*10, 1957.

Geiger, Ruth: CNS cultures. J. Neuropsychiat. *1:*185, 1960.

Gerard, R. W.: The biological roots of psychiatry. Am. J. Psychiat. *112:*81, 1955.

Gerard, R. W., Kluckhohn, C., and Rapaport, A.: Biological and cultural revolution. Behav. Sci. *1:*6, 1956.

Gerty, F.: The physician and psychotherapy. Am. J. Psychiat. *116:*1, 1960.

Gesell, A., et al.: The First Five Years of Life. New York. Harper & Bros. 1955.

Gesell, A., and Ilg, Frances L.: Infant and Child in the Culture of Today. New York. Harper & Bros. 1943.

Gesell, A., Ilg, Frances, and Ames, Louise: Youth. The Ages from 10 to 16. New York. Harper & Bros. 1956.

Gibbs, F. A., and Gibbs, E. L.: Atlas of Electroencephalography. 2nd Ed. Cambridge, Mass. Addison-Wesley Publishing Co. 1950.

Gibson, Eleanor, and Walk, R. D.: The visual cliff. Scientific American *202:*64, 1960.

Gill, M., Newman, R. and Redlich, F. C.: The Initial Interview in Psychiatric Practice. New York. International Universities Press. 1954.

Gillespie, C. C.: Lamarck and Darwin. Scientific American *46:*408, 1958.

Gillespie, C. D.: Psychological Effects of War on Citizen and Soldier. New York. W. W. Norton & Co. 1942.

Gillin, J.: Cross-cultural aspects of socio-cultural therapy. Estudios anthropologios. Mexico. Manuel Samio. 1956.

Ginsberg, B. E.: Genetics as a tool in the study of behavior. Perspectives in Biology. I. Chicago. University of Chicago Press. 1959.

Glad, D. D.: Operational Values in Psychotherapy. New York. Oxford University Press. 1959.

Glass, A. V.: Psychotherapy in the combat zone. Am. J. Psychiat. *110:*725, 1959.

Glass, B.: Discussion of genetics. Symposium. Am. J. Psychiat. *113:*504, 1956.

Glueck, B., Ed.: Current Therapies of Personality Disorders. New York. Grune and Stratton. 1946.

Goldhamar, H., and Marshall, A.: Psychosis and Civilization. Glencoe, Ill. The Free Press. 1953.

Goldsmith, Margaret: Franz Anton Mesmer. New York. Doubleday, Doran. 1934.

Goldstein, K.: The Organism. New York. American Book Co. 1939.

Gombrich, E. H.: The Story of Art. New York. Phaidon. 1951.

Goodenough, Florence L.: Developmental Psychology. New York. Appleton-Century-Crofts. 1934.

Goody, W.: Time and the nervous system: the brain as a clock. Lancet *2:*1155, 1959.

Gordon, H. L.: Psychiatric concepts in Bible, Talmud and Zohar. *In* Jews in the Arts and Sciences. J. Acad. Arts & Sciences, 1955.

Gottschalk, L.: Understanding History. New York. Alfred A. Knopf. 1950.

Grantham, E. C.: Prefrontal lobotomy for relief of pain, with a report of a new operative technique. J. Neurosurg. *8:*405, 1951.

Green, H.: Perverted appetites. Physiol. Rev. *5:*1, 1925.

Green, R. M.: Asclepiades. His Life and Writing. New Haven. Elizabeth Licht Publ. 1955.

Greenacre, Phyllis: Trauma, Growth and Personality. New York. W. W. Norton & Co. 1952.

Greenspoon, J.: Communication in therapy. Am. J. Psychol. 68:409, 1955.
Griffiths, Ruth A.: The Abilities of Babies: A Study in Mental Measurement. New York. McGraw-Hill Book Co. 1954.
Grinker, R. R.: Psychosomatic Research. New York. W. W. Norton & Co. 1953.
Grinker, R. R.: Anxiety as a significant variable for a unified theory of human behavior. A.M.A. Arch. Gen. Psychiat. 1:537, 1959.
Grinker, R. R.: A transactional model for psychotherapy. A.M.A. Arch. Gen. Psychiat. 1:132, 1959.
Grinker, R. R., et al.: Neurology. Springfield, Ill. Charles C Thomas. 1958.
Grinker, R. R., and Robbins, F. P.: Psychosomatic Case Book. New York. The Blakiston Co. 1954.
Grinker, R. R., and Spiegel, J. P.: Men Under Stress. Philadelphia. The Blakiston Co. 1945.
Grotjahn, M.: Beyond Laughter. New York. McGraw-Hill Book Co. 1957.
Group for the Advancement of Psychiatry: Methods of Forceful Indoctrination. New York. July 1957.
Groves, E. R., and Blanchard, Phyllis: Introduction to Mental Hygiene. New York. Henry Holt & Co. 1930.
Gruenberg, E. M.: The epistemology of mental disease. Scientific American 190:38, 1954.
Gruenberg, Sidonie M., Ed.: The Family in a World at War. New York. Harper & Bros. 1942.
Guhl, A. M.: The social order of chickens. Scientific American 194:43, 1956.
Guilford, J. P.: Structure of human intellect. Science 122:875, 1955.
Gull, W. W.: Anorexia nervosa. Trans. Clin. Soc. London 7:11, 1874.
Gumpian, M. E.: Psychoanalysis as Science. Stanford University Press. 1953.
Gutheil, E. A., et al.: Music and Your Emotions. New York. Liveright Publishing Corp. 1952.
Guttmacher, M. S., and Weihofen, H.: Psychiatry and the Law. New York. W. W. Norton & Co. 1952.
Guyton, R.: The Ethics of Sexual Acts. New York. Alfred A. Knopf. 1948.

Hahn, E. F.: Stuttering: Significant Theories and Therapies. Stanford University Press. 1943.
Halliday, J. L.: Psychosocial Medicine. New York. W. W. Norton & Co. 1948.
Hamburger, V.: The life history of a nerve cell. Scientific American 145:263, 1957.
Hamilton, Edith: Mythology. New York. Mentor, 1957.
Hamilton, Edith: The Greek Way. New York. Mentor. 1957.
Handlon, V. H.: A metatheoretical view of assumptions regarding the etiology of schizophrenia. Arch. Gen. Physiol. 27:153, 1960.
Hanemann, E.: The age of psychology. Life 42:68, 1957.
Hankoff, L. D.: The placebo response in 43 schizophrenic patients. Arch. Gen. Psychiat. 2:43, 1960.
Hardin, G.: The threat of clarity. Am. J. Psychiat. 114:392, 1957.
Harlow, H.: Love in infant monkeys. Scientific American 200:68, 1959.
Harriman, P. L., Ed.: Encyclopedia of Psychology. New York. Philosophical Library. 1946.
Hart, B.: The Psychology of Insanity. Cambridge University Press. 1957.
Hastings, D.: Follow-up in psychiatric illness. Am. J. Psychiat. 114:1057, 1958.
Hauser, A.: The Social History of Art. Vol. I. New York. Alfred A. Knopf. 1951.
Hayakawa, S. I.: Language in Thought and Action. Rev. ed. New York. Harcourt, Brace & Co. 1949.
Heath, R. C., et al.: Studies in Schizophrenia: A Multidisciplinary Approach to Mind-Brain Relationships. Cambridge, Mass. Harvard University Press. 1952.
Heath, R. C., Monroe, R. B., and Meekle, W. A.: Stimulation of the amygdaloid nucleus in a schizophrenic patient. Am. J. Psychiat. 111:862, 1955.
Hebb, D. O.: A Textbook of Psychology. Philadelphia. W. B. Saunders Co. 1958.
Heidegger, M.: Sein und Zeit. Halle. Niemeyer. 1927.

Heidegger, M.: Existence and Being. Chicago. Regnery Press, 1949.

Heilbroner, R. L.: The Wordly Philosophies. New York. Simon & Schuster. 1953.

Heinroth, O.: Beiträge zur Biologie. Intern. Ornith. Kongs. 5:25, 1910.

Hendrick, I.: Facts and Theories of Psychoanalysis. Rev. ed. New York. Alfred A. Knopf. 1957.

Hendrickson, W. J., and Holmes, D. J.: Control of behavior as a causal factor in intensive psychiatric treatment in an adolescent ward. Am. J. Psychiat. 115:969, 1959.

Herriegel, E.: Zen in the Art of Archery. New York. Pantheon Books. 1953.

Herrmann, P.: Conquest by Man. New York. Harper & Bros. 1954.

Hersher, L., Moore, A. V., and Richmond, J. B.: Effect of post-partum separation of mother and kid on maternal care in the domestic goat. Science 128:1342, 1958.

Herskovits, M. J.: Man and His Works. New York. Alfred A. Knopf. 1950.

Hess, E.: "Imprinting" in animals. Scientific American 198:81, 1958.

Higdon, E. K.: New Missionaries for New Days. St. Louis. The Bethany Press. 1956.

Hilgard, E. R.: Introduction to Psychology. New York. Harcourt, Brace & Co. 1957.

Hilgard, E. R., Kornetsky, C. H., Flanary, H. G., and Wikler, A.: Studies on anxiety associated with the anticipation of pain. Arch. Neurol. & Psychiat. 67:612, 1952.

Himwich, H. E.: Brain Metabolism and Cerebral Disorders. Baltimore. Williams and Wilkins Co. 1951.

Hinckley, R. G., and Hermann, Lydia: Group Treatment in Psychotherapy. Minneapolis. University of Minnesota Press. 1951.

Hinsie, L. E., and Shatzky, J.: Psychiatric Dictionary. London. Oxford University Press. 1940.

Hoch, P., Ed.: Failures in Psychiatric Treatment. New York. Grune and Stratton. 1948.

Hoch, P., and Knight, R. P., Eds.: Epilepsy: Psychiatric Aspects of Convultive Disorders. New York. Grune and Stratton. 1947.

Hoch, P., and Zubin, J., Eds.: Psychosexual Development. New York. Grune and Stratton. 1949.

Hoch, P., and Zubin, J., Eds.: Relation of Psychological Tests to Psychiatry. New York. Grune and Stratton. 1951.

Hoch, P., and Zubin, J., Eds.: Current Problems in Psychiatric Diagnoses. New York. Grune and Stratton. 1953.

Hoch, P., and Zubin, J., Eds.: Depression. New York. Grune & Stratton. 1954.

Hoch, P., and Zubin, J. Eds.: Psychiatry and the Law. New York. Grune and Stratton. 1955.

Hoch, P., and Zubin, J. Eds.: Experimental Psychopathology. New York. Grune and Stratton. 1957.

Hoch, P., and Zubin, J., Eds.: Problems of Addiction and Habituation. New York. Grune and Stratton. 1958.

Hoebel, E. A.: The Law of Primitive Man. Cambridge. Harvard University Press. 1954.

Hoffman, F. J.: Freudianism and the Literary Mind. Baton Rouge, La. Louisiana State University Press. 1945.

Hollender, M. H.: The Psychology of Medical Practice. Philadelphia. W. B. Saunders Co. 1958.

Hollingshead, A. B., and Redlich, F. C.: Social Class and Mental Illness. New York. John Wiley & Sons. 1958.

Holt, R. R., and Luborsky, L.: Personality Patterns of Psychiatrists. New York. Basic Books. 1958.

Hora, T.: Existential group psychotherapy. Am. J. Psychotherapy 13:83, 1959.

Horney, Karen: The Neurotic Personality of Our Time. New York. W. W. Norton & Co. 1937.

Horney, Karen: New Ways in Psychoanalysis. New York. W. W. Norton & Co. 1939.

Horton, D.: The functions of alcohol in primitive societies: a cross cultural study. Quart. J. Stud. Alcohol 9:199, 1933.

Hoskins, R. G.: The Biology of Schizophrenia. New York. W. W. Norton & Co. 1946.

Howitt, M. K.: Fact and artifact in the biology of schizophrenia. Science 124:429, 1956.

Hubbard, L. R.: The Modern Science of Mental Health. New York. Hermitage House. 1950.

Huff, D.: How to Lie With Statistics. New York. W. W. Norton & Co. 1954.

Hull, C. L.: Principles of Behavior. New York. Appleton-Century Co. 1943.

Hume, E. H.: Doctors Courageous. New York. Harper & Bros. 1950.

Hunt, J. McV., Ed.: Personality and the Behavior Disorders. New York. The Ronald Press. 1944.

Husserl, E.: Ideen zu einer reinen Phänomenologie. Halle. Niemeyer. 1922.

Huston, P. E.: The relation of psychiatry and psychology. Am. J. Psychiat. *110:*814, 1954.

Huxley, T. H.: Man's Place in Nature. London. Thomas, Ltd. 1898.

Ilg, Frances L., and Ames, Louise B.: Child Behavior. New York. Harper & Bros. 1955.

Inbau, F. E.: Lie Detection and Criminal Interrogation. Baltimore. Williams and Wilkins Co. 1943.

Ingle, D. J.: Principles of Research in Biology and Medicine. Philadelphia. J. B. Lippincott Co. 1958.

Ivanov-Smolensky, A. G.: Essays on the Pathophysiology of the Higher Nervous Activity. Moscow. Foreign Languages Publishers. 1954.

Jackson, C.: The Lost Weekend. New York. Farrar and Rinehart. 1944.

Jackson, J. H.: Selected Writings. London. Hodder. 1931–32. 2 vols.

Jacobsen, C. F., et al.: Neuroses in chimpanzees. J. Nerv. & Ment. Dis. *82:*1, 1933.

Jacobsen, E., and Skaarup, Y.: Experimental induction of conflict behavior in cats: its use in pharmacological investigations. Acta pharmacol. et toxicol. *11:*117, 1955.

Jacobsen, E., and Sonne, Else: The effects of benactyzine on stress-induced behavior in the rat. Acta pharmacol. et toxicol. *11:*135, 1955.

Jacoby, H. J.: Analysis of Handwriting. London. Allen and Unwin. 1939.

James, W.: Psychology. New York. Henry Holt & Co. 1920.

James, W.: Varieties of Religious Experience. New York. Longmans, Green and Co. 1938.

Janet, P.: Psychological Healing. London. Allen and Unwin. 1925.

Jaspers, K.: Reason and Existence. New York. Longmans, Green and Co. 1938.

Jeans, J. H.: The new world picture of modern physics. Nature, Sept. 8, 1934.

Jellinek, E. M., Ed.: Alcohol Addiction and Chronic Alcoholism. New Haven. Yale University Press. 1942.

Jennings, H. S.: The Biologic Basis of Human Nature. New York. W. W. Norton & Co. 1930.

Jennings, H. S.: Social life and interrelationships in certain protozoa. Sociometry 8:9, 1945.

Jensen, D. D.: Learning. Science *126:*1341, 1957.

Johnson, R. C.: Psychical Research. New York. Philosophical Library. 1956.

Jones, E.: The God Complex. Essays in Applied Psychoanalysis. London. Hogarth Press. 1951.

Jones, E.: Life of Freud. 3 Vols. New York. Basic Books. 1953–58.

Jones, M.: The Therapeutic Community. New York. Basic Books. 1953.

Josselyn, Irene: The Adolescent and His World. New York. Family Service Association. 1952.

J.A.M.A.: Alcoholism in rats. *167:*645, 1958.

Jung, C. G.: Psychological Types. New York. Harcourt, Brace & Co. 1923.

Jung, C. G.: The Psychology of Dementia Praecox. 2nd Ed. New York. Nervous and Mental Disease Publishing Co. 1937.

Kalinowsky, L. B., and Hoch, P. H.: Shock Treatments, Psychosurgery and Other Somatic Treatments in Psychiatry. 2nd Ed. New York. Grune and Stratton. 1952.

Kallmann, F. J.: Heredity in Health and Mental Disorder. New York. W. W. Norton & Co. 1942.

Kallmann, F. J.: Heredity and eugenics. Am. J. Psychiat., *115*:586, 1959.

Kallmann, F. J., and Rypins, Senta J.: Genetics of Schizophrenia. New York. J. J. Augustin. 1938.

Kanner, L.: Child Psychiatry. 3rd Ed. Springfield, Ill. Charles C Thomas. 1957.

Kaplan, O. J., Ed.: Mental Disorders in Later Life. 2nd Ed. Stanford. Stanford University Press. 1956.

Kardiner, A.: The Individual and His Society. New York. Columbia University Press. 1939.

Kardiner, A.: War Stress and Neurotic Illness. New York. Paul B. Hoeber. 1947.

Kardiner, A.: Sex and Mortality. Indianapolis. Bobbs Merrill. 1955.

Kardiner, A., Karush, A., and Lionel, O.: A methodologic study of Freudian theory. J. Nerv. Ment. Dis. *129*:11–19, *133*:43, 207, 221, 341, 351, 1959.

Kasanin, J. S.: Language and Thought in Schizophrenia. Berkeley, Calif. University of California Press. 1946.

Katz, D.: Animals and Man. New York. Longmans, Green & Co. 1937.

Kaufmann, W., Ed.: International Symposium on Anthropology. Chicago. University of Chicago Press. 1952.

Kaufmann, W., Ed.: Existentialism from Dostoevsky to Sartre. New York. Meridian. 1956.

Kelley, D. M.: 22 Cells in Nuremberg. New York. Greenberg Publisher. 1947.

Kempf, E.: The social and sexual behavior of the infra-human primates and some comparable facts in human behavior. Psychoanalyt. Rev. *4*:127, 1917.

Kety, S. S.: The Biology of Mental Health and Disease. New York. Paul B. Hoeber. 1952.

Kety, S. S.: Behavioral theories of schizophrenia. Science *129*:1528, 1959.

Kierkegaard, S.: The Concept of Dread (1844). Princeton. Princeton University Press. 1944.

King, J. A.: Parameters relevant to determining the effect of early experiences upon the adult behavior of animals. Psychol. Bull. *5*:46, 1958.

King, J. A.: The social behavior of prairie dogs. Scientific American *201*:12, 1959.

Kinsey, A. C., Pomeroy, W. B., and Martin, C. E.: Sexual Behavior in the Human Male. Philadelphia. W. B. Saunders Co. 1949.

Kinsey, A. C., Pomeroy, W. B., Martin, C. E., and Gebhard, P. H.: Sexual Behavior in the Human Female. Philadelphia. W. B. Saunders Co. 1953.

Klapman, J. W.: Group Psychotherapy: Theory and Practice. 2nd Ed. New York. Grune and Stratton. 1957.

Klein, Henriette, Potter, H. W., and Syk, Ruth B.: Anxiety in Pregnancy and Childbirth. New York. Paul B. Hoeber. 1950.

Klein, Melanie: Contributions to Psychoanalysis. London. Hogarth Press. 1948.

Klein, Melanie: The Psychoanalysis of Children. 3rd Ed. New York. Hillary. 1949.

Klerman, G. L., et al.: Sedation and tranquilization. A.M.A. Arch. Gen. Psychiat. *3*:28, 1960.

Klerman, G. L., et al.: Sociopsychological characteristics of resident psychiatrists and their use of drug therapy. Am. J. Psychiat. *117*:111, 1960.

Klopfer, B.: The Rorschach Technique. Yonkers, N. Y. World Book Co. 1942.

Kluckhohn, C., and Murray, H. A., Eds.: Personality in Nature, Society and Culture. 2nd Ed. New York. Alfred A. Knopf. 1953.

Klumpyner, G., Hand, J., and Spanger, J. C.: Army psychiatry in Korea following the cease fire agreement. Am. J. Psychiat. *113*:352, 1956.

Koehler, W.: The Mentality of Apes. 3rd Ed. New York. Universal Distributors. 1948.

Korchin, S. J., et al.: Experience of perceptual distortion as a source of anxiety. Arch. Neurol. & Psychiat. *80*:98–113, 1958.

Kraepelin, E.: General paresis. New York. J. Nerv. & Ment. Dis. Publ., 1913.

Kraepelin, E.: Dementia Praecox and Paraphrenia. Edinburgh. E. and S. Livingstone. 1919.

Kraepelin, E.: Manic-Depressive Insanity and Paranoia. Edinburgh. E. and S. Livingstone. 1921.

Krafft-Ebing, R.: Psychopathia Sexualis. New York. Pioneer. 1939.

Krapf, E. E.: On the pathogenesis of epileptic and hysterical seizures. Bull. World Health Organ. *16*:749, 1957.

Krech, D., and Crutchfield, R. S.: Theory and Problems of Social Psychology. New York. McGraw-Hill Book Co. 1948.

Kretschmer, E.: Physique and Character. New York. Harcourt, Brace & Co. 1925.

Krieg, W. J. S.: Functional Neuroanatomy. Philadelphia. The Blakiston Co. 1947.

Kroeber. A. L., Ed.: International Symposium on Anthropology. Chicago. University of Chicago Press. 1952.

Kroeber, A. L.: Anthropology Today. Chicago. University of Chicago Press. 1953.

Kropotkin, P. A.: Mutual Aid—A Factor of Evolution. New York. Penguin Books. 1939.

Krout, M. H.: Introduction to Social Psychology. New York. Harper & Bros. 1942.

Kruse, H. D.: Integrating the Approaches to Mental Disease. New York. Paul B. Hoeber. 1957.

Kubie, L. S.: Neurotic Distortion of the Creative Process. Lawrence, Kansas. University of Kansas Press. 1942.

Kubie, L. S.: Practical and Theoretical Aspects of Psychoanalysis. Rev. ed. International Universities Press. 1950.

Kuhn, L., and Russo, S.: Modern Hypnosis. New York. Psychological Library. 1947.

Kuo, Z. Y.: Genesis of the cat's responses towards the rat. J. Comp. Psychol. *11*:1, 1930.

La Barre, W.: The Human Animal. University of Chicago Press. 1955.

Lacey, L. I., Smith, R., and Green, A.: Use of conditioned autonomic responses in the theory of anxiety. Psychosom. Med. *17*:208, 1955.

Laing, R. D.: An examination of Tillich's theory of anxiety and neurosis. Brit. J. Med. Psychol. *30*:88–91, 1957.

Laird, C.: The Miracle of Language. New York. Fawcett Publications. 1957.

Langer, Susanne K.: Philosophy in a New Key. New York. Mentor. 1956.

Lansing, A. J.: Cowdry's Problems of Aging. Biological and Medical Aspects. 3rd Ed. Baltimore. Williams and Wilkins Co. 1952.

Laughlin, H. P.: The Neuroses in Clinical Practice. Philadelphia. W. B. Saunders Co. 1956.

Lawton, G., Ed.: New Goals for Old Age. New York. Columbia University Press. 1943.

Lawton, G.: Aging Successfully. New York. Columbia University Press. 1946.

Lazarsfeld, P. F.: Mathematical Thinking in the Social Sciences. Glencoe, Ill. Free Press. 1954.

LeBeau, J.: Anterior cingulectomy in man. J. Neurosurg. *11*:268, 1955.

LeBlond, C. P.: Extra-hormonal factors in mental behavior. Proc. Soc. Exper. Biol. & Med. *38*:66, 1938.

Leighton, A. H., Clausen, J. A., and Wilson, R. N.: Exploration in Social Psychiatry. New York. Basic Books. 1957.

Leighton, D., and Kluckhohn, G.: Children of the People. Cambridge. Harvard University Press. 1947.

Lemkau, P. V.: Basic Issues in Psychiatry. Springfield, Ill. Charles C Thomas. 1959.

Levine, Edna S.: Youth in a Soundless World. New York. New York University Press. 1956.

Levine, S.: Stimulation in infancy. Scientific American *202*:81, 1960.

Levine, S., and Levin, G. W.: Critical periods for effects of infantile experience on maturation of stress response. Science *129*:43, 1959.

Levitt, E. E., Beiser, H., and Robertson, R. E.: A follow-up evaluation of cases treated at a community child guidance clinic. Personal Communication. 1958.

Levy, D.: The relation of animal psychology to psychiatry. *In* Galdston, I., Ed.: Medicine and Science. New York. International Universities Press. 1954.

Levy, D.: Maternal Overprotection. New York. Columbia University Press. 1943.

Levy-Bruhl, L.: Primitive Mentality. New York. The Macmillan Co. 1923.

Lewin, B., and Ross, Helen: Psychoanalytic Education in the U.S. New York. W. W. Norton & Co. 1960.

Lewin, K.: A Dynamic Theory of Personality. New York. McGraw-Hill Book Co. 1935.
Lewin, K.: Principles of Topological Psychology. New York. McGraw-Hill Book Co. 1936.
Lewin, K.: Resolving Social Conflicts. New York. Harper & Bros. 1948.
Liddell, H. S.: Discussion of Konrad Lorenz. Proc. Center Post-Grad. Training. New York. Oct. 23, 1958.
Liebman, J. L.: Peace of Mind. New York. Simon and Schuster. 1946.
Liebman, S., Ed.: Emotional Problems of Childhood. Philadelphia. J. B. Lippincott Co. 1958.
Lief, A., Ed.: The Common-Sense Psychiatry of Dr. Adolf Meyer. New York. McGraw-Hill Book Co. 1948.
Lilly, J. C.: Some considerations regarding basic mechanisms of positive and negative types of motivation. Am. J. Psychiat. *115*:113, 1956.
Lindauer, M.: House Hunt. Scientific American *196*:70, 1958.
Lindbergh, C. A.: Spirit of St. Louis. New York. Scribner's. 1953.
Lindeman, E. C., Ed.: Plutarch's Lives. New York. Mentor. 1953.
Linden, M. D.: Relationship between social attitudes toward aging and the delinquencies of youth. Am. J. Psychiat. *114*:444, 1957.
Lindesmith, A. R.: Opiate Addiction. Bloomington, Indiana. Principia Press. 1947.
Lindner, R. M.: Rebel without a Cause. New York. Grune and Stratton. 1944.
Lindsay, G., Ed.: Handbook of Social Psychology. 2 vols. Cambridge, Mass. Addison-Wesley Publishing Co. 1954.
Linn, L.: Some seven mental aspects of the body image. Internat. J. Psychoanalysis *36*:36, 1955.
Linn, L.: A Handbook of Hospital Psychiatry. New York. International Universities Press. 1955.
Linn, L.: The renaissance of neuropsychiatry. Psych. Quart. July 1955.
Linn, L.: Sources of uncertainty in studies of drugs affecting mood, mentation, or activity. Am. J. Psychiat. *116*:97, 1959.
Linton, R.: The Study of Man. New York. D. Appleton-Century Co. 1936.
Linton, R.: The Tree of Culture. New York. Alfred A. Knopf. 1955.
Lippman, H. S.: Treatment of the Child in Emotional Conflict. New York. McGraw-Hill Book Co. 1956.
London, L. S., and Caprio, F. S.: Sexual Deviations. Washington, D. C. Linacre Press. 1950.
Lorenz, K.: King Solomon's Ring. New York. Basic Books. 1952.
Lorenz, Marcia: Behavior and language patterns. Psychiatry *18*:353, 1955.
Lowrie, R. H.: Primitive Society. New York. Liveright. 1947.
Lundberg, F. and Farnham, Marynia: Modern Woman, the Lost Sex. New York. Harper & Bros. 1947.
Lurie, W.: The impertinent questioner: the scientist's guide to the statistician's mind. Amer. Science *46*:58, 1958.

Malinowski, B.: The Sexual Life of Savages in Northwestern Melanesia. New York. Liveright. 1929. 2 vols.
Mantegazza, P.: The Sexual Relations of Mankind. New York. Eugenics Publishing Co. 1935.
Marcel, G.: Le Mystère de l'Être. Paris. Aubier. 1951.
Masland, R. L., Saison, S. B., and Gladwin, T.: Mental Subnormality. New York. Basic Books. 1958.
Maslow, A. H., and Mittelman, B.: Principles of Abnormal Psychology. New York. Harper & Bros. 1941.
Masserman, J. H.: Behavior and Neurosis. Chicago. University of Chicago Press. 1943. (See for earlier references.)
Masserman, J. H.: A note on the dynamics of suicide. Dis. Nerv. System *8*:324, 1947.
Masserman, J. H.: Mental hygiene in a world crisis. Dis. Nerv. System *2*:210, 1948.
Masserman, J. H.: Psychological Medicine and World Affairs. *In* Harris, N. G., Ed.: Modern Trends in Psychological Medicine. New York. Paul B. Hoeber. 1948.

Masserman, J. H.: Modern reorientations in psychoanalytic therapy. Dis. Nerv. System 10:3, 1949.

Masserman, J. H.: Some current concepts of sexual behavior. Psychiatry 14:67, 1951.

Masserman, J. H.: Psychoanalysis and biodynamics—an integration. Internat. J. Psycho-Analysis 34:1, 1953.

Masserman, J. H.: Can sociology be weaned from its formulae? In Hsu, F. L. K., Ed.: Aspects of Culture and Personality. New York. Abelard-Schuman, Inc. 1954. p. 161.

Masserman, J. H.: Moreno's "Transference, counter-transference, and tele." Group Psychotherapy 7:309, 1954.

Masserman, J. H.: The conceptional dynamics of person, religion and self. Psychoanal. Rev. 41:303, 1954.

Masserman, J. H.: Practice of Dynamic Psychiatry. Philadelphia. W. B. Saunders Co. 1955.

Masserman, J. H.: Emotional reactions to death and suicide. In Liebman, S., Ed.: Stress Situations. Philadelphia. J. B. Lippincott Co. 1955. p. 117.

Masserman, J. H.: Moreno's "Interpersonal therapy, group psychotherapy and the function of the unconscious." Group Psychotherapy 8:62, 1955.

Masserman, J. H.: The role of drug therapies in current and future psychiatric practice. Psychiatric Research Reports no. 4. Washington, D. C. American Psychiatric Association, 1956, pp. 95, 125.

Masserman, J. H.: In Gerty, Francis: Round-table discussion. Psychiatric Research Reports. Washington, D. C. American Psychiatric Association, 1956, pp. 114–129.

Masserman, J. H.: Say ID isn't so—with music. In Masserman, J. H., Ed.: Science and Psychoanalysis. New York. Grune and Stratton. 1958.

Masserman, J. H., Ed.: Biological Psychiatry. I. New York. Grune and Stratton. 1959.

Masserman, J. H.: Masochism—a biodynamic review. In Masserman, J. H., Ed.: Science and Psychoanalysis. II. New York. Grune and Stratton. 1959. p. 73.

Masserman, J. H.: The biodynamic approaches. In Arieti, S., Ed.: American Handbook of Psychiatry. New York. Basic Books. 1959. Vol. II, pp. 1680–1696.

Masserman, J. H.: Experimental approaches to psychotherapy. In Gottlieb, J. S., and Tourney, G.: Scientific Papers and Discussions. A.P.A. Divisional Meeting, District Branches Publication No. 1. Washington, D. C. American Psychiatric Association. 1960. p. 125.

Masserman, J. H.: Humanitarian psychiatry. Acta Psychotherap. 8:395–399, 1960; also in American Practitioner 11:915, 1960.

Masserman, J. H.: The office therapy of psychosomatic disorders. Arch. Gen. Psychiat. 3:320, 1960.

Masserman, J. H., Ed.: Current Psychiatric Therapies. New York. Grune and Stratton. Annually from 1961.

Masserman, J. H., et al.: The neuroses. In Spiegel, E. A., Ed.: Progress in Neurology and Psychiatry. New York. Grune and Stratton. Annually from 1948.

Masserman, J. H., and Balken, Eva R.: The psychoanalytic and psychiatric significance of phantasy. Psychoanalyt. Rev. 26:343 and 555, 1939.

Masserman, J. H., Hecker, A. L., Pessin, J., and Booth, B. E.: Philosophy and methodology in the training of 500 psychiatric residents. Am. J. Psychiat. 106:362, 1949.

Masserman, J. H., and Jacques, Mary G.: Do lie detectors lie? Nation 174:368, 1952.

Masserman, J. H., Levitt, M., McAvoy, T., Kling, A., and Pechtel, C.: Cingulates and behavior. J. Nerv. & Ment. Dis. 126:148, 1958.

Masserman, J. H., and Moreno, J. L., Eds.: Progress in Psychotherapy. New York. Grune and Stratton. Annually, 1956 to 1960.

Masserman, J. H., and Pechtel, C.: Conflict-engendered neurotic and psychotic behavior in monkeys. J. Nerv. & Ment. Dis. 118:408, 1953.

Masserman, J. H., Pechtel, C., and Gross, Z.: Abnormalities of behavior. In Stone, C. P., Ed.: Annual Review of Psychology. Palo Alto, Calif. Stanford Ann. Reviews. 1954, p. 263.

Masserman, J. H., and Pechtel, C.: The osmatic responses of normal and neurotic monkeys. Ann. New York Acad. Sc. 58:256, 1954.

Masserman, J. H., and Pechtel, C.: How brain lesions affect normal and neurotic behavior. Am. J. Psychiat. 112:872, 1956.

Masserman, J. H., and Pechtel, C.: Normal and neurotic olfactory behavior in monkeys. Tr. Soc. Biol. Soc. *11*:30, 1956.

Masserman, J. H., and Pechtel, C.: Neurophysiologic and pharmacologic influences on experimental neuroses. Am. J. Psychiat. *113*:510, 1956.

Masserman, J. H., Pechtel, C., and Aarons, L.: Differential responses in young vs. old animals to training, conflict, drugs and brain lesions. *In:* Am. J. Psychiat. *116:* 1018, 1960.

Masserman, J. H., Schreiner, L., Rioch, D. McK., and Pechtel, C.: Behavioral changes following thalamic injury in cats. J. Neurophysiol. *16*:234–246, 1953.

Masserman, J. H., and Yum, K. S.: An analysis of the influence of alcohol on experimental neuroses in cats. Psychosom. Med. 8:36, 1946.

May, R.: The Meaning of Anxiety. New York. The Ronald Press. 1950.

Mayer-Gross, W., Slater, E., and Roth, M.: Clinical Psychiatry. Baltimore. Williams & Wilkins Co. 1955.

McDonald, J. M.: Psychiatry and the Criminal. Springfield, Ill. Charles C Thomas. 1957.

McGill, V. J.: Emotions and Reason. Springfield, Ill. Charles C Thomas. 1954.

McKinney, F.: Psychology of Personal Adjustment. New York. John Wiley & Sons. 1949.

Mead, Margaret: From the South Seas. New York. Morrow. 1939.

Mead, Margaret: Male and Female: A Study of the Sexes in a Changing World. New York. William Morrow & Co. 1949.

Mead, Margaret: Sex and Temperament. New York. Mentor. 1952.

Mead, Margaret, and Macgregor, F. C.: Growth and Culture. New York. G. P. Putnam's Sons. 1951.

Menninger, K. A.: Love against Hate. New York. Harcourt, Brace and Co. 1942.

Menninger, K. A.: The Human Mind. 3rd Ed. New York. Alfred A. Knopf. 1945.

Menninger, K. A.: A Guide to Psychiatric Books. New York. Grune and Stratton. 1950.

Menninger, K. A.: A Manual for Psychiatric Case Study. New York. Grune and Stratton. 1952.

Menninger, K. A.: Theory of Psychoanalytic Technique. New York. Basic Books. 1958.

Menninger, W. C.: Psychiatry in a Troubled World. New York. The Macmillan Co. 1948.

Mikesell, W. H., Ed.: Modern Abnormal Psychology. New York. Philosophical Library. 1950.

Miller, J. G.: Information input overload and psychopathology. Am. J. Psychiat. *116:* 695, 1960.

Miller, J. G., Ed.: Experiments in Social Process. New York. McGraw-Hill Book Co. 1950.

Moench, L. C.: Office Psychiatry. Chicago. Year Book Publishers. 1952.

Moloney, J. C.: Understanding the Japanese Mind. New York. Philosophical Library. 1954.

Monrad-Krohn, G. H.: Clinical Examination of the Nervous System. 10th Ed. New York. Harper & Bros. 1954.

Monrad-Krohn, G. H.: The third element of speech: prosody in the neuro-psychiatric clinic. J. Ment. Sc. *103*:326–331, 1957.

Moravia, A.: Two Adolescents. New York. Farrar and Straus. 1950.

Moreno, J. L.: Group Psychotherapy. 3rd Ed. New York. Beacon House. 1957.

Morris, C. W.: Six Theories of Mind. Chicago. University of Chicago Press. 1932.

Moses, Paul J.: The Voice of Neurosis. New York. Grune and Stratton. 1954.

Mullahy, P.: Oedipus—Myth and Complex. New York. Hermitage Press. 1948.

Mullahy, P.: Contributions of Harry Stack Sullivan. New York. Hermitage Press. 1952.

Muller, H. J.: The Uses of the Past. New York. Mentor. 1952.

Muncie, W.: Psychobiology and Psychiatry. 2nd Ed. St. Louis. C. V. Mosby Co. 1948.

Munroe, Ruth: Schools of Psychoanalytic Thought. New York. Dryden Press. 1955. pp. 174–219.

Murphy, G.: Personality: A Biosocial Approach to Origins and Structure. New York. Harper & Bros. 1947.

Murphy, G.: In the Minds of Men. New York. Basic Books. 1953.

Murphy, G. and Bachrach, A. J., Eds.: An Outline of Psychology. New York. Modern Library. 1954.

Murray, H. A.: Explorations in Personality. New York. Oxford University Press. 1938.

Murray, H. A.: Thematic Apperception Test. Cambridge, Mass. Harvard University Press. 1943.

Nagel, E.: Sovereign Reason. Glencoe, Ill. Free Press. 1954.

Nagel, E., and Newman, J. R.: Godel's Proof. Scientific American *194:*71, 1956.

Nakao, H.: Emotional behavior produced by hypothalamic stimulation. Am. J. Physiol. *194:*411, 1958.

Nash, H.: The design and conduct of argument on the psychological effects of drugs. J. Nerv. Dis. *128:*129, 1959.

Naumburg, Margaret: Studies of the Free Art of Expression of Behavior Problem Children and Adolescents as a Means of Diagnosis and Therapy. New York. Nervous and Mental Disease Publishing Co. 1947.

Naumburg, Margaret: Schizophrenic Art. New York. Grune and Stratton. 1950.

Neill, A. S.: The Problem Family. New York. Hermitage Press. 1949.

Newman, H. H., Ed.: The Nature of the World and of Man. Chicago. University of Chicago Press. 1926.

Newman, H. H.: Acute Alcoholic Intoxication. Stanford University Press. 1941.

Newman, H. H., Freeman, F., and Holzinger, J. J.: Twins: A study of heredity and environment. Chicago. University of Chicago Press. 1937.

Newman, S., and Mather, V. G.: Analysis of spoken language of patients with affective disorders. Am. J. Psychiat. *94:*913, 1938.

New York Academy of Medicine: Radio in Health Education. New York. Columbia University Press. 1945.

Nicole, J. E.: Psychopathology: A Survey of Modern Approaches. 4th Ed. Baltimore. Williams & Wilkins Co. 1947.

Nicoll, M.: Dream Psychology. London. Oxford University Press. 1917.

Niebuhr, R.: The Self and the Drama of History. New York. Charles Scribner's Sons. 1955.

Nielsen, J. M.: A Textbook of Clinical Neurology. New York. Paul B. Hoeber. 1941.

Nielsen, J. M.: Agnosia, Apraxia, Aphasia: Their Value in Cerebral Localization. 2nd Ed. New York. Paul B. Hoeber. 1946.

Nielsen, J. M., and Thompson, George N.: The Engrammes of Psychiatry. Springfield, Ill. Charles C Thomas. 1947.

Nijinski, Romola: Nijinsky. New York. Garden City Publishing Co. 1941.

Nordenskiöld, Erik: The History of Biology. New York. Tudor Publishing Co. 1928.

Norris, A. S.: Prenatal factors in intellectual and emotional development. J.A.M.A. *172:*413, 1960.

Noveck, Simon, Ed.: Judaism and Psychiatry. New York. Basic Books. 1956.

Novey, S.: Some philosophical speculations about the concept of genital character. Internat. J. Psychoanalysis *36:*88, 1955.

Nowlis, H. H.: The influence of success and failure on the resumption of an interrupted task. J. Exper. Psychol. *28:*304, 1941.

Noyes, A. P., and Kolb, L. C.: Modern Clinical Psychiatry. 5th Ed. Philadelphia. W. B. Saunders Company. 1958.

Oberndorf, C. P.: A History of Psychoanalysis in America. New York. Grune and Stratton. 1953.

Odier, C.: Anxiety and Magic Thinking. New York. International Universities Press. 1955.

Offenkrantz, W.: Psychiatric management of suicide problems in military service. Am. J. Psychiat. *114:*33, 1957.

Ogburn, W. F., and Menkoff, M. F.: Sociology. Boston. Houghton Mifflin Co. 1940.

Ogden, C. K., and Richards, S. A.: The Meaning of Meaning. New York. Harcourt, Brace & Co. 1923.

O'Kelly, L. I.: An experimental study of regression. J. Comp. Psychol. *30:*55, 1940.

Olds, J.: Pleasure centers in the brain. Scientific American *195:*105, 1956.

Olds, J.: Self stimulation of the brain. Science *127:*315, 1958.

Olds, J., Kellam, K. F., and Bach, Rita P.: Self stimulation of the brain used as a screening method for tranquilizing drugs. Science *124:*265, 1956.

O'Neal, P., and Robins, L. N.: The relation of childhood behavior to adult psychiatric status. Am. J. Psychiat. *114:*961, 1958.

Opler, M. K.: Psychoanalytic techniques in social analysis. Am. J. Sociol. *15:*91, 1942.

Opler, M. K., Ed.: Culture and Mental Health. New York. The Macmillan Co. 1959.

Oppenheimer, R.: Analogy in science. Am. Psychol. *11:*127, 1956.

Orgel, S. Z.: Psychiatry Today and Tomorrow. New York. International Universities Press. 1946.

Orr, D. W.: Transference and countertransference. A historical survey. J. Am. Psychoanalyt. A. *2:*621, 1954.

Orton, S. T.: Reading, Writing and Speech Problems in Children. New York. W. W. Norton & Co. 1937.

Ostow, M., and Scharfstein, Ben-Ami: The Need to Believe. New York. International Universities Press. 1954.

Palmer, H.: The Philosophy of Psychiatry. New York. Philosophical Library. 1952.

Parloff, M. B., et al.: Communication of values and therapeutic change. Arch. Gen. Psychiat. *2:*300, 1960.

Parsons, T.: The Social System. Glencoe, Ill. Free Press. 1951.

Pasamanick, B., and Lilienfeld, A.: Association of maternal and fetal factors with development of mental deficiency. J.A.M.A. *159:*155, 1955.

Paterson, D. G.: Physique and Intellect. New York. The Century Co. 1930.

Pattie, F. A.: The gregarious behavior of normal chicks and chicks hatched in isolation. J. Comp. Physiol. *21:*161, 1936.

Pavlov, I. P.: Lectures on Conditioned Reflexes: 25 Years of Objective Study of the Higher Nervous Activity (Behavior) of Animals. New York. International Publishers. 1928.

Pechtel, C., Masserman, J. H., Schreiner, L., and Levitt, M.: Differential effects of lesions of the mediodorsal nuclei of the thalamus on normal and neurotic behavior in the cat. J. Nerv. & Ment. Dis. *121:*26, 1955.

Pechtel, C., and Masserman, J. H.: Cerebral localization: not where, but in whom? Am. J. Psychiat. *116:*51, 1959.

Peele, T. L.: The Neuroanatomical Basis for Clinical Neurology. New York. McGraw-Hill Book Co. 1954.

Pei, Mario: The Story of Language. New York. J. B. Lippincott Co. 1949.

Pellman, C.: Overcoming Stammering. New York. Beechurst Press. 1947.

Penfield, W.: Speech and Brain Mechanisms. Princeton University Press. 1959.

Penfield, W. and Jasper, H.: Epilepsy and Functional Anatomy of the Human Brain. Boston. Little, Brown & Co. 1954.

Penfield, W., and Kristiansen, K.: Epileptic Seizure Patterns: A Study of the Localizing Value of Initial Phenomena in Focal Cortical Seizures. Springfield, Illinois. Charles C Thomas. 1951.

Penfield, W., and Milner, B.: Memory deficit produced by bilateral lesions in the hippocampal zone. Arch. Neurol. & Psychiat. *79:*475, 1958.

Penfield, W., and Roberts, L.: The interpretive cortex. Science *159:*1722, 1959.

Peon, R. H.: Modification of electrical activity in cochlear nucleus during attention in unanesthetized cats. Science *123:*331, 1956.

Perd, R.: Logical analysis. Am. J. Psychiat. *114:*397, 1957.

Piaget, J.: The Child's Conception of Physical Causality. New York. Harcourt, Brace & Co. 1930.

Piaget, J.: The Language and Thought of the Child. 2nd Ed. New York. Harcourt, Brace & Co. 1932.

Piaget, J.: The Construction of Reality in the Child. New York. Basic Books. 1954.

Piaget, J.: The child and modern physics. Scientific American *196:*40, 1957.

Piaget, J., and Inhelder, B.: The Child's Concept of Space. London. Rutledge and Kegan. 1942.

Piers, G., and Singer, M. B.: Shame and Guilt. Springfield, Illinois. Charles C Thomas. 1953.

Pittinger, R. E., and Smith, H. L.: A basis for some contributions of linguistics to psychiatry. Am. J. Psychiat. *20:*610, 1957.

Plank, M.: The Universe in the Light of Modern Physics. London. Allen and Unwin. 1937.

Pollak, Otto: Social Science and Psychotherapy for Children. New York. Russell Sage Foundation. 1952.

Polyani, M.: Scientific outlook, its sickness and its cure. Science *125:*480, 1957.

Polyani, M.: Personal Knowledge Towards a Post-scientific Philosophy. Chicago. University of Chicago Press. 1958.

Popham, R. L.: Some social and cultural aspects of alcoholism. Amer. Psych. Assoc. *4:*22, 1955.

Porter, R. W.: Experimental observations on gastrointestinal lesions in behaviorally conditioned monkeys. Psychosom. Med. *20:*379, 1958.

Potter, S.: The Theory and Practice of Gamesmanship. New York. Henry Holt & Co. 1954.

Powdermaker, Florence B., and Frank, J. D.: Group Psychotherapy. Cambridge. Harvard University Press. 1953.

Price, C. R.: Science and the supernatural. Science *122:*359, 1955.

Pringle, K., and Bossio, V.: Early prolonged separation and emotional maladjustment. J. Child Psychol. & Psychiat. *1:*37, 1960.

Proust, M.: Remembrance of Things Past. New York. Random House. 1934.

Pumpian-Mindlin, E., Ed.: Psychoanalysis as Science. Stanford. Stanford University Press. 1952.

Pumpian-Mindlin, E.: Changing concepts of therapy in a Veterans Administration Mental Hygiene Clinic. Am. J. Psychiat. *113:*1095, 1957.

Puner, Helen W.: Freud, His Life and His Mind. New York. Howell-Soskin. 1947.

Rabiner, E.: Transference-countertransference phenomena in choice of shock. Arch. Neurol. & Psychiat. *81:*517, 1959.

Radiguet, R.: Devil in the Flesh. London. Graywalls Press. 1949.

Rado, S., and Daniels, G.: Changing Concepts in Psychoanalytic Medicine. New York. Grune and Stratton. 1956.

Raines, G. N., and Rohrer, T. H.: The operational matrix of psychiatric practice. Consistency and variability in interview impression of different psychiatrists. Am. J. Psychiat. *111:*721, 1955.

Rank, O.: The Myth of the Birth of the Hero. New York. Nervous and Mental Disease Publishing Company. 1914.

Rank, O.: Will Therapy and Truth and Reality. New York. Alfred A. Knopf. 1947.

Rapaport, A.: What is semantics? Scientific American *40:*123, 1952.

Rapaport, A.: Scientific approach to ethics. Scientific American *125:*796, 1957.

Rappaport, D.: Manual of Diagnostic Psychological Testing. Josiah Macy, Jr., Foundation. 1944.

Razran, G.: Pavlov and Lamarck. Science *128:*758, 1958.

Redlich, F., Bingham, June, and Levine, J.: The Inside Story. New York. Alfred A. Knopf. 1953.

Rees, J. R.: The Shaping of Psychiatry by War. New York. W. W. Norton & Co. 1945.

Reich, W.: Character Analysis: Principles and Technique for Psychoanalysts in Practice and in Training. 3rd Ed. New York. Orgone Institute Press. 1949.

Reichenback, H.: The Rise of Scientific Philosophy. Berkeley. University of California Press. 1956.

Reik, T.: Listening with the Third Ear. New York. Farrar, Straus and Young. 1949.

Reiss, Max, Ed.: Psychoendocrinology. New York. Grune and Stratton. 1958.

Rennie, T. A. C., and Woodward, L. E.: Mental Health in Modern Society. New York. Commonwealth Fund. 1948.

Rensch, B.: The intelligence of elephants. Scientific American *196:*44, 1957.

Reymert, M. L., Ed.: Feelings and Emotion. New York. McGraw-Hill Book Co. 1950.

Reynolds, G. S., and Sommers, P.: Effects of ethyl alcohol on avoidance behavior. Scientific American *132:*43, 1960.

Reznikoff, M. A., and Toomey, L.: Evaluation of Changes Associated with Psychiatric Treatment. Springfield, Ill. Charles C Thomas. 1959.

Rhine, J. B.: New Frontiers of the Mind. New York. Farrar and Rinehart. 1937.

Ribble, Margaretha: The Rights of Infants. New York. Columbia University Press. 1943.

Richter, C. P.: On the phenomenon of sudden death in animals and man. Psychosom. Med. *19:*191, 1957.

Riesman, D.: The Lonely Crowd. New Haven. Yale University Press. 1958.

Riese, W.: Principles of Neurology in the Field of History and Their Present Use. New York. Nervous & Mental Disease Monographs. 1950.

Riese, W.: An outline of history of ideas in psychotherapy. Bull. Hist. Med. *25:*442, 1951.

Riese, W.: Philosophical presuppositions of present-day medicine. Bull. Hist. Med. *30:*163, 1956.

Rinkel, M., and Himwich, H. E., Eds.: Insulin Treatment in Psychiatry. New York. Philosophical Library. 1959.

Rioch, D. McK.: Certain aspects of "conscious" phenomena and their neural correlates. Am. J. Psychiat. *111:*810, 1955.

Rioch, D. McK.: The application of the experimental method to psychiatric therapy. J. Hillside Hospital *5:*3, 1956.

Rioch, D. McK.: Problems of "perception" and "communication" in mental illness. A.M.A. Arch. Gen. Psychiat. *1:*81, (July) 1959.

Ripley, H. S., and Jackson, Joan: Therapeutic factors in AA. Am. J. Psychiat. *116:*44, 1960.

Roback, A. A.: History of American Psychology. New York. Library Publications. 1952.

Robbins, B. S.: The myth of latent emotion. Psychotherapy *1:*3, 1955.

Roberts, D., and Torkelson, E. H.: Preparing the mind for battle. Infantry J. *56:*34, 1945.

Roberts, W.: Rapid escape learning without avoidance learning motivated by hypothalamic stimulation in cats. J. Comp. & Physiol. Psychol. *51:*391, 1950.

Roberts, W.: Both rewarding and punishing effects from stimulation of posterior hypothalamus of cat with same electrode and same intensity. J. Comp. & Physiol. Psychol. *51:*4, 1958.

Roe, Anne, and Simpson, G. C.: Behavior and Evolution. New Haven. Yale University Press. 1958.

Rogers, Carl R.: Counselling and Psychotherapy. Boston. Houghton Mifflin Co. 1942.

Rorschach, H.: Psychodiagnostics: A Diagnostic Test Based on Perception. New York. Grune and Stratton. 1942.

Rose, A. M., Ed.: Mental Health and Mental Disorder. New York. W. W. Norton & Co. 1955.

Rosenzweig, S., and Kogan, K.: Psychodiagnosis. New York. Grune and Stratton. 1949.

Ross, F. H., and Hills, Tynette: The Great Religions. New York. Fawcett Publications. 1956.

Ross, W. D., and Kehal, R. A.: Practical Psychiatry for Industrial Physicians. Springfield, Ill. Charles C Thomas. 1956.

Rostand, J.: Can Man Be Modified? New York. Basic Books. 1959.

Rosvold, H. E.: The effects of electroconvulsive shock on gestation and maternal behavior: I. J. Comp. & Physiol. Psychol. *42:*207, 1949.

Royce, V.: The search for meaning. Scientific American *47:*515, 1959.

Ruch, F. L.: Psychology and Life. Chicago. Scott, Foresman & Co. 1953.

Ruesch, J.: Transference reformulated. Acta psychother., Suppl. vol. 3, 1955, p. 596.
Ruesch, J.: Disturbed Communication. New York. W. W. Norton & Co. 1957.
Ruesch, J., and Bateson, G.: Communication. New York. W. W. Norton & Co. 1951.
Ruesch, J., and Kess, W.: Non-verbal Communication. Berkeley. University of California Press. 1956.
Russell, B.: Outline of Philosophy. London. Allen and Unwin. 1927.
Russell, B.: Power, a New Social Analysis. New York. W. W. Norton & Co. 1938.
Russell, B.: Philosophical Development. New York. Simon and Schuster. 1959.
Russell, B.: The social responsibilities of scientists. Science *131*:391, 1960.

Sackel, M.: The Pharmacological Shock Treatment of Schizophrenia. New York. Nervous and Mental Disease Publishing Co. 1938.
Salzman, L.: Spiritual and faith healing. J. Pastoral Care *11*:14, 1957.
Salzman, L.: Masochism. *In* Masserman, J. H., Ed.: Science and Psychoanalysis. Vol. II. New York. Grune & Stratton. 1959.
Sanger, W. S.: The History of Prostitution. New York. Eugenics Publishing Co. 1937.
Sargant, W. W., and Slater, E.: An Introduction to Physical Methods of Treatment in Psychiatry. 3rd Ed. Baltimore. Williams and Wilkins Co. 1954.
Sargent, S. S. and Smith, Marian W., Eds.: Culture and Personality. New York. Viking Fund. 1949.
Sarton, G.: A History of Science. Cambridge. Harvard University Press. 1952.
Sartre, J. P.: L'Existentialisme est un Humanisme. Paris. Nagel. 1946.
Sartre, J. P.: Being and Nothingness. New York. Philosophical Library. 1956.
Saslow, G., and Peters, Ann D.: A follow-up study of "untreated" patients with various behavior disorders. Psychiatric Quart. *30*:283, 1956.
Sauer, E. G. F.: Celestial navigation in birds. Scientific American *199*:42, 1958.
Saul, L. J.: Emotional Maturity. Philadelphia. J. B. Lippincott Co. 1947.
Saul, L. J.: The Hostile Mind. New York. Random House. 1956.
Saul, L. J.: Technic and Practice of Psychoanalysis. Philadelphia. J. B. Lippincott Co. 1958.
Saul, L. J.: Freud's death instinct and the second law of thermodynamics. Internat. J. Psychoanalysis *39*:323, 1959.
Schaffner, B., Ed.: Group Processes. New York. Josiah Macy, Jr., Foundation. 1955.
Scheelman, I.: Dynamics and treatment of antisocial psychopathology in adolescents. Nerv. Child *11*:35, 1955.
Schein, E. H.: The Chinese indoctrination program for prisoners of war. Psychiatry *19*:149, 1956.
Schelling, T. C.: The Strategy of Conflict. Cambridge, Mass. Harvard University Press. 1960.
Scher, J. M.: The structured ward. Am. J. Orthopsychiat. *28*:291, 1958.
Schilder, P.: The Image and Appearance of the Human Body. New York. International Universities Press. 1950.
Schilder, P.: Medical Psychology. New York. International Universities Press. 1953.
Schiller, C. H. (Tr.): Instinctive Behavior. New York. International Universities Press. 1957.
Schilpp, P. A., Ed.: Albert Einstein: Philosopher–Scientist. Evanston. Library of Living Philosophies. 1949.
Schmarl, R. B.: The scientist. Am. Sci. *47*:100A, 1949.
Schmerhorn, R. A.: Psychiatric disorders among Negroes: a sociologic note. Am. J. Psychiat. *112*:878, 1956.
Schmideberg, Melitta: The dilemma of the analyst. Samiksa *11*:189, 1957.
Schmideberg, Melitta: Values and goals in psychotherapy. Psychiatric Quart. *32*:233, 1958.
Schmidt, P. F.: Models of scientific thought. Am. Sci. *45*:173, 1957.
Schmidt, W.: The Origin and Growth of Religion. New York. The Humanities Press. 1935.

Schneck, J. M., Ed.: Hypnosis in Modern Medicine. Springfield, Ill. Charles C Thomas. 1953.

Schnierla, T. C.: Learning and orientation in ants. Comp. Psychol. Monographs 6:139, 1929.

Schoenfeld, C.: God and Country. New York. Philosophical Library. 1955.

Schuetz, A.: Multiple realities. Phil. & Phenom. Res. 5:533, 1945.

Scott, J. P.: The process of socialization in higher animals. Milbank Fund Publications. New York. 1953.

Scott, J. P.: Animal Behavior. Chicago. University of Chicago Press. 1958.

Scott, W. E.: Data on song in birds. Science 14:522, 1901.

Scull, C., Nance, M., and Roll, G. F.: Research in the Soviet Union. J.A.M.A. 167:2120, 1958.

Sèchehaye, Marguerite A.: Symbolic Realization: A New Method of Psychotherapy Applied to a Case of Schizophrenia. New York. International Universities Press. 1951.

Sèchehaye, Marguerite A., Ed.: Renee. The Autobiography of a Schizophrenic Girl. New York. Grune and Stratton. 1951.

Seitz, P. F. D.: The effects of infantile experiences upon adult behavior in animal subjects. I. Effects of litter size during infancy upon adult behavior in the rat. Am. J. Psychiat. 110:916, 1954.

Seligman, Kurt: The History of Magic. New York. Pantheon Books. 1948.

Senn, M. J., Ed.: Problems of Infancy and Childhood. New York. Josiah Macy, Jr., Foundation. 1953.

Shaffer, G. W., and Lazarus, R. S.: Fundamental Concepts in Clinical Psychology. New York. McGraw-Hill Book Co. 1952.

Shakespeare, W.: Complete Works. New York. Harper & Bros. 1954.

Shapiro, A. K.: The placebo effect. Am. J. Psychiat. 116:298, 1959.

Sheldon, W. H., Stevens, S. S., and Tucker, W. B.: The Varieties of Human Physique. New York. Harper & Bros. 1940.

Sheldon, W. H., and Stevens, S. S.: The Varieties of Temperament. New York. Harper & Bros. 1942.

Sherrington, C. S.: The Integrative Action of the Nervous System. New Haven. Yale University Press. 1948.

Shipley, J .T.: Dictionary of Word Origins. New York. Philosophical Library. 1945.

Shrader, Caroline, Van Gundy, Justine, and Husband, R. W., Eds.: Psychology Through Literature. New York. Oxford University Press. 1943.

Sibol, J.: The strangest birds in the world. Life, March 25, 1957, p. 88.

Simpson, G. G.: The Meaning of Evolution. New Haven. Yale University Press. 1949.

Sivadon, P. D.: Techniques of sociotherapy. Psychiatry 20:205, 1957.

Skinner, B. F.: The experimental analyses of behavior. Am. Sci. 45:343, 1957.

Skinner, B. F.: Verbal Behavior. New York. Appleton-Century-Crofts. 1957.

Smith, A., and Kinder, E. F.: Changes in psychological test performances of brain-operated schizophrenics after 8 years. Science 129:149, 1959.

Smith, H. W.: Man and His Gods. Boston. Little, Brown and Co. 1952.

Smith, Jackson: Occupational stress and emotional illness. J.A.M.A. 161:1038, 1956.

Smith, Jackson: Psychiatry: Descriptive and Dynamic. Baltimore. Williams and Wilkins Co. 1960.

Smith, Kendon: The naturalistic conception of life. Am. Sci. 46:413, 1958.

Soden, W. H., Ed.: Rehabilitation of the Handicapped. New York. The Ronald Press. 1949.

Soibelman, Doris: Therapeutic and Industrial Uses of Music. New York. Columbia University Press. 1948.

Solomon, H. C., and Yakovlev, P. I.: Manual of Military Neuropsychiatry. Philadelphia. W. B. Saunders Co. 1944.

Sonneman, U.: Existence and Therapy. New York. Grune and Stratton. 1954.

Sophocles: Oedipus Rex. Chicago. University of Chicago Press. 1954.

Sparer, P. J., Ed.: Personality, Stress and Tuberculosis. New York. International Universities Press. 1956.

Sperry, R. W.: The eye and the brain. Scientific American 194:56, 1956.

Sperry, R. W.: The growth of nerve circuits. Scientific American 201:68, 1959.

Spiegel, E. A.: Progress in Neurology and Psychiatry—An Annual Review. New York. Grune and Stratton. 1946 to present.

Spiegel, E. A., et al.: The thalamus and temporal orientation. Science *121:*771, 1955.

Spitz, R. A.: A note on the extrapolation of ethnological findings. Internat. J. Psychoanalysis *361:*162, 1955.

Stagner, R.: Psychology of Personality. New York. McGraw-Hill Book Co. 1937.

Stagner, R.: Psychology of Industrial Conflict. London. Chapman & Hall. 1956.

Stanton, A. H., and Schwartz, M. S.: The Mental Hospital. New York. Basic Books. 1954.

Stebel, W.: Conditions of Nervous Anxiety and Their Treatment. New York. Liveright. 1950.

Stein, L.: Secondary reinforcement established with subcortical stimulation. Science *127:*464, 1958.

Stern, A.: Science and the philosopher. Am. Sci. *44:*281, 1956.

Stern, Edith M.: Mental Illness: A Guide for the Family. New York. The Commonwealth Fund. 1945.

Stevens, S. S.: A Handbook of Experimental Psychology. New York. John Wiley & Sons. 1951.

Stevenson, G. S.: Mental Health Planning for Social Action. New York. McGraw-Hill Book Co. 1956.

Stevenson, Ian: Is human personality more plastic in infancy and childhood? Am. J. Psychiat. *114:*153, 1957.

Stone, A.: The Premarital Consultation: A manual for physicians. New York. Grune and Stratton. 1956.

Stone, L.: Brief psychotherapy. Psychoanalyt. Quart. *20:*215, 1951.

Storch, A.: Primitive Archaic Forms of Inner Experiences and Thought in Schizophrenia. New York. Nervous and Mental Disease Publishing Co. 1924.

Stott, D. H.: Infantile illness and subsequent mental and emotional development. J. Genet. Psychol. *94:*233–251, 1959.

Strauss, E.: On Obsessions. New York. Nervous and Mental Disease Publishing Co. 1948.

Strecker, E. A., Ebaugh, F. G., and Ewalt, J. R.: Practical Clinical Psychiatry. 7th Ed. Philadelphia. The Blakiston Co. 1957.

Strupp, H. H.: The psychotherapist's contribution to the treatment process. Behav. Sc. *3:*34, 1958.

Sullivan, H. S.: Conceptions of Modern Psychiatry. Washington, D. C. William Alanson White Psychiatric Foundation. 1947.

Sullivan, H. S.: The Interpersonal Theory of Psychiatry. New York. W. W. Norton & Co. 1953.

Sullivan, H. S.: The Psychiatric Interview. New York. W. W. Norton & Co. 1954.

Summers, M., Tr.: Malleus Maleficarum. London. Pushkin Press. 1948.

Symonds, P. M.: Dynamic Psychology. New York. Appleton-Century-Crofts. 1949.

Symposium on Preventive and Social Psychiatry. Walter Reed Army Institute of Research. Washington. 1957.

Szasz, T. S.: On the psychoanalytic theory of instincts. Psychoanalyt. Quart. *21:*25, 1952.

Szasz, T. S.: On the experiences of the analyst in the psychoanalytic situation. J. Am. Psychoanalyt. A. *4:*197, 1956.

Szasz, T. S.: Psychiatry and the law. A.M.A. Arch. Neurol. & Psychiat., 75:297, 1956.

Szasz, T. S.: Problems in contemporary psychoanalytic training. A.M.A. Arch. Gen. Psychiat., 3:82, 1960.

Szasz, T. S.: Three problems in contemporary psychoanalytic training. A.M.A. Arch. Gen. Psychiat., 4:106, 1960.

Szent-György, A.: Bioenergetics. New York. Academic Press. 1957.

Szymanski, J. S.: Modification of the innate behavior of cockroaches. J. Animal Behavior *2:*81, 1912.

Tanner, J. M.: Prospects in Psychiatric Research. Springfield, Ill. Charles C Thomas. 1953.

Tempereau, C. E.: Fear of flying in Korea. Am. J. Psychiat. *113*:218, 1956.

Teuber, H-L., and Weinstein, S.: Ability to discover hidden figures after cerebral lesions. Arch. Neurol. & Psychiat. *76*:369, 1956.

Thomas, A., Stern, M., and Lilienfeld, A.: Relationship of psychosis and psychosomatic disease. J. Nerv. & Ment. Dis. *123*:249, 1956.

Thompson, Clara: Emotional climate of psychoanalytic institutes. Psychiatry *21*:45, 1958.

Thompson, Clara, and Mullahy, P.: Psychoanalysis: Evolution and Development. New York. Hermitage House. 1950.

Thompson, Clara, Mazer, M., and Witenburg, E., Eds.: An Outline of Psychoanalysis. New York. Modern Library. 1955.

Thompson, W. R.: Early Environment—Its Importance for Later Behavior. *In* Hoch, P. H., and Zubin, J.: Psychopathology of Childhood. New York. Grune and Stratton. 1955.

Thompson, W. R.: Influence of prenatal maternal anxiety on emotionality in young rats. Science *125*:698, 1957.

Thompson, W. R., and Heron, J.: Protected pups, helpless dogs with a poor personality. Canadian J. Psychol. *8*:17, 1954.

Thompson, W. R., and Melzack, R.: Whirling behavior in dogs as related to early experiences. Science *123*:939, 1956.

Thorpe, J. G., and Baker, A. A.: Statistics, science, and psychiatry. Arch. Gen. Psychiat. *1*:338, 1959.

Thurber, J.: The psychosemanticist will see you now, Mr. Thurber. Science *123*:705, 1956.

Tillich, P.: Love, Power, and Justice. New York. Oxford University Press. 1954.

Time: Faithfulness. May 30, 1955, p. 30.

Tinbergen, N.: The Study of Instinct. Oxford. Clarendon Press. 1951.

Tomkins, S. S., Ed.: Contemporary Psychopathology. Cambridge. Harvard University Press. 1943.

Tourney, G., Senf, Rita, Dunham, H. W., Slem, R., and Gottlieb, J. S.: The effect of resocialization techniques on chronic schizophrenic patients. Am. J. Psychiat. *116*:993, 1960.

Tow, T. M.: Personality Changes Following Frontal Leucotomy: A Clinical and Experimental Study of the Functions of the Frontal Lobes in Man. New York. Oxford University Press. London. Amen House. 1955.

Toynbee, A. J.: Greek Historical Thought. New York. Mentor, 1952.

Toynbee, A. J.: A Study of History. New York. Oxford. Vols. 1–6, 1947. Vols. 7–10, 1957.

Toynbee, A. J.: Greek Civilization and Character. New York. Mentor. 1953.

Tyhurst, J. S.: Psychological and social aspects of civilian disaster. Canad. M.A.J., *76*: 385, 1957.

Tylor, E. B.: Primitive Culture. New York. Brentano. 1924.

Uhr, L., and Miller, V. G.: Drugs and Behavior. New York. John Wiley and Sons. 1960.

Underwood, B. J.: Psychological Research. New York. Appleton-Century-Crofts. 1957.

Unger, H. S.: Marriage annulment. Am. J. Psychiat. *117*:85, 1960.

Van Loon, H. W.: The Story of Mankind. New York. Pocket Library. 1957.

Veblen, T. B.: The Theory of the Leisure Class. New York. Modern Library. 1934.

Verrill, A. H.: The Strange Story of Our Earth. New York. Fawcett Publications. 1956.

Vexhall, J. von: Umwelt und Innenwelt der Tiere. Berlin. Springer. 1920.

Vieth, Ilsa: Psychiatric nosology: from Hyppocrates to Kraepelin. Am. J. Psychiat. *714*: 385, 1957.

Villiger, E.: Brain and Spinal Cord. Philadelphia. J. B. Lippincott Co. 1918.

Vischer, A. L.: Old Age—Its Compensations and Rewards. London. Allen and Unwin. 1947.

Viteles, M. S.: The new Utopia. Science *122:*1167, 1955.

Von deWall, W.: Music in Hospitals. New York. Russell Sage Foundation. 1946.

Von Witzlehen, H.: History, psychiatry and the behavioral sciences. Behav. Sci. *2:*57, 1957.

Wald, S.: The significance of vertebrate metamorphoses. Science *128:*1481, 1958.

Wallinger, J. V.: Severe alcoholism in career military personnel. U.S. Armed Forces M.J. 7:551, 1956.

Walpole, H. R.: Semantics. New York. W. W. Norton & Co. 1951.

Walter, W. G.: The Living Brain. New York. W. W. Norton & Co. 1953.

Walter, W. G.: Where vital things happen. Am. J. Psychiat. *116:*673, 1960.

Warcollier, R.: Mind to Mind. New York. Grune and Stratton. 1948.

Warner, W. J.: Common denominators in theory for psychotherapy. Group Psychotherapy 8:82, 1955.

Warren, H. C., Ed.: Dictionary of Psychology. Boston. Houghton Mifflin Co. 1934.

Waterman, P. F.: The Story of Superstition. New York. Grosset and Dunlap. 1929.

Watson, J. B.: Psychology from the Standpoint of a Behaviorist. 3rd Ed. Philadelphia. J. B. Lippincott Co. 1929.

Watson, R. E.: Experimentally induced conflict in cats. Psychosom. Med. *16:*341, 1954.

Watson, R. I.: Psychology of the Child: Personal, Social, and Disturbed Child Development. New York. John Wiley and Sons. 1959.

Wayne, G. G.: Some unconscious determinants in physicians motivating the use of particular treatment methods with special reference to electroconvulsive treatment. Psychoanal. Rev. *42:*83, 1955.

Weaver, W.: Science and people. Science *122:*1255, 1955.

Wechsler, I. S.: A Textbook of Clinical Neurology. 8th Ed. Philadelphia. W. B. Saunders Co. 1958.

Weider, A., Ed.: Contributions toward Medical Psychology. New York. The Ronald Press. 1953. 2 vols.

Weinstein, J. J.: Religion looks at Psychiatry. CCAR Journal, January, 1954.

Weinstock, H. I.: Summary and final report of the central fact-gathering committee. American Psychoanalytic Association, Jan. 15, 1958.

Weiss, E., and English, O. S.: Psychosomatic Medicine. 3rd Ed. Philadelphia. W. B. Saunders Co. 1957.

Wendt, H.: In Search of Adam. Cambridge. Riverside Press. 1956.

Whatnough, Joshua: Language: A Modern Synthesis. New York. Mentor. 1957.

Wheelis, A.: The vocational hazards of psychoanalysis. Internat. J. Psychoanalysis *37:* 171, 1956.

Wheelis, A.: The Quest for Identity. New York. W. W. Norton & Co. 1958.

White, M., Ed.: The Age of Analysis. New York. Mentor. 1956.

White, R. W.: The Abnormal Personality. 2nd Ed. New York. The Ronald Press. 1956.

Whitehead, A. N.: Science and the Modern World. New York. The Macmillan Co. 1925.

Whitehead, A. N.: Modes of Thought. New York. The Macmillan Co. 1938.

Whitehead, A. N.: Science and the Modern World. New York. Mentor. 1954.

Whitehorn, J. C.: Understanding psychotherapy. Am. J. Psychiat. *112:*328, 1955.

Whitehorn, J. C.: Orienting medical students toward the whole patient. J.A.M.A. *164:* 538, 1957.

Whiting, J. W. M., and Child, I. L.: Child Training and Personality. New Haven. Yale University Press. 1953.

Whitty, C. W. M., and Lewin, W.: Vivid day-dreaming: an unusual form of confusion following anterior cingulectomy. Brain *80:*72, 1957.

Whitwell, P. R.: Historical Notes on Psychiatry. London. Lewis. 1936.

Wiener, N.: Cybernetics. New York. John Wiley & Sons. 1948.

Wild, J.: The Challenge of Existentialism. Bloomington, Ind. Indiana University Press. 1955.

Willard, Helen S.: Principles of Occupational Therapy. Philadelphia. J. B. Lippincott Co., 1954.

Williams, R. J.: Chemical anthropology—an open door. Am. Sci. *46*:618, 1958.

Winthrop, H.: The pejorative bias in clinical and personality research. Psychiatry *20:* 401, 1957.

Wisdom, J. O.: The Unconscious Origin of Berkeley's Philosophy. London. Hogarth Press. 1953.

Witmer, H. L.: Psychiatric Interviews with Children. New York. The Commonwealth Fund. 1946.

Wittels, F.: Freud and His Time. New York. Liveright. 1931.

Wittkower, E.: A Psychiatrist looks at Tuberculosis. London. National Association for the Prevention of Tuberculosis. 1949.

Wolberg, L. R.: Hypnoanalysis. New York. Grune and Stratton. 1945.

Wolberg, L. R.: Medical Hypnosis. New York. Grune and Stratton. 1948.

Wolberg, L. R.: The Technique of Psychotherapy. New York. Grune and Stratton. 1954.

Wolff, H. G.: Every man has his breaking point—the conduct of prisoners of war. Mil. Med. *125*:85, 1960.

Wolff, W.: The Personality of the Preschool Child. New York. Grune and Stratton. 1946.

Woods, R. L., Ed.: The World of Dreams. New York. Random House. 1947.

Wright, Rebekah: Hydrotherapy in Hospitals for Mental Diseases. Boston. Tudor Press. 1932.

Yacorzynski, G. K.: Medical Psychology. New York. The Ronald Press. 1951.

Yerkes, R. M.: Champanzees, a Laboratory Colony. New Haven. Yale University Press. 1943.

Zangwill, O. L.: An Introduction to Modern Psychology. New York. Philosophical Library. 1950.

Ziff, P.: Semantic Analysis. Ithaca, N. Y. Cornell University Press, 1960.

Zilboorg, G., and Henry, G. W.: History of Medical Psychology. New York. W. W. Norton & Co. 1941.

Ziskind, E.: Psychophysiologic Medicine. Philadelphia. Lea & Febiger. 1954.

Zuckerman, S.: The Social Life of Monkeys and Apes. London. Kegan, Paul, Trench & Trubner. 1932.

Glossary of psychiatric terms

IN THIS glossary are assembled the definitions, simply worded and operationally phrased in so far as possible, of about twelve hundred of the more obscure terms found in current psychiatric literature. No attempt has been made to define specifically or fully words of generalized or multiple meanings (e.g., *psychoanalysis* or *personality*) or of highly controversial connotation (e.g., *psychotherapy*), since such concepts are dealt with extensively in the body of the text. On the other hand, many terms which are rapidly passing from technical use (e.g., *conversion*) have been included, although with the hope that their obsolescence will be hastened so that future psychiatric glossaries may be briefer and scientifically more exact. In any case, it is recommended that the glossary be used in frequent cross-reference with the index for fuller textual explanations of the dynamic and clinical significance of many of the terms employed. Definitions of special significance are indicated by ✦ for the convenience of the student desiring a rapid review of the leading concepts in the field.

ablutomania. Incessant preoccupation with thoughts of washing; frequently part of an *obsessive-compulsive neurosis* (q.v.).

abnormal behavior. Any phenomenon or pattern of behavior considered to be outside the limits generally set for a given time, place and culture.

abreaction. Release of *repressed* (q.v.) ideation and emotion, especially during hypnosis or psychoanalytic therapy or under the influence of drugs (see *catharsis*).

absence. Short-term impairment or clouding of consciousness (cf. *epilepsy, minor*).

abulia. Marked impairment of initiative, energy and drive; popularly, lack of "pep" or "will power."

acarophobia. Morbid dread of small inanimate objects, or of infestation with minute living forms (e.g., insects, worms).

accident-proneness. *Neurotic* (q.v.) neglect or carelessness which renders the patient subject to injury, especially at his work (H. Dunbar).

acousticophobia. Morbid dread of sounds.

acro-esthesia. Increased pain sensitivity in the extremities.

acrophobia. Morbid dread of heights.

acting-out. In psychoanalytic therapy, a common defense pattern in which a patient unconsciously expresses his conflicts in neurotic behavior in relation to the therapist or others, rather than acquiring insight through analytic processes.

adiadokokinesia. Inability to perform rapid alternating or cyclic movements.

adrenal syndrome. *Adrenalectomized* animals (adrenal glands removed) develop severe motor weakness and other signs of profoundly disturbed metabolism (*Addison's disease* in man) which can be partially relieved by the administration of sodium and adrenal steroids.

aerophagia. Compulsive, though not

Page 275

necessarily conscious, swallowing of air, which may accompany neurotic gastrointestinal dysfunctions.

aerophobia. Morbid dread of air, gases, drafts or noxious influences transmitted through them.

✦affect. Generalized feeling tone, usually distinguished from *emotion* in being more persistent and pervasive, less directly reflected in physiologic deviations and with more generalized ideational content.

✦affective psychoses. *Psychoses* (q.v.) characterized prominently by marked changes in mood: e.g., depression or mania.

ageusia. Impaired sense of taste, common in depressive states, less so in gastrointestinal neuroses.

agitated melancholia. A *depressive psychosis* (q.v.) characterized by marked restlessness, professions of hopelessness and recurrent self-mutilatory or suicidal tendencies.

agnosia. An *aphasic disorder* (q.v.) characterized mainly by an inability to recognize objects or symbols.

agoraphobia. Abnormal dread of large, open, exposed or solitary places.

agrammatism. *Aphasic* (q.v.) impairment of logical or grammatical order in speech.

ah-ah! experience. A sudden flash of recognition or understanding; cf. *Gestalt* and *insight.*

aichmophobia. Abnormal dread of sharp or pointed objects.

ailurophobia. Abnormal dread of cats or other felines.

akinesia. Impairment of motility.

alalia. Inability to talk.

Alcoholics Anonymous. A lay organization, with branches in many large cities, organized for the purpose of treating alcoholic addicts by personal, religious and social rehabilitation.

alexia. Impairment of understanding of written speech; visual aphasia; less accurately, "word-blindness."

algophobia. Morbid dread of pain.

allelic. Pertaining to opposed genes which transmit alternative hereditary characteristics.

alloplastic. Refers to aberrant interpersonal (social) conduct (e.g., *sociopathic*, q.v.), as distinguished from *autoplastic* neurotic or hysteric symptoms (e.g., sensori-motor or organic dysfunctions—Ferenczi and F. Alexander).

✦Alzheimer's disease. A generalized fibrillary degeneration of the cerebral cortex with glial plaque formation occurring in late middle life and manifested by a variable but usually rapidly progressive symptomatology comprising aphasia, apraxia, intellectual deterioration, habit disintegration, explosiveness of affect, and, occasionally, convulsive seizures.

amaurotic family idiocy. (Tay-Sachs disease.) A hereditary degenerative disease of the brain causing blindness, dementia, muscular dystrophies and early death in children.

amaxophobia. Morbid dread of vehicles.

✦ambivalence. Incompatibility of simultaneous attitudes, generally unconscious, with regard to alternative possibilities of action, e.g., mixed love and hate for the same person.

✦amentia. Lack of development of *intellectual* (q.v.) capacities.

amimia. Impairment of gestural communication.

✦amnesia. Loss of memory or recall. *Anterograde a.* signifies forgetfulness for events following some *amnemonic trauma,* such as a cerebral concussion or an epileptic seizure, as distinguished from *retrograde a.,* or loss of memory for events preceding such traumata. *Lacunar or patchy a.* connotes an inability to recall specific events or portions of them, with preserved memory for episodes between them.

Amytal interview. Psychiatric examination of a patient placed under the influence of Sodium Amytal. See *narcosynthesis* and *Sodium Amytal.*

anabolism. Constructive metabolism, storing potential energy.

anaclisis. Passive leaning; i.e., excessive dependency.

anal erotism. In psychoanalytic terms, fixation of libido at anal phases of development, with *"anal character"* traits (q.v.) of covert hostility, covered by obsessive-compulsive orderliness, cleanliness, avarice, stubbornness, etc.

analgesia. Impairment of pain or touch perception.

analysis, distributive. In psychobiologic therapy (Diethelm) the *guided* investigation and interpretation of the patient's past behavior, as distinguished from the *spontaneous* free-associations of psychoanalytic technique.

analytic psychology. The metapsychologic system of C. Jung. See *psychology, analytic.*

anamnesis. The patient's account of his life history.

anancastic. *Obsessive-compulsive* (q.v.).

anergasia. In psychobiologic terminology (Meyer), a behavior disorder caused by organic defects of the central nervous system.

anesthesia. Abolition of sensation.

anhedonia. Abolition of pleasurable feelings.

anima. In Jungian terminology, the inner "being," as distinguished from the *persona* or outer character of the personality.

animism. The concept that all objects are endowed with life and inner purpose.

anomia. An *aphasic disorder* (q.v.) characterized by an inability to associate objects or persons with their names.

anorexia. Loss of appetite.

anorexia nervosa. A behavior syndrome generally characterized by loss of appetite and weight, gastrointestinal and menstrual disturbances and motor hyperactivity (often in neurotic patterns) despite severe nutritive debility (cf. Appendix 3).

anthropometry. Physical measurement of the body.

✛anxiety. A state of apprehensive tension which arises during motivational and adaptational conflicts. Anxiety is experienced in circumstances of direct or symbolic danger, or when phobic, compulsive or other accustomed defenses are transgressed.

anxiety hysteria. A *neurosis* characterized by severe *anxiety* (q.v.) complicated by *hysterical* or *conversion symptoms* (qq.v.).

anxiety neurosis. A *neurosis* (q.v.) characterized by continuous diffuse anxiety, usually with recurrent exacerbations of its physiologic concomitants (*anxiety syndrome,* q.v.).

✛anxiety syndrome. The physiologic concomitants of anxiety, generally experienced as palpitation (consciousness of racing or pounding heart), shallow, rapid or constricted respiration, globus (sensations of tightness or a lump in the throat), trembling, "fluttering" in the abdomen, sweaty, flushed or pale skin, and subjective feelings of diffuse apprehensiveness which may mount to feelings of impending catastrophe and panic. Incontinence may occur in severe attacks.

✛aphasia. Impairment of communicative functions. *Sensory* or *impressive* aphasia includes inability to perceive *auditory, tactile* or *visual* speech-symbols; *semantic* aphasia denotes impaired recall (amnestic a.), recognition (anomia), or correlation (syntacic a., aphrasia) of speech symbols; *motor expressive aphasia* indicates a loss of verbal, written or mimetic speech expression. These types of aphasia are all present in varying degree in *organic aphasia* and, when complete, constitute *global aphasia.* In *functional* or *neurotic* (q.v.) aphasia one or several specific dysfunctions may appear in relative isolation.

aphemia. Loss of spoken speech.

aphephobia. Morbid dread of touching.

aphonia. Loss of voice.

aphrasia. Impaired ability to organize speech symbols into language forms; usually, slow, halting speech with blocking, lacunae or *agrammatism* ("telegram style").

aphrodisia. Sexual excitement.

apoplexy. An organic illness caused by an acute hemorrhage or obstruction in the blood vessels of the brain (a "stroke"), usually resulting in contralateral paralysis and some degree of *aphasia* and *dementia* (qq.v.).

apperception. Recognition of the context and significance of a situation in terms of the individual's past experience.

apprehension. 1. Apperception. 2. Anticipatory dread.

apraxia. Impaired ability to utilize objects.

arithmomania. Obsessive-compulsive counting or other mathematical preoccupations.

asexuality. Absence of sexual interests and activities.

✛association, free. 1. The psychoanalytic technique of requiring the patient to express or describe all thoughts, sensations and emotions as they occur during the analytic hour. 2. The verbalizations so elicited.

associations, clang. Rhyming or other sound-associations, usually nonsensical, sometimes observed in *manic states* (q.v.).

associations, dream. In psychoanalytic technique, ideas associated with parts or wholes of previous dreams, as related during the analytic hour.

astasia-abasia. Neurotic inability to stand or walk, usually not accompanied by paralysis of the limbs.

asthenia. Weakness; absence of energy.

asthenic. See *types, Kretschmer.*

asthenophobia. Morbid dread of being weak.

atavism. The reversion to primitive or animal-like forms of behavior.

ataxia. Incoordination, generally used in relation to motor functions. Stransky called the incoordination between idea and affect in schizophrenia *intrapsychic ataxia.*

athetosis. Large, slow, involuntary, sinuous and repetitive movements.

athletic. See *types, Kretschmer.*

attitude. A readiness to react in accordance with referential patterns predetermined by individual experience.

✦aura. Sensations or other prodromal experiences (sometimes *hallucinatory*) which regularly or irregularly precede each episode of a paroxysmal disorder, e.g., *migraine* or *epilepsy* (q.v.).

autism. Introversive self-preoccupation.

autochthonous. Appearing in consciousness as though independently self-engendered; generally applied to *obsessive ideas* (q.v.).

auto-erotism. Erotic behavior directed toward the individual's own body (Ellis). In early infancy, it may be diffuse and "polymorphous-perverse" (Freud).

✦automatism. Mechanical, repetitious, apparently undirected, symbolic behavior, often without conscious control; seen in *fugue states* or *schizophrenia* (q.v.).

autonomic epilepsy. Attacks of severe involuntary excitation of the autonomic nervous system, sometimes attributable to lesions at the base of the brain (Penfield).

✦autonomic nervous system. That portion of the nervous system that regulates the glands, circulation and internal organs. Its *parasympathetic* (craniosacral) division is in general anabolic and inhibitory; its *orthosympathetic* (thoraco-lumbar) division is in general catabolic and excitatory, but (a) there are specific exceptions in organ-innervation, and (b) the two divisions are intimately interactive.

autonomous processes. Those initiated or controlled by the organism in the *biosphere* (q.v.) (Angyal).

autoplastic. Behavior limited to internal functions, as opposed to *alloplastic* interpersonal conduct (q.v.).

auxiliary ego. See *psychodrama.*

avalanche concept. A theory that nervous energy may accumulate until it breaks through in an explosive discharge with wide diffusion, as in an *epileptic attack* (q.v.).

bacillophobia. Morbid dread of microorganisms.

ballistophobia. Morbid dread of projectiles.

balneology. Study of the effects of baths.

barylalia. Thick, heavy speech.

bath, continuous. A prolonged immersion (one to twelve hours) in flowing water at body temperature, generally used to calm excited patients.

bathophobia. Morbid dread of depths and heights.

bedlam. Wild confusion or pandemonium. (From the Hospital of St. Mary of Bethelehem, a "lunatic asylum" established in London in 1402.)

behavior. The conduct of organisms, integrating internal ("physiologic") and external ("objective, social") actions.

✦behaviorism. A system of psychology (J. B. Watson) that studies the conduct of human beings exclusively on the principle of association and professes to exclude consciousness and other subjective and conative considerations as irrelevant *epiphenomena.*

benign. In medicine or psychiatry, any mild, self-limiting and recoverable disorder, as a *benign* depressive reaction, or a *benign* tumor.

bestiality. In sexology, coitus with animals.

bibliomania. A morbid affinity for books.

binome. A two-word name or diagnosis (e.g., *dementia praecox*) in the manner of the Linnaean system of classifying plants.

✦biodynamics. The historical, comparative and experimental study of the dynamic processes manifested in the behavior of organisms.

biosphere. The field of interaction of the organism with its environment (Angyal).

birth trauma. In Rankian theory the deprivation of womb-security at birth, constituting a "psychic shock" which leaves an unconscious but ineradicable anxiety.

bisexual. Having the propensities or physical characteristics (hermaphroditism) of both sexes.

blepharospasm. Tense closure of the eyelids.

blocking. Functional inhibition of recall, ideation or communication.

brady -arthria, -kinesia, -lexia, -logia, -phrenia. Slowness of speech, movement, reading, ideation or thinking respectively.

brontophobia. Morbid dread of thunder or storms.

bulimia. Morbidly increased hunger.

cachexia. Marked malnutrition or debility.

cacogeusia. Persistent unpleasant taste, frequently occurring in severe depressive states.

cacophony. Unpleasant, disharmonious sounds; discord.

camptocormia. A neurotically forward-flexed posture of the body.

carphology. Stereotyped picking or plucking movements, sometimes seen in deliria, severe organic psychosis or advanced schizophrenia.

✦castration complex. In psychoanalytic theory, fear of traumatic degenitalization in either sex as punishment for forbidden erotic desires. The term, however, has been used with a variety of connotations ranging from fear of literal castration (Freud) to symbolic deprivation of any cherished possession.

catabolism. Destructive metabolism, releasing kinetic energy.

catalepsy. Muscular hypertonicity and fixity of posture, sometimes occurring in severe hysterical or schizophrenic states.

catamnesis. The historical (follow-up) account of a patient's conduct after an illness or behavior disorder.

✦cataplexy. A sudden, passing attack of muscular weakness, with or without loss of consciousness. May occur in conjunction with *narcolepsy* (q.v.).

✦catastrophic reaction. Severe disintegration of behavior under excessive stress, especially in patients whose adaptive capacities are impaired by cerebral injury (K. Goldstein).

✦catatonia. A clinical form of *schizophrenia* (q.v.) characterized by motor disturbances (hyperactivity, rigidity, or, rarely, *flexibilitas cerea, q.v.*), stupor, occasional marked excitement, and a relatively acute or episodic course.

✦catharsis. The partial dissipation of the morbid residua of a repressed traumatic experience by therapeutic verbalization or acting-out, accompanied by affective discharge or *abreaction*. This occurs during psychoanalytic therapy, or it may be induced by hypnosis (*hypnocatharisis*) or drugs (*narcoanalysis*) with or without interpretation and guided retraining by the therapist (*narcosynthesis*)—a form of rapid therapy often effective in acute combat neuroses (Horsley, Grinker).

✦cathexis. In psychoanalysis, "libidinal charge," or investment of an object or idea with special significance or value-tone for the individual; e.g., individualized love, hatred or ambivalent combinations of affect with reference to a thing or person.

cenophobia. Morbid dread of empty spaces.

censor. In psychoanalytic theory, that function of the *Ego* or *Superego* (qq.v.) that bars dangerous impulses or ideas from consciousness, or distorts and disguises them by *displacement, reversal* or *symbolization*, as in dreams.

cephalalgia. Headache.

cerebellar ataxia. Incoordination of motion or speech caused by lesions of the cerebellum.

✦character. The interrelated patterns of behavior of an individual; distinguished by some from *personality* in that the latter may mean more specifically the *social* manifestations of character patterns.

character, anal. In psychoanalytic theory a person *fixated* at, or *regressed* to, the "anal-erotic" phase of infantile development, and thereby either (a) *"anal retentive,"* i.e., egotistic, dogmatic, stubborn, miserly and self-constricted in his object-relationships or (b) *"anal aggressive,"* i.e., covertly hostile and mysophilic, but with defensive patterns of perfectionism, meticulosity and excessive orderliness. Under special stress, "anal characters" are prone to develop *obsessive-compulsive-phobic* (q.v.) symptomatology (K. Abraham).

character, genital. In psychoanalytic theory, an individual who has reached and maintained the "genital phase" of libidinal development and is thereby capable of *object-love* in normal adult relationships and responsibilities.

character, oral. In psychoanalytic

theory, an individual adult *fixated* at or *regressed* to the phase of "oral erotism" (q.v.) in infantile development and thereby either (a) *"oral dependent,"* i.e., passive, generally optimistic but parasitic and lacking in initiative and responsibility, or (b) *"oral aggressive,"* i.e., insecure, grasping, sensitive, demanding and actively "incorporative." *Oral character* types are theoretically subject to *depressive reactions* (q.v.) under stress (K. Abraham).

character, pedantic. 1. An affectively inhibited, introspectively critical, overly meticulous personality apt to be lost in preoccupations with minute details and repetitiously sterile ruminations. 2. The exemplification of such responses on the ink-blot test (see *test, Rorschach*).

cherophobia. Morbid dread of gaiety.

chorea. A neuromuscular disorder characterized by spasmodic, irregular involuntary movements, sometimes accompanied by outbursts of excitement; usually due to encephalitis.

choreomania. Compulsive dancing movements. "Epidemics" of neurotic choreomania swept Europe during the Middle Ages.

chromatophobia. Morbid dread of color.

cibophobia. Morbid dread of food.

clang association. Plays on words related only by sound; sometimes seen in *manic states* (q.v.).

claustrophobia. Morbid dread of closed or constricted spaces.

clavus. A sensation of stabbing pain, usually in the head.

climacophobia. Morbid dread of climbing.

climacterium. A period in life usually associated in women with the menopause; sometimes refers also to (a) the corresponding age (42 to 50) and (b) supposed glandular changes in men.

clonus. Rapid, oscillatory movements produced by muscular spasm, seen following the tonic phase in major epilepsy.

co-conscious. A term used by Morton Prince to mean alternate systems of thought and action, which may appear involuntarily in automatic writing (A. Muhl), or may successively and completely displace each other in *multiple personalities* (q.v.).

collective unconscious. A term used by Jung to mean that portion of the un-

conscious common to (a) a given "race" (*racial u.*), (b) to all mankind or (c) to all living things (*atavistic u.*).

coma. Deep, unresponsive stupor.

combat (battle) neuroses. Acute *neuroses* usually characterized by exhaustive anxiety, severe phobias, recurrent nightmares and marked regression, and sometimes by *conversion* symptoms (qq.v.).

complex. In psychoanalytic theory, a group of associated conations, ideas and affects which, though repressed, latent and unconscious, covertly influence conscious attitudes and behavior.

complex, Electra. An obsolescent psychoanalytic term used to denote the incestuous attachment of the female child to her father. [From the Greek myth of Electra's love for her father Agamemnon and her revenge on her mother Clytemnestra for Agamemnon's murder.]

+complex, inferiority. In Adlerian individual psychology, unconscious feelings of inferiority or inadequacy. stemming from excessive disciplinary subordination or physical inadequacies (organ inferiority) in childhood, for which the individual may try to *overcompensate* by excessive ambitiousness, aggressiveness, domination, or special accomplishment to overcome the handicap.

+complex, Oedipus. In early psychoanalytic theory, the erotic attachment of the child to the parent of the opposite sex, repressed because of the *fear of castration* (q.v.) by the jealous parent. [From the Greek myth in which Laius, King of Thebes, exiles his infant son Oedipus, who is rescued by a shepherd. Later, Oedipus in his wanderings unknowingly kills his father and marries Jocasta, his mother. When he discovers this, he blinds (symbolically castrates) himself, and is later destroyed by the Fates.]

complex, symptom-. An association of symptoms into a *syndrome* (q.v.).

compromise formation. In psychoanalytic theory, interadaptations of two or more unconscious tendencies or modes of action. Biodynamically, when these are highly conflictful the resultant behavior may be *neurotic* or *psychotic* (qq.v.).

+compulsion. An act carried out (despite some conscious rejection and resistance by the patient) in accordance with a persistent idea (*obsession*), and in order to avoid inexplicable anxiety should the impulse not be followed.

compulsion, repetition. A pressing tendency to alleviate the residual anxiety of past traumatic experiences by reexploring or reenacting them in fantasy or in actuality; [e.g., a soldier with a *combat neurosis* (q.v.) may have repeated nightmares recapitulating his traumatic experiences, or a guilt-ridden criminal may return to the scene of his crime]. In classic psychoanalytic theory, this *"masochistic"* behavior was thought to be one manifestation of the *"death instinct"* since it seemed contrary to and outweighed the *pleasure principle* (qq.v.).

conation. A general term for concepts of motivation; e.g., needs, instincts, drives, urges, wants, desires, strivings, etc. (qq.v.).

concretism. A tendency toward ideation and behavior at simple and direct (i.e. *"realistic," "concrete"*) levels of apperception of the environment; generally distinguished from *abstract* or *categorical* ideation or concept formation (K. Goldstein).

concussion. Generalized, disruptive injury of the brain by a blow.

+condensation. A symbolic process by which many concepts may be represented by one. For instance, in symbolic imagery a snake may represent phallic erotism, slinking danger, low bestiality, pitiless aggressivity, mystic fascination, etc. So, too, a *phobia* or a *conversion symptom* (q.v.) may *condense* and represent in *compromise form* many otherwise incompatible symbolizations and adaptations.

+conditioning. In Pavlovian reflexology and Watsonian behaviorism, the process by which innate responses ("unconditioned reflexes"), when associated with new sensory stimuli, may thereafter be evoked by these stimuli acting alone.

conduct. Behavior, especially in its consciously directed and social implications.

+confabulation. A tendency to substitute detailed but fantastic, inconsistent and variable accounts—each version currently believed by the patient during its telling—to fill in gaps of memory produced by organic cerebral disease [e.g., as in *alcoholic* (Korsakoff) or *senile psychoses,* qq.v.].

confusion. 1. Disorientation. 2. Disordered thinking, affect or behavior, as in *delirium* (q.v.).

congenital. Existing at birth.

conscience. 1. Conscious judgment by an individual as to whether his conduct conforms with his experientially determined anticipations of ultimately favorable or unfavorable results; i.e. unconscious evaluation of consequences. 2. In psychoanalytic theory, the inhibitory function of the *Superego* (q.v.).

consciousness. In the mentalistic psychologies, direct awareness.

consensus. Relative group agreement (by authority, compromise, majority or integration—McIver).

constitution. Generally, the biologic make-up of an organism, especially in its hereditary features. However, the term is used with a very wide range of meanings (see *type*).

constitutional inadequacy. A concept loosely implying, usually *post hoc,* some sort of hereditary biologic inferiority.

content, latent. In psychoanalysis, the unconscious meanings and determinants of symbols (as in dreams or free-associations) as opposed to their superficial description or *manifest content.*

contrectation. Erotic or wooing activity, especially by touching and caressing, as distinguished from coitus.

+conversion. In psychoanalytic theory, the process whereby sexual *libido* is "converted" and redirected into bodily (*autoplastic*) aberrations of behavior. The term is now mainly used to designate *hysterical* (q.v.) sensorimotor dysfunctions, such as blindness or paralysis.

convulsion. Intense, involuntary muscular spasms, *clonic* (between very brief rhythmic periods of relative relaxation) or *tonic* (sustained).

coprophagia. The direct or symbolic ingestion of excrement.

coprophilia. Pleasure in handling excreta or their symbolic representations.

coprophobia. Morbid dread of excreta.

cosmic identification. Equation of the self with the universe, theoretically present in covert form in infants, and sometimes observable in dreams and in schizophrenic behavior (e.g., in *delusions* of omniscience and omnipotence).

+counter-transference. 1. In psychoanalytic theory, the symbolic libidinal relationships, partly unconscious, of the analyst with the analytic patient (*analysand*) which may impair the ideal objectivity of the analytic process. 2. In general, the therapist's attitudes toward the patient, based on the former's interpersonal evaluations of the latter.

couvade. The symbolic enactment of childbirth by a male, certain aspects of which are common in many ethnic groups, and which may be represented in neurotic or psychotic behavior.

craving. A wanting or longing, mainly conscious, but less specific than a *desire* (q.v.), e.g., a craving for love or freedom.

cretinism. Congenital thyroid deficiency, causing bodily deformities, markedly retarded development and amentia.

+criminality. Asocial, antisocial or illegal conduct which, nevertheless, is in accordance with the conscious standards and intent of the individual. Theoretically, though not always practically, distinguishable from (1) *neurotic* or *psychopathic behavior* (qq.v.), in which the aberrant conduct is deviantly symbolic rather than indulged in for extrinsic gain, and (2) from *psychotic behavior* (q.v.) in which excesses of uncontrollable affect or distortions of generally accepted reality occasion the antisocial act.

cry, epileptic. A short, shrill piercing sound that may herald a major epileptic seizure.

cryptogenic. Of unknown causation, as cryptogenic (*idiopathic*) epilepsy.

cryptomnesia. Recall of events not recognized by the subject as part of his actual experience.

cunnilingus. Use of the tongue in erotic play with the female genitals.

+cyclothymia. A tendency to persistent, irrational or exaggerated shifts in mood, especially with regard to alternations of euphoria (*hypomania, mania*) and depression (*hypothymia, melancholia*).

cynophobia. Morbid dread of dogs, or of rabies.

cypridophobia. Fear of the adverse consequences (disease, etc.) of sexual intercourse (coitus).

daemonophobia. Extreme dread of ghosts, spirits, devils, etc.

Dauerschlaf. See *prolonged sleep.*

death instincts. In Freudian theory, the latent drives toward destruction, senescence and death collectively termed *Thanatos* (q.v.).

+defense mechanism. 1. In psychoanalytic theory a process by which the

Ego (the orientative and integrative portion of the personality) partially satisfies the unconscious instinctive drives of the *Id* by behavior that conforms with the self-regulative demands of the *Superego* (qq.v.). 2. In general, adaptive modes of behavior constituting compromises among the needs of the organism and its experientially contingent apperceptions and evaluations of its milieu (cf. Chapter 3).

degenitalize. To purge of genital reference, e.g., as in "Platonic love."

déjà entendu. The feeling or belief that a completely new auditory perception had somehow been experienced before.

déjà éprouvé. The delusion that an intended action had been accomplished.

déjà vu. A feeling, accompanied by a sense of inexplicable familiarity, that an experience being lived for the first time is a repetition of one in the past.

+delinquency. Asocial, antisocial, illegal or culturally nonconforming conduct in a minor.

délire du toucher. An almost incessant compulsion to touch objects.

+delirium. In modern usage, a state of disorientation and confusion (often with rapidly changing, generally fearful *hallucinations*) induced by the toxic effects of organic diseases or drugs (e.g., alcoholic *delirium tremens*).

+delusion. A fixed belief widely deviant from the cultural norm, and impervious to persuasion or reason.

+dementia. Deterioration of perceptive, integrative and manipulative (e.g., "*intellectual*") capacities due to organic disease of the brain.

dementia praecox. A form of *schizophrenia* (q.v.) characterized by onset or rapid exacerbation at puberty, and formerly thought to lead inevitably to *dementia* (q.v.) (Kraepelin). The term is, fortunately, rapidly becoming obsolete.

+dementia, schizophrenic. A term referring to the supposed "mental degeneration" in *schizophrenia* (q.v.). Actually, however, there is only disinterest in, and abandonment, disuse or distortion of, complex intellectual and social processes, but no demonstrable deterioration of capacities (*dementia*) occurs unless secondary organic cerebral changes supervene as a result of the patient's physical debility or intercurrent diseases.

dendrophilia. Exaggerated love of plants, especially trees.

✦denial. In psychoanalysis, an unconscious defense whereby the patient refuses to recognize or accept unwelcome conations or concepts.

✦depersonalization. A subject's feeling or belief that he has lost his identity. *D.* is evanescent in *hypnogogic states* or in *neurotic* reactions, but may be persistent and accompanied by cosmic delusions in the *psychoses* (qq.v.).

✦depression. A state characterized affectively by maintained dejection in mood, ideologically by gloomy ruminations or foreboding, and physiologically by the *depressive syndrome* (q.v.). Depressions range in intensity and persistence from evanescent "blues" to deep melancholia. See *psychoses, depressive.*

depression, neurotic. A depressive state with prominent neurotic features (e.g., *anxiety, phobias, compulsions*).

✦depression, reactive. A self-limited depressive state the content, intensity and duration of which have rational reference to "actual" rather than "symbolic" frustrations, deprivations or adversities in the life of the patient. Distinguished from *psychosis* by the criteria listed under the latter (q.v.).

✦depression - syndrome, physiologic. Depressive states are typically accompanied by varying degrees of anorexia, insomnia, loss of weight, constipation or other gastrointestinal dysfunctions, easy fatigability and diminished sexual desire. In women, disturbances of menstruation are common; in men, relative impotence. Energy is generally decreased, so that ideation and action are slowed, but *diurnal variations* (morning retardation, partially dispelled toward evening) may occur. However, there may be episodes of markedly increased appetite (*bulimia*); or a persistent, aimless, motor restlessness (*agitation*) may supervene.

depth psychology. A term used by Freud to distinguish *psychoanalysis* from other psychologic systems which "deal only with the superficial phenomena of behavior."

✦dereistic. Unreal, delusional; i.e., not in accordance with generally accepted interpretations of space, time and logic. Generally applied to schizophrenic fantasies and their "irrational" organization.

desensitization. In psychiatric therapy, a process by which a patient gradually reexplores a conflictual situation and dissipates his anxiety through the formation of new and more satisfactory adaptations. See *working through.*

desire. A conscious and fairly specific wanting, e.g., for food or warmth.

✦deterioration. 1. Degeneration of intellectual capacities due to organic cerebral disease (e.g., *alcoholic d., paretic d., senile d.*), as manifested by variable *amnesias, aphasias, apraxias,* disturbances of category formation and impairment of energy (*power factor*) or loss of other intellectual functions.

determinism. 1. A belief in some form of causality. 2. The doctrine of preordained, unalterable fate.

detumescence. Relaxation of erectile sexual organs, especially during or after intercourse.

dextrophobia. Dread of objects to the right.

✦diagnosis. Determination of the nature and intensity of a morbid process or processes. In modern psychiatry, diagnosis entails a balanced survey of the nature, context and extent of all significant behavioral aberrations, as distinguished from mere superficial classification by "disease entities," (*taxonomic nosology*).

diaschisis. 1. Physical or chemical severance of neural connections. 2. Disturbed function in one portion of the nervous system caused by disease in a related portion (Monakow).

diathesis. A predisposition (usually conceived as constitutional) to a particular disease or disorder.

dikephobia. Morbid dread of justice.

dilapidation. Advanced *deterioration* (q.v.).

diplegia. Paralysis of homologous parts of the body (e.g., both arms).

diplopia. Doubling of objects in the field of vision.

dipsomania. 1. Morbid addiction to alcoholic drinks. 2. Recurrent bouts of extreme drunkenness, between periods of sobriety.

disorientation. Impaired awareness of place, time or person.

✦displacement. The transfer of symbolic meaning and value from one object or concept to another: e.g., a mother may cherish a pet excessively after her child's death; a man may redirect unconscious hate of his father onto his boss; or a girl may conceal displaced concern over her genital functions in obsessive-compulsive oral hygiene.

dissimulation.   Conscious attempts to deceive; lying, *malingering.*

✦dissociation.   1. The severance of normal relationships and sequences among conations, thoughts and affects. 2. Complex combinations of behavior patterns, which though integrated among themselves, may appear unrelated to the rest of the personality, giving rise to "double" or *"multiple personality"* (Prince) or to "encapsulated *paranoia"* (Bleuler) (qq.v.).

✦distortion.   An adaptive alteration of a perception or concept to conform with the subject's wishes or prejudices; e.g., a *distorted* apperception and evaluation of the personality characteristics of a loved or hated person.

dizygotic.   Twins from separate ova.

dolicomorphic.   Long, thin "body-type," *asthenic.* See *types, Kretschmer.*

dominance.   1. In heredity, the tendency of some hereditary characteristics, attributable to genes, to dominate weaker (*recessive*) ones simultaneously present in the individual (Mendel). 2. In ethology and sociology, the primacy accorded an individual or group in some competitive activity.

Don Juan.   A legendary roué, seducer and profligate; in psychiatry, a term sometimes used to describe compulsive, restless sexual promiscuity in the male.

✦dream-function.   In psychoanalytic theory, a process by which dream-fantasies express unconscious wishes and reexplore and allay anxieties through symbolic representation and resolution.

dream-interpretation.   1. In psychoanalysis, the recognition of unconscious *dream-functions* (q.v.) through the analysis of dreams, thus opening "the royal road to the Unconscious" (Freud). 2. Information given the patient about such analyses.

dream-stimulus.   An experiential ("external" sensory or "internal" physiologic) apperception which precipitates a dream, or serves as a nidus about which dream fantasies cluster. E.g. a man may quarrel with his wife, dream the next night that she is perishing in a fire, and wake with the clang of fire-engines merging with the actual ringing of his alarm-clock. In this example the latter constitutes the *sensory* or precipitating component of the dream-stimulus, as distinguished from the *primary* unconscious source of the dream itself—the man's hatred of his wife.

dream-text.   The fantasied occurrences in a dream (*manifest content*) as distinguished from their unconscious symbolisms and dynamisms (*latent content*).

dream-timing.   1. The duration and sequence of dreaming. Examples such as cited under *dream-stimulus* (q.v.) indicate that dreams, though prolonged in subsequent narration, are temporally highly condensed fantasies. 2. A normal mean of 8 dream-periods per night as signaled by electroencephalography; deprivation through deliberate waking may occasion serious disturbances in waking thought and action (Dement).

dromomania.   Morbid, compulsive traveling; vagabondism.

dynamics.   The study of the presumably constant space-time interrelationships among phenomena. In biology, *biodynamics.*

dysarthria.   Impairment of spoken speech; especially, difficulty of enunciation.

dysbasia.   Disturbances of gait.

dysbulia.   Impairment or vacillation of "will-power"; pervasive indecision.

dyscrasia.   Imbalanced regulation of metabolism, particularly by endocrine disturbances.

dysergasia.   In psychobiology (A. Meyer) a behavior disorder attributable mainly to toxic organic disturbances in the nervous system; e.g., *delirium* (q.v.).

dysesthesia.   Distortion or perversion of tactile sensations or perceptions.

dysgeusia.   Distorted taste.

dyskinesia.   Disturbances of movement, as by *tics* or *spasms* (qq.v.).

dyslogia.   Incoherence of spoken speech.

dysmetria.   Impaired ability to adjust bodily movements to the required space, time or effort.

dysmnesia.   Impaired or distorted memory.

dysmorphophobia.   Morbid dread of bodily deformity.

dysorexia.   Perverted appetite.

dyspareunia.   Unpleasant or painful sensations during sexual intercourse, in women.

dysphagia.   Difficulty in eating, especially in swallowing.

dysphemia. Functional speech disorder.
dysplasia. Abnormal development of the body or of special tissues and organs.
dyspraxia. Impairment of skilled movements, especially in the use of tools.
dysthymia. Morbid alterations or fixations in mood, especially toward *depression.*
dystonia. Disturbed muscular tension.
dystrophy. Defective or faulty nutrition of a body part.
dystropy. In psychobiology (A. Meyer), any abnormal or morbid behavior, especially in its social aspects.

ecdemomania. Morbid, compulsive wandering.
ecdysiasm. A morbid tendency to disrobe to provoke (frustraneous) erotic stimulation in the opposite sex.
echolalia. Automatic repetition by the patient of the examiner's speech, sometimes observed in schizophrenic disorders.
echopraxia. Automatic imitation by the patient of the examiner's movements or mannerisms, sometimes seen in schizophrenic disorders.
ecology. Study of the geographic distribution of organisms according to species, age-groups, incidence of disease, or other factors.
+economics. 1. In dynamic psychiatry, the study of the respective weighting, interaction and balance of adaptive processes to produce final behavior. 2. In psychoanalytic theory, the distribution of *libido* according either to the *pleasure-principle,* the psychosexual development or the *death - instincts* (qq.v.).
ecphoria. The revival of a memory-trace, neurologically conceived as an *engram* (q.v.).
ectoderm. The outer tissue layer of the embryo from which develop the skin and its appendages, the sense organs, and the brain and nervous system.
ectomorphic. See *types, Sheldon.*
ectype. Any type widely deviant from "normal" (see *types*).
effort syndrome. A term sometimes used to describe war neuroses characterized mainly by lassitude, marked fatigability and various degrees of phobic anxiety.
egersis. Persistent wakefulness.
+ego or Ego. In psychoanalytic theory, that portion or stratum of the "mind" or personality which is in contact with the environment through the senses,

perceives and evaluates the milieu through intellectual functions, and directs behavior into acceptable compromises between the blind drives of the *Id* and the inhibitions (conscience) and idealizations (*Ego-ideal*) of the *Superego* (qq.v.).
+ego-analysis. In psychoanalysis, the investigation of the methods (*"defenses"*) by which the *Ego* (a) resolves conflicts among *Id* drives or between these and Superego inhibitions, thus averting disruptive *anxiety,* and (b) adapts by "normal" or "neurotic" *mechanisms* to the demands of reality as conceptually interpreted.
ego, auxiliary. In Moreno's *"psychodramatic therapy"* an individual who assumes some mimetic role in acting out scenes or plays supposed to represent a patient's intrapsychic conflicts.
ego-cathexis. Love of self—a concept more limited than unconsciously pervasive *narcissism* (q.v.).
ego-dystonic. Unacceptable to the *Ego* q.v.), as contrasted with *ego-syntonic.*
+ego-ideal. In psychoanalytic theory, that portion or function of the Superego which orientates and directs the personality toward ends and goals—usually those of other persons with whom the subject has, in the past, identified his own interests.
egomania. Morbid self-centeredness and selfishness.
ego-syntonic. Acceptable to the Ego.
+eidetic imagery. Vivid, detailed, accurate, voluntarily controllable recall of previous sensory impressions, reported to be present in 60 per cent of children and in some adults (cf. *types, Jaensch*).
eisoptrophobia. Dread of mirrors.
ejaculatio deficiens. Impaired ejaculation.
ejaculatio precox. Ejaculation and detumescence before completion of coitus, or even before *intromission* (q.v.).
ejaculation. Extrusion of semen from the penis, usually with detumescence.
+electroshock therapy. A form of treating psychiatric disorders by passing an electric current through the brain, usually with the induction of convulsions and coma.
eleemosynary. Dealing with the administration of charity.
eleutheromania. Excessive seeking for complete freedom.
ellipsis. The omission of words, phrases

or thoughts from their context, due to unconscious *repression* (q.v.) or organic *aphasia*.

embolalia. The insertion of irrelevant, nonsensical or repetitive words or phrases into speech; occurs in some aphasic and schizophrenic states.

emetophobia. Morbid dread of vomiting.

+emotion. A state of excitation manifested during conative press or conflicts, and reflected in characteristic physiologic reactions and motor expressions.

+empathy. The "objective" or "intellectual" recognition of the nature and significance of another's behavior, as distinguished from *sympathy*, derived from corresponding conative and affective experiences.

emprosthotonos. Spastic flexion of the body.

enantiopathic. Provoking opposite feelings.

encephalitis. Inflammation of the brain.

encephalomalacia. Softening and atrophy of the brain.

endocrinopathy. Disordered functioning of the ductless glands which, through the secretion of hormones, control the growth and metabolism of the body.

endocrinotherapy. Use of *hormones* (q. v.) in treatment.

endoderm (or **entoderm**). The inner germ layer of the embryo from which develop the internal organs of respiration and digestion.

endogenous. Arising from within the body.

endomorphic. See *types, Sheldon.*

end-pleasure. The pleasurable release of tension in sexual orgasm, as opposed to the tension-building *fore-pleasure* of pregenital activity.

engram. The supposed neural pathway or *trace* left in the nervous system by every sensorimotor experience.

enisophobia. Dread of having committed "an unpardonable sin."

enteroptosis. Abnormally low position of the abdominal organs.

enuresis. Impaired control of urination; generally, persistent bed-wetting.

eonism. Female sexual behavior in a male.

eosophobia. Dread of dawn.

+epicritic sensitivity. Accurate appreciation of light touch, temperature and point-to-point distance on the skin; distinguished from grosser *protopathic* sensations of pain or pressure (Head).

+epilepsy. A group of disorders characterized mainly by motor convulsions and/or disturbances of consciousness, often traceable by electroencephalography to cerebral dysrhythmias; generally episodic, except in the *continuous partial epilepsy* of Wilson and in *status epilepticus*. Distinguished from *toxic convulsions* and *hysterical seizures* in etiology, course and prognosis (qq.v.). Cf. *epilepsy, major.*

epilepsy, akinetic. An epileptic syndrome in which muscular spasms are absent.

epilepsy, autonomic. Episodic disturbances of the internal organs attributable to abnormal excitations of the *sympathetic nervous system* (q.v.) sometimes caused by tumors at the base of the brain (Penfield).

epilepsy, continuous partial (—partialis continua). Continuous, jerky, spastic movements of a body segment, episodically exacerbated.

epilepsy, cryptogenic. Epilepsy of unknown etiology.

+epilepsy, Jacksonian. Recurrent convulsive movements beginning in one extremity and accompanied by minimal disturbances of consciousness. These may arise from circumscribed cerebral lesions (Hughlings Jackson).

+epilepsy, major (grand mal). Typically, episodic disturbances or abolition of consciousness, with tonic contractions rapidly involving the whole body (*opisthotonos*) followed by violent clonic movements during which there may be urinary or fecal incontinence. The attack may be heralded by a prodromal *aura* (sensory, affective or hallucinatory experiences) and the convulsions may be immediately preceded by an expulsive *epileptic cry*. If the patient is not prepared for the seizure he generally falls, and may bite his tongue or injure himself during the convulsions. *Postdromata* often consist of lassitude, muscular weakness or soreness, headache, and amnesia for the seizure. Epilepsy may be distinguished from *toxic convulsive states* (e.g., strychnine, tetany) and *hysterical seizures* (qq.v.) by its etiology, symptoms and course.

+epilepsy, minor (petit mal). Epilepsy characterized by relatively mild muscular movements or sometimes only by momentary impairments of consciousness (*absences*) during which the patient may automatically continue his previous activity (*minor epileptic fugue*).

epilepsy, psychic. Episodes of *amnesia, paramnesia, automatism,* dreamlike or *fugue* states, *hallucinosis* (qq.v.) or other disorder of conscious control or experience (*epileptic equivalents*) which may replace convulsive seizures in epileptic patients.

✦epileptic character. Thought by some to comprise personality traits of intense affective ambivalence, obsessive-compulsive tendencies, hypersensitivity, mysticism and religiosity, and a propensity for vacillating instability between extremes of impulsive behavior. However, it is highly probable that the concept of an "epileptic character type" has no independent validity, and in the relatively few patients in whom such traits are marked, they represent secondary neurotic reactions to the epileptic disorder rather than a correlated constitutional deviation.

✦epileptic equivalent. Any episodic sensory, motor or experiential phenomena that may replace convulsive seizures in epilepsy (v. *psychic epilepsy*).

✦epileptic fugue. A state of disturbed, clouded, bewildered or dreamlike consciousness with integrated but automatic and occasionally violent activity (q.v.) following epileptic seizures. The fugue may persist from minutes to (in rare cases) days, and is thereafter generally submerged in almost complete amnesia.

epileptic furor. A state of disturbed consciousness, great excitability or uncontrolled activity which may follow an epileptic seizure.

✦epileptic status. Incessant or nearly continuous epileptic seizures which, in extreme cases, may lead to exhaustion and death if not therapeutically controlled.

✦epinosic gain. Secondary advantages derived from an illness or behavior disorder, as distinguished from the essential *paranosic* determinants and phenomena of the illness itself.

epiphenomena. False, spurious or irrelevant appearances.

epistasis. The predominance of some hereditary traits over *hypostatic* ones, the opposed traits not being related to *allelic genes* (q.v.).

epistemology. The study of the basis or validity of knowledge.

epistemophilia. Morbid seeking for or preoccupation with learning or knowledge.

equivalent. Any deviant or substitutive symptomatic expression of a morbid process, as an *epileptic e.* or a *migraine e.* (qq.v.).

eremiophobia. Morbid dread of loneliness.

erethism. 1. Increased excitability. 2. Marked excitation; e.g., *sexual erethism* means hypersensitivity to erotic stimuli leading to strong passions.

ergasia. In psychobiology (A. Meyer) the totality of an organism's behavior, as opposed to its *part-functions.* See *reaction types.*

ergasiology. In psychobiology (A. Meyer) the study of the determinants of the total behavior of an individual. See *reaction types.*

ergasiomania. Compulsive preoccupation with work or other incessant activity.

ergasiophobia. Morbid dread of activity.

erogenous. Causing genital or other erotic arousal. In psychoanalytic theory the *erogenous* (*libidinal*) *zones* are the *oral, anal* and *genital;* but the hair, ears, nose, breasts, or almost any other portion of the body may subserve erogenous or *fetishistic* (q.v.) purposes.

Eros. In Greek mythology, the god of passion. In psychoanalytic theory Eros comprises all libidinal instincts or strivings related to love of self or others, as distinguished from *Thanatos,* the instincts of destruction and death.

erotize. To endow with sexual or, in psychoanalytic theory, other *libidinal* (q.v.) meaning.

erotographomania. Morbid preoccupation with writing love letters.

erotomania. Excessive preoccupation with sexual phantasies and activities; usually used with reference to morbidly increased heterosexuality.

erythrophobia. Dread of red color, usually as symbolic of sexuality and/or sanguineous physical injury.

esthesiometer. An instrument for measuring sensibility, especially touch or two-point discrimination.

ethnic. Pertaining to the races of mankind. See *race.*

etiology. Pertaining to causation, particularly of disease.

euergasia. In psychobiology (A. Meyer) the normal functioning of the total organism.

eugenics. The study and control of factors that would improve the hereditary characteristics of a race (Galton). *Positive e.* promotes optimal mating among highly qualified (*"aristogenic"*) parents; *negative e.* deals with the prevention of reproduction in "undesirable" (*"cacogenic"*) stock through contraception, sterilization, etc.

eunuch. A male with female bodily characteristics; generally caused by castration before puberty.

euphoria. An exaggerated sense of well-being, usually accompanied by carefree activity.

eurhythmia. Optimal harmony, proportion or balance in behavior.

eurotophobia. Morbid fear of the female genitalia.

eutelegenesis. Controlled artificial impregnation.

euthanasia. The induction of death, particularly in the incurably ill, by rapid and painless methods.

euthenics. Racial improvement by the provision of optimal diet, environment, medical care, etc.

euthymia. Pleasant, tranquil feeling tone.

eviration. Impairment or distortion of male attitudes or activities.

exegesis. The exposition and interpretation of an authoritative text or doctrine.

exhibitionism. Erotic pleasure in exposing the body, with or without concomitant desires to stimulate a sex partner.

exogenic, exogenous. Arising outside the body.

expansiveness. Behavior characterized by various mixtures of *euphoria*, talkativeness, overgenerousness and some degree of *grandiosity* (qq.v.).

exteriorization. The turning of interests outward; e.g., into work or social pursuits.

+extinction. The disappearance of a *conditioned reflex* (Pavlov) when it is repeatedly elicited without *reinforcement* by the *unconditioned reflex* (qq. v.) through the provision of a reward.

+extroversion. Interest and participation in the "external" world, as distinguished from *introversion,* or preoccupation with endogenous, "self-centered" fantasies and *autistic* behavior (Jung).

fabrication. Fantastic lying without direct intent to deceive, as in *confabulation* (q.v.).

facies. Facial conformation or expression.

falsification, retrospective. Distortion of the occurrences in, and evaluation of, past experiences to conform with present attitudes, concepts or delusions. (cf. *screen-memory.*)

fantasy. Imagery; imagined scenes or occurrences.

fantasy test. One in which the subject is asked to describe scenes and events evoked in his imagination by some given stimulus, as by the standard pictures of the Thematic Apperception Test (Morgan-Murray). See *tests, projective.*

fellatio. Erotic contact between mouth and penis.

fertilization. Union between ovum and sperm; in general, stimulation to creative production.

festination. Involuntary increase in tempo of movement, particularly in gait, as in *paralysis agitans.*

fetish. 1. In general, any object or act endowed with special power or significance. 2. In sexology, any object (e.g., a lock of hair), body part (ear, breast) or maneuver (e.g., stroking or biting) charged with special sentimental or erotic interest.

+fixation. 1. The persistence of a definite goal or pattern of behavior. 2. In psychoanalytic theory, the continuation into later life of some pregenital (e.g., *oral* or *anal*) phase of interest in, or evaluation of, objects (*libidinal cathexis,* qq.v.).

flagellantism. Erotic pleasure or stimulation in whipping or being whipped.

flexibilitas cerea. See *catalepsy* and *catatonia.*

folie a deux, a trois, etc. A neurotic or psychotic interpersonal relationship participated in by two, three or more people.

folie du doute. Persistent, obsessive doubting, vacillation and indecision, usually with compulsive ruminations over every act.

fore-conscious. That portion of the unconscious subject to voluntary recall.

fore-pleasure. Contrectative or other preliminary erotic pleasure preceding genital orgasm (*end-pleasure*).

formes frustes. Atypical forms of a disease.

formication. Sensations of crawling in the skin.

fornication. Extramarital coitus.

frigidity. Absence of genital eroticism in women.

frustration. Prevention of attainment and satisfaction.

✦fugue. A state in which the patient's consciousness and behavior, though they may be well integrated, show an apparent break in continuity with previous patterns. *Epileptic fugues* (q.v.) leave an almost complete *amnesia* for their duration; *hysterical fugues* leave a *lacunar* and generally penetrable *amnesia* (qq.v.).

functional. Often misused with regard to symptoms or illnesses to mean of "neurotic" or "psychotic" etiology, as distinguished from "organic" causation. Strictly, all conduct is functional.

galeophobia. Morbid dread of cats.

gammacism. Child-like talk.

gamomania. Morbid preoccupation with desires to marry.

gamophobia. Dread of marriage.

Ganser syndrome. The miming of confusion, disorientation or other supposed psychotic behavior, especially among prisoners, whether deliberate (*malingering*) or neurotic (*hysterical psychosis*) or, as is usually the case, in mixed forms.

gatophobia. Morbid dread of cats; *ailurophobia*.

Gaussian distribution. The statistical incidence of data in close approximation to the *normal curve of error* (De Moivre-Gauss-Laplace), in accordance with the formula

$$y = \frac{n}{\sqrt{2\pi}\sigma} e - \frac{x^2}{2\sigma^2}$$

Observational or experimental data must be demonstrably deviant from this expectancy for special significance.

gelasmus. Hysterical laughter.

gene. An element or unitary function in a *chromosome* (the chromatin particles in the nucleus of a cell) which carries specific hereditary traits to descendants of the cell.

✦general paresis (dementia paralytica). A behavior disorder the organic precipitating cause of which is syphilitic infection of the brain; in late cases, a frank *psychosis* characterized by dementia, dysarthria, habit deterioration and pathognomonic neurologic signs

may appear and dominate the clinical picture.

genital. Pertaining to the organs or act of reproduction.

genophobia. Morbid dread of sexuality.

geophagy. Eating of dirt.

gephryophobia. Morbid dread of crossing water (i.e., over bridges).

geriopsychoses. The psychoses of senility.

germ plasm. Tissues that produce sperm or ova, parts of which are therefore presumably immortal (Weismann).

gerontophilia. Fascination with old people.

Gestalt. Configuration; setting in a total field. See *psychology, Gestalt*.

gibberish. Nonsensical speech, as in motor aphasia or some forms of advanced schizophrenia.

gigantism. Bodily overgrowth and deformity due to endocrine dyscrasias, particularly of the pituitary gland.

glioma. A tumor composed of *glia*, the non-neural supporting tissue cells of the brain.

globus hystericus. Feeling of a lump or constriction in the throat, as in the *anxiety syndrome* (q.v.). Derived from an ancient notion that in hysteria the uterus (*hysterus*) wanders about the body.

glossodynia. Pain or burning in the tongue.

glossolalia. "Speaking with tongues"; unintelligible (*jargon*) talk. 1. Denotes "spiritual presence" in some forms of Pentecostal worship. 2. *Neologisms* and *word salad* (qq.v.) during schizophrenic excitement.

glove anesthesia. Loss of sensation in a hand not following sensory nerve distribution; nearly always hysterical.

gonads. The sex glands.

✦grandiosity. Delusions of being wealthy, famous, powerful, omniscient, etc.

grand mal. A major form of epilepsy. See *epilepsy, major*.

graphomania. Morbid preoccupation with writing.

graphophobia. Morbid dread of writing.

grasping reflex. Closure of the hand when the palm is struck or stroked; normal in neonates, but indicative of a lesion in the frontal lobe of the brain in adults.

group-analysis. 1. Psychoanalytic investigations or therapy applied to groups. 2. The study of interpersonal tensions in a society (the *phyloanalysis* of T. Burrow).

✦**guilt.** Conscious or unconscious dread of loss of love or retributive punishment for impulses or deeds forbidden in earlier experiences.

gumma. A degenerative syphilitic lesion of the brain.

gymnophobia. Morbid dread of nakedness.

gynandromorphism. Possessing both male and female characteristics, sometimes on opposite sides of the body.

gynephobia. Morbid dread of women.

habit. A constant pattern of behavior, more or less unconsciously fixated and determined.

habit deterioration. Generally refers to a disintegration of adequate social and cultural adaptations (e.g., reversion to uncleanliness), constriction of interests and activities and disorganization of conative and affective control.

habitus. Physique, particularly as to "type" (q.v.).

hadephobia. Morbid dread of hell.

✦**hallucination.** An auditory, visual, tactile (*haptic*) or other apperception accepted as real by the subject but occasioned by no apparent external sensory stimuli. Hallucinations differ from *hypnagogic* or *dream-imagery* (qq.v.) in that no corrective reorientation occurs immediately after the imagery ceases, or on waking. On the other hand, the rapidly changing, fearful hallucinations of *toxic deliria* are recognized by the patient to have been unreal after his recovery.

hallucinations, Lilliputian. Diminutive (*microptive*) hallucinations; rarely, these occur in epileptic aura.

hallucinosis. The state of being actively hallucinated.

hamartophobia. Morbid dread of sinning.

haptephobia. Morbid dread of being touched.

hebephrenia. See *schizophrenia, hebephrenic.*

hebetude. Marked dulling and inertia in conation, affect and thought; a state of listlessness and apathy, especially when extreme.

hedonic charge. Refers to the invest-

ment of a concept or act with pleasurable affect.

hedonics. The study of the phenomena and dynamics of pleasure and displeasure.

hedonism. The doctrine that all behavior is, or should be, directed toward securing a maximal balance of pleasure, and avoiding displeasure in so far as possible.

hedonophobia. Dread of pleasure.

heliophobia. Morbid dread of sunlight.

hemeralopia. Impaired vision in bright light; distinguished from *nyctalopia*, or blindness only at night or in dim light.

hemianopsia. Impaired sight in a lateral half of the field of vision.

hemiballismus. Violent jerking, twitching, twisting or rolling movements on one side of the body, usually due to a lesion in the subthalamic nuclei of the opposite side.

hemichorea. Unilateral *chorea* (q.v.).

hemicrania. Unilateral headache, particularly in *migraine* (q.v.).

hemiparesis. Unilateral muscular weakness.

hemiplegia. Paralysis of one side of the body.

hereism. The doctrine of matronly fidelity and virtue.

hermaphrodite. Possessed of well-developed parts of the genital organs of both sexes; *bisexual.*

hermeneutics. The interpretation (and, especially, non-critical elaboration) of an authoritative text or doctrine.

hetairism. Concubinage, limited or free.

hetero-erotism. In psychoanalytic theory, the investment of *libido* (narcissistic energy) in external objects; *object-love* or *object-libido* as distinguished from *auto-erotism.*

heteronymous processes. Angyal's term for the influences of the environment on the organism in the *biosphere* (q.v.).

heterosexual. Pertaining to relationships between the sexes.

heuristic. Favoring the discovery of knowledge or of more adequate theoretic formulae.

hippus. Concentric oscillations of the pupil on stimulation by light.

holergasia. In psychobiology (A. Meyer) a "sweeping" reaction involving the total personality; generally equivalent to *psychosis* (q.v.).

holistic. 1. Referring to considerations

of the whole or total configuration. 2. The philosophy of the interdependence of wholes (J. C. Smuts).

+homeostasis. The tendency of organisms to maintain their metabolic processes in so far as possible within optimal limits for individual and race survival (C. Bernard, W. Cannon).

homicidomania. Persistent impulse to kill.

homilophobia. Morbid dread of sermons.

homogamy. Inbreeding.

homonymous. Bilaterally corresponding; e.g., *left homonymous hemianopsia* signifies loss of vision in the left field of both eyes.

homosexuality. Erotic interest or relations between individuals of the same sex.

homunculus. An imaginary little man.

Hoover's sign. If a patient with hysterical hemiplegia is placed on his back and asked to raise the "paralyzed" leg, there will be no pressure on an examiner's palm placed under the opposite heel.

hormic psychology. A psychology based on the concept of instincts (e.g., W. McDougall's).

hormone. A secretion from an endocrine gland that regulates growth, metabolism, or some special body function (e.g., insulin regulates sugar metabolism; the pituitary and ovarian secretions regulate menstruation, etc.).

hydrocephalus. Enlargement of the cranium from the pressure of spinal fluid inside (*internal h.*) or outside (*external h.*) the cerebrum.

hydrodipsomania. Excessive, almost insatiable thirst; rare and generally episodic. Sometimes seen in epilepsy and in brain tumors.

hydrophobia. 1. Rabies. 2. Neurotic dread of water. The latter connotation is so likely to be confused with the first that the etymologic hybrid "*aquaphobia*" has come into use.

hydrotherapy. Treatment of disease by various types of baths or by the internal administration of water.

hyelophobia. Morbid dread of materialism; or, philosophically, of materialistic doctrines.

hygrophobia. Morbid dread of dampness.

hypacusia. Impaired hearing.

hypengyophobia. Morbid dread of responsibility.

hyperacusis. Morbid auditory alertness or hypersensitivity.

hyperechema. Exaggeration of auditory sensations.

hyperesthesia. Increased sensitivity to stimuli, especially tactile.

hyperhidrosis. Excessive sweating.

hyperkinesis. Excessive or exaggerated muscular activity.

hypermnesia. Excessive crowding or unusual clarity of memory images.

hyperopia. Inability to focus on near objects; far-sightedness.

hyperpathia. Constant pain and markedly increased sensitivity in a body part.

hyperplasia. Overgrowth of tissue.

hyperprosexia. Morbid overattentiveness.

hypersomnia. Excessive sleeping.

hyperthymia. Lability of affect, usually toward *euphoria* (q.v.) and generally accompanied by increased activity to submanic levels (*hypomania*).

hypertonia. Morbid increase of muscular tension.

hypesthesia. Decreased sensibility, especially to touch and pain.

hypnagogic. Producing, or induced by, sleep or related states (e.g., *hypnagogic imagery*, q.v.).

hypnocatharsis. See *catharsis*.

hypnogenic spot. A region on the body (of an appropriately trained hypnotic subject) pressure upon which induces hypnosis.

+hypnosis (hypnotism). A trancelike passive state produced by monotonous, reiterated suggestion of relaxation, sleep and control by the hypnotist, in which the subject shows increased amenability and responsiveness to directions or commands, provided that these do not conflict seriously with the subject's own conscious or unconscious wishes. "Forgotten" memories may be recalled, and altered states of sensibility, perception or motor function may be induced. Acceptable acts may also be compulsively performed by the subject after the hypnotic trance has been terminated (*post-hypnotic suggestion*), and the patient may profess a directed forgetfulness for his experiences during the trance (*post-hypnotic amnesia*).

hypnotic. Any procedure or drug that promotes or induces sleep.

hypnotist. Anyone who practices *hypnotism* (q.v.).

hypobulia. Impairment of "will power."

hypochondriasis. A state of morbid preoccupation and fearful rumination about one's health, especially in the absence of serious organic disease.

hypokinesis. Diminished motility.

hyponoic. Stemming from, or determined by, unconscious processes (Kretschmer).

hypophysial cachexia (Simmonds' disease). Emaciation, anemia, *asthenia*, loss of hair and other bodily disturbances attributable to organic disease of the pituitary gland.

hypoplasia. Lack of development of a tissue or body part.

hyposomnia. Sleep of inadequate depth or abnormally short duration.

hypothalamus. A portion of the *diencephalon* (mid-brain) which plays an important part in the sympathetic nervous control of body temperature, blood pressure, heart rate, and water, fat and sugar metabolism. For the role of the hypothalamus in emotional expression, see Index.

+hysteria. 1. A state of neurotic sensorimotor dysfunction, e.g., *hysterical* blindness, paralysis or convulsions. 2. A lay term for great emotional and motor excitation ("hysterics"); should not be used in this sense in psychiatric description or diagnosis.

hysterical psychosis. A hysterical state which simulates psychotic behavior (e.g., a *Ganser syndrome*, q.v.).

hystero-epilepsy. 1. Hysterical convulsions simulating, but rarely duplicating, an epileptic seizure. 2. Occasionally used to denote a true epileptic attack precipitated by neurotigenic stresses.

iatrogenic. Induced in whole or part by a physician; e.g., an *iatrogenic neurosis* is one to which the professional ministrations of a physician contributed.

ichthyophobia. Morbid dread of fish.

iconomania. Morbid preoccupation with symbolic images.

ictus. A sudden, acute attack or seizure, e.g., *ictus epilepticus* connotes an epileptic convulsion without aura or other warning.

+id or Id. In psychoanalytic theory, a general term for all unconsciously determined instincts or libidinal strivings, (q.v.), constituting the conative "portion" of the personality.

idealization. Wishful over-evaluation of an object, person or concept.

ideas, fixed. A general term for *obsessions* and *delusions* (qq.v.).

ideas of persecution. *Obsessions* or *delusions* (qq.v.) that one is being consistently discriminated against or mistreated.

ideas of reference. *Obsessions* or *delusions* (qq.v.) that one is continually the object of, or is influenced by, the thoughts and actions of others.

+identification. Wishful adoption, mainly unconscious, of the personality characteristics or identity of another individual, generally one possessing advantages which the subject envies and desires.

ideogenetic. Induced by or related to vague sense impressions rather than organized images.

idiocy. Severe intellectual deficiency connoting a "mental age" rating on standard *intelligence tests* (q.v.) less than one-quarter the subject's chronological age. Idiots are incapable of making adequate extra-institutional adjustments.

+idiocy, moral (moral insanity of Prichard). Almost obsolete terms connoting a serious lack of "moral sense" or "moral development," i.e., the inadequate establishment of social responsibilities and adaptations. Cf. *criminality* and *psychopathy*.

idiopathic. Of unknown etiology.

idiosyncrasy. A delimited behavior pattern in one individual considered peculiar by another but not sufficiently so to be called neurotic or psychotic.

idiot-savant. An individual whose average intelligence is that of *idiocy* (q.v.) but who nevertheless possesses superior special abilities, e.g., memorizing, chess-playing, puzzle-solving.

+illusion. A misinterpretation of a sensory percept; usually fleeting or correctable by closer or supplementary examination of the stimulus which induced the illusion.

illusion, memory. A false memory.

imagery, hypnagogic. Distortions of perception, imagery and interpretation that sometimes occur in the trancelike state preceding sleep; those that occur between sleep and full waking are termed *hypnopompic*.

imago. A psychoanalytic term for a subject's unconscious conception of parents, siblings, or others, especially as derived from childhood evaluations.

+imbecility. General intellectual deficiency such that the average intelligence level is between about one-quarter and one-half normal. Imbeciles nearly always require institutional care.

impotence. Impaired ability to erect the penis for sexual intercourse, whether due to neurotic inhibition or to organic disease.

incest. Culturally prohibited sexual relations between members of a family, as between father and daughter, or brother and sister.

incorporation, oral. In psychoanalysis, the fantasy of permanent preemption of some desired object or person through symbolic swallowing, possibly stemming from *oral incorporative* attitudes of the suckling to its mother.

incubus. A male demon believed in the Middle Ages to violate women, or enter their bodies and thus influence their behavior.

individuation. In the *analytic psychology* of C. Jung and the *psychobiology* of A. Meyer, the progressive differentiation and unique integrations of the developing organism.

infatuation. A wishful, fantastically distorted over-evaluation of a love object, occasioned by pressing unconscious needs.

inferiority, organ. The concept that neuroses are basically caused by an hereditary or congenital inferiority of some organ or system of the body, for which the individual then strives to *"overcompensate"* (A. Adler).

influencing-machine. A fantastic device which a deluded patient believes his enemies use to control his thoughts and actions (Tausk).

+inhibition. 1. In general, the internal checking or restraint of a conation, affect, thought or act. 2. In psychoanalytic theory the prevention of *Id* instincts from reaching conscious recognition and response, because of specific *Ego* controls directed by the *Superego* (qq.v.). 3. In Pavlovian reflexology (a) the submergence of a positive or *excitatory conditioned reflex* by a contrary *inhibitory* one, and (b) the supposed occurrence of a radiating *inhibitory process* over the cerebral cortex controlling the corresponding neural reflex arcs.

+insanity. A vague legal term variously connoting inability "to distinguish right from wrong," or "a mental state in which the patient is unable to care for himself or constitutes a danger to others." To be distinguished from the psychiatric concept of *psychosis* (q.v.).

+insight. 1. Clinically, the patient's own explanation of his illness, progressively judged "distorted," "incomplete," "good," etc. by the observer in so far as it coincides with his own theoretic formulations. 2. In psychoanalysis, the extent of a patient's true (as opposed to merely professed or *verbal*) understanding of the origins and unconscious dynamisms of his behavior. 3. In Gestalt psychology, the phenomenon of sudden grasp ("ah-ah!" *erlebnis*) of a perceptual configuration or of the solution to a problem.

insomnia. Lack or disturbance of sleep.

+instinct. 1. A conative psychologic term with variable meaning, but generally connoting an inborn tendency toward certain specific patterns of behavior (e.g., the *sex instinct,* the *exploratory instinct,* etc.). 2. In older psychoanalytic theory, a primary tendency toward life and reproduction (*Eros*) or toward destruction, dissolution and death (Thanatos) (qq.v.).

insulin therapy. A form of treatment of psychiatric disorders by the production of hypoglycemic (low blood sugar) states (with or without convulsions or coma) by the injection of insulin.

+intelligence. The sum total and degree of development of the organism's capacities to perceive, differentiate, integrate and manipulate its environment (Tolman). Spearman contends that there is an over-all index (g) of general intelligence, plus factors for perseveration (p), fluency (f), will (w) and speed (s). Others divide intelligence into less interdependent capacities: e.g. *abstract i., mechanical i.* and *social i.* (Thorndike), or various special (statistically determined) *vectors* of intellectual capacity such as memory (m), verbal comprehension (v), verbal fluency (w), space visualization (s), number facility (n) and, possibly, other factors of induction, deduction, speed of reaction time, perception, judgment, closure (including flexibility) and rate of reversal of ambiguous perceptions (Thurstone). In any case, the ordinary *tests* (q.v.) of "general intelligence" (e.g., the Stanford-Binet or Kuhlman) indicate only rough averages of these abilities; moreover they often do not take adequate account of intercurrent conative and affective factors, or of the previous training and experiences of the subject.

✦intelligence quotient (I.Q.). A figure indicating the subject's performance on some *test of intelligence* (q.v.) in relation to the statistical norm for his age; e.g., a child of 12 (chronological age) whose performance totalled the 8½ year level (mental age) on the Binet-Stanford test would have an I.Q. of 8½ ÷ 12 or 71. See *intelligence.*

intelligence test. See *tests, intelligence.*

intrauterine fantasy. Of returning to the utter peace, passivity and security of the mother's womb (*Nirvana fantasy*).

introjection. A psychoanalytic term connoting the fantasied reincorporation of a loved or hated object or person into the subject's own *Ego* or *Superego* (qq. v.). For example a widow may unconsciously attempt to regain her dead husband by a fantasy that he is "forever within" her, and then, in her own behavior, display some of his remembered characteristics. Such *mental mechanisms* are often associated with fantasies of *oral incorporation* (q.v.).

intromission. Insertion of the penis into the vagina.

introversion. Self-preoccupation; turning of interests inward; *autism* (q.v.).

✦intuition. A sudden understanding, or conviction not reached by conscious reasoning; usually an integration of unconscious knowledge which reaches consciousness as an illuminating *insight* or *inspiration.*

inversion. Assumption of a feminine sexual role by men, or a masculine one by women.

inversion, amphigenous. Combined male and female roles assumed by a person of either sex.

inversion of affect. A defensive changing of an affect to its opposite; e.g., love into hate, or fear into avidity.

inversion, sexual. Feminine sexual interests or activity displayed by men, or masculine interests by women; homosexuality.

investment, affective. The transposition or attribution of special interest, meaning and value to an object or person; *affective charge;* in psychoanalysis, *cathexis* (q.v.).

involutional period. Referring to an indefinite time in late middle life (age forty to fifty-five) when general retrogressive physiologic changes, especially in the gonadal functions of women (menopause), occur or are thought to occur. Many so-called *involutional psychoses* (q.v.), however, are only indirectly related to menopausal or other involutional changes.

iophobia. Morbid dread of poison.

irrumation. Penile-oral intercourse.

isolation. The defensive separation of an impulse, concept or act from its memory-context or from its affective charge of anxiety.

isolation, sensory. A method for producing disturbances of orientation, affect and consciousness by depriving a subject of sensory stimulation.

jactation or jactitation. Incessant tossing or jerking movements.

Janet's test. Reveals the spurious nature of a claimed anesthesia when the blindfolded patient, on direction to do so, replies "no" or "I don't feel it" when the affected part is touched.

jaw-jerk. Reflex elevation of the jaw when the mandible is struck.

kakidrosis. Disagreeably odoriferous sweating.

keraunophobia. Morbid dread of lightning.

kinesalgia. Pain on movement.

kinesophobia. Morbid dread of movement.

kleptomania. Obsessive - compulsive stealing, the objects taken being usually of unconsciously symbolic rather than of intrinsic value.

koinotropy. Interest in social relationships (A. Meyer).

kopophobia. Morbid dread of exhaustion.

✦Korsakoff psychosis. A toxic psychosis (usually alcoholic) characterized by inflammatory or retrogressive changes in peripheral nerves (*polyneuritis*), disorientation, *amnesia* with *confabulation* and intellectual deterioration (*dementia*) (qq.v.).

la belle indifférence. A term used by Janet to describe the "happy indifference" or tolerance shown by neurotic patients toward their unconsciously adaptive symptoms.

lability. Instability, particularly with regard to affect or emotion.

laliophobia. Morbid dread of talking or stuttering.

lapsus calami. A "slip of the pen" revealing an unconscious wish or association.

lapsus linguae. A "slip of the tongue" revealing an unconscious wish or association.

latency period. In psychoanalytic theory, the period between five and puberty when libidinal drives (oral, anal, genital) recede from direct expression because of the progressive formation of *Ego-defenses* (Chapter 3).

lateropulsion. Walking sideways, usually with *festination*, as in *paralysis agitans* (qq.v.).

Laurence - Moon - Biedl syndrome. An hereditary disease characterized by pigmentary degeneration of the retina, idiocy, and various dystrophies including *polydactylism* (supernumerary fingers or toes) and webbing of the extremities.

law of retaliation (lex talionis). The concept of retribution in kind: "an eye for an eye, a tooth for a tooth."

lécheur. One who applies his mouth to the genitals of others.

leptosome. One with a spare, lanky (*asthenic*) habitus (cf. *type*, Kretschmer).

lesbianism. Homosexual love between women.

letheomania. Intense addiction to narcotic drugs.

✛libido. 1. In psychoanalytic theory, the energy associated with the instincts of the *Id*. 2. In a more limited sense (medical and lay) the desire for sexual relationships; sex drive.

libido, free-floating. In psychoanalytic theory, instinctual energy unattached to external personal or material relationships, leaving undirected, objectless yearnings for dependency, aggressivity or love.

Little's disease. Mental deficiency and spastic muscular dystrophies caused by injury to the brain at birth.

locomotor ataxia. A disease caused by syphilitic degeneration of the spinal cord and characterized mainly by progressive loss of muscular control or recurrent painful organic disturbances (e.g., *gastric crises*). See *tabes*.

logorrhea. Incessant flow of talk.

logospasm. Explosiveness in speaking.

✛love. 1. An affect or sentiment evoked by a person (concept or object) that fulfills one's needs or expectations. (This definition is not recommended for domestic consumption.) 2. "[Love is the effort of] two solitudes to protect and touch and greet each other"—Rainer Maria Rilke. Also see *rapport, sentiment* and *infatuation.*)

lues. Syphilis.

lunacy. A legal term, equivalent to *insanity* (q.v.).

lycanthropy. The delusion of being a wolf, or a human being in wolf form.

lygophilia. A morbid preference for dark or obscure places.

lyssophobia. Morbid dread of becoming insane.

macrocephaly. Abnormally large head, usually *hydrocephalic*.

macrogenitosomia. Sexual maturation in childhood, usually due to pituitary or adrenal tumors.

macropsia. The perception of objects as larger than normal; usually *hysterical* (q.v.).

macrosplanchnic. Cf. *types, Viola.*

magic omnipotence, fantasy of. Reversion to infantile feelings of *cosmic identification* (q.v.) or control (cf. *Ur-defenses*).

magnetism, animal. Mesmer's theory (now obsolete) of hypnotic phenomena.

maieusiophobia. Morbid dread of childbirth.

malaria therapy. The treatment of paresis by the recurrent fevers of a mild form of artifically induced malaria.

✛malingering. The deliberate simulation of disease; usually, however, by neurotic individuals.

mammalingus. Erotic licking or sucking of the breast.

mania. See *psychoses, manic.*

-mania. A suffix denoting morbid preoccupation with some impulse, idea or activity. Addiction to alcoholic drinks is called *dipsomania;* morbid preoccupation with arithmetic or mathematics, *arithmomania;* with bones, *osteomania;* with books, *bibliomania;* with buying indiscriminately, *oniomania;* with dancing movements, *choreomania;* with dead bodies, *necromania;* with being diseased, *nosomania;* with the taking of drugs, *pharmacomania;* with eating, *phagomania;* with erotic phantasies and activities, *erotomania;* with delusions of fame, riches, power, *megalomania;* with fires, *pyromania;* with freedom, *eleutheromania;* with hatreds, *mesomania;* with heterosexual desire in women, *nymphomania;* with homosexual desire in women, *nymphomania, inverted;* with extreme homesickness, *nostomania;* with images, *iconomania;* with killing, *homicidomania;* with light, *photomania;* with love letters, *erotographomania;* with marrying, *gamomania;* with morphine, *opiomania;* with narcotic drugs, *letheomania;* with obscene writing, *pornographomania;* with poetry, *metromania;* with pulling of the hair, *trichotillomania;* with selfishness, *egomania;* with a single conation, concept or activity, *monomania;* with specific foods, *opsomania;* with stealing, *kleptomania;* with suicide, *thanatomania;* with thirst, *hydrodipsomania;* with traveling, *dromomania;* with wandering, *ecdemomania;* with wanderlust, *poriomania;* with washing, *ablutomania;* with wealth, *plutomania;* with words or names, *onomatomania;* with work, *ergasiomania;* with writing, *graphomania.*

maniaphobia. Morbid dread of "insanity."

✛mannerism. A characteristic expression, gesture or movement. When stereotyped and unconsciously repetitious, but minor, it is termed a *tic.* Such movements may become symbolically bizarre and persistent in *schizophrenia* (q.v.).

marihuana. A narcotic drug derived from the plant *Cannabis sativa.* When smoked in cigarettes it may produce feelings of elation and a fantastic, sometimes grandiose hallucinosis.

✛masochism. 1. In sexology, erotic pleasure derived from physical pain. 2. In older psychoanalytic theory, the satisfaction of destructive instincts (Thanatos) turned against the self. 3. In biodynamics, the satisfaction of bodily needs through learned adaptive patterns, certain aspects of which may appear unpleasant or painful to an observer (cf. index).

masochism, moral. A type of masochism that actuates self-induced social "suffering," e.g., the persecuted reformer, the religious martyr.

massotherapy. Treatment by kneading, passive motion or massage.

mass-reflex. Flexion of the legs, abdominal spasm, sweating and incontinence produced by sensory stimulation below the level of a transverse lesion of the spinal cord.

mastigophobia. Exaggerated dread of punishment.

masturbation. Erotic manipulation of one's own genitals.

masturbation, psychic. Erection and orgasm during erotic fantasies, without external stimulation of the genitals.

matrix (adj. matricial). The mother-material or context from which a thing or concept originates, takes form and develops, and within which it remains imbedded and connected.

✛mechanism. 1. In psychoanalytic theory, the mechanics of interaction among psychic "structures": e.g. the *Ego* "defends itself" against the *Id* by the "mechanism" of *repression* (qq.v.). 2. In biodynamics, a process of contingent and total organismic adaptation devoid of any implication of an isolated pattern.

megalomania. Markedly grandiose delusions of fame, riches, power or religious exaltation.

✛melancholia. A severe *depressive psychosis* (q.v.).

mellissophobia. Morbid dread of bees.

meningitis. Inflammation of the proximal coverings of the brain (meninges).

✛mental hygiene. A term employed (but not coined) by A. Meyer to designate the development of optimal modes of personal and social conduct and the prevention of psychiatric disorders.

mental level. 1. Popularly, equivalent to the average intelligence of a subject. 2. In Jung's metapsychology, refers to the levels of (a) consciousness, (b) the personal unconscious, (c) the *collective unconscious,* or (d) the deepest (and partially *atavistic*) "substrate of mentation."

merycism. Chewing of regurgitated food (cud).

mesmerism. An almost obsolete term for hypnotism (from Anton Mesmer).

mesoderm. The middle germinal layer of the embryo from which are derived the bones, muscles, heart, vascular system and portions of the urogenital tracts.

mesomorphic. See *types, Sheldon.*

✛metapsychology. A psychological theory that cannot be verified or disproved by observation or reasoning.

Metrazol therapy. An obsolescing treatment of psychiatric disorders by producing coma and/or convulsions by the intravenous injection of Metrazol (pentamethylene tetrazol), alone or in combination with anticonvulsant drugs.

metromania. Morbid preoccupation with poetry.

micropsia. The appearance of objects as visually small or diminutive; usually *hysterical* (q.v.).

microsplanchnic. See *type, Viola.*

+migraine. A disorder characterized by recurrent attacks of severe localized or one-sided (hemicranial) headaches, which are often preceded or accompanied by visual disturbances, gastrointestinal dysfunctions and physical fatigue or prostration.

+migraine equivalents. Various transient paresthesias, motor disturbances or organic dysfunctions that may replace an attack of *migraine.*

+mind. 1. A generalized metapsychologic abstraction comprising a person's motivations, affects, intelligence, values, beliefs, etc. 2. Operationally, the phenomena of body in internal (including speech) and external action.

miosis. Maintained contraction of the pupil.

misanthropy. Hatred of mankind.

misocainia. Marked aversion to anything new or unaccustomed.

misogamy. Marked aversion to marriage.

misogyny. Marked aversion to women.

misomania. Preoccupation with multiple hatreds.

+M'Naghten rule. A legal precedent from the murder trial of Daniel M'Naghten (England, 1843) to the effect (a) that any act committed by an idiot, imbecile or lunatic cannot be adjudged a crime, and (b) that such persons cannot be tried and punished by criminal procedure if it can be shown that they were aware neither of the "nature" of their act, nor that it was "wrong." This precedent is incorporated into the criminal law of twenty-nine of our States.

mnemic or mnemonic. Pertaining to memory.

mongolism. A congenital deficiency characterized by idiocy or imbecility with dysplastic bodily development including a fold of skin over the inner canthus which gives the eyes a "mongoloid" appearance.

monocular diplopia. Double vision in one eye; nearly always hysterical.

monomania. Incessant preoccupation with a single conation, concept or activity.

monothetic. A system of thought or practice based upon a single principle or formula.

monozygotic. Identical twins, developed from a single ovum, as distinguished from *dizygotic* or *fraternal* twins developed simultaneously, but from separate ova.

morale. The spontaneous coordination and persistence of members of a group working toward a common goal.

mores. The traditional standards of a group, as distinguished from *folkways* or customs.

+moron. 1. A mentally defective person, with average intelligence (I.Q.) of from 50 (*low grade m.*) to 79 (*high grade m.*) as estimated by standard intelligence tests with a "norm" of about a hundred. 2. A lay or journalistic term incorrectly applied to sexual perverts.

mother-fixation. Infant-like dependence on the mother.

mother-surrogate. Any person who, in the subject's interpersonal attitudes, he unconsciously regards in the role of his mother.

+mourning. A state of grief and sadness over a loss; theoretically distinguished from *depression* or *melancholia* (q.v.) by the absence of marked self-recrimination, persistent agitation, a severe depressive syndrome or suicidal impulses. Compare *psychoses, depressive.*

+multiple (disseminated) sclerosis. A diffuse, remissive, but generally progressive organic disease of the central nervous system manifested variously by tremor, scanning speech and nystagmus (the *Charcot triad*), ataxia, sensory disturbances and optic atrophy. There may be neurotic or psychotic reactions to these disabilities, or there may be symptoms indicative of organic damage to the brain (cf. *organic psychoses*).

mutism. Persistent refusal, conscious or unconscious, to speak; sometimes seen in schizophrenia.

myasthenia. Muscular weakness or fatigability. When due to an organic progressive disturbance in neuromuscular metabolism, it is a prominent symptom of the generally fatal disease *myasthenia gravis.*

myoclonia. Spasmodic muscular contractions.

mysophobia. Morbid dread of dirt or contamination.

+narcissism or narcism. [From Narcissus, who, for rejecting the devotion of *Echo*, was condemned by Nemesis to fall in love with his own reflected image.] In psychoanalysis, equivalent to original self-love, or to the *reidentification* with, or fantasied *reincorporation* of, objects or persons given a temporary investiture (*cathexis*) of *object-love*. The first form is called *primary narcissism,* the re-derived form *secondary narcissism.*

+**narcolepsy.** Recurrent episodes of trancelike or sleep states, occurring with no, or almost no, warning, and persisting from a few seconds to several hours. They may be of *neurotic* etiology; also cf. *epileptic equivalents.*

narcomania. A morbid desire for or preoccupation with sleep, or means of producing it (drugs, hypnosis, etc.).

+**narcosynthesis.** A therapeutic procedure, particularly applicable to recent combat neuroses, in which the patient is given an hypnotic drug (e.g., Pentothal) to alleviate his acute anxiety, permitted to express his repressed memories, affects and conflicts (cf. *catharsis*) and then guided by the therapist to conative and emotional reintegration, behavioral readjustments and social rehabilitation. See *Sodium Amytal.*

necromania. Morbid love of dead bodies.

necromimesis. Acting as though dead.

necrophilia. Morbid attraction toward corpses, or, more generally, death.

necrophobia. Morbid dread of dead bodies.

+**need.** A physiologic (metabolic) deficiency or imbalance translated dynamically into behavior (characterized variously as motivated by desires, drives, goals, instincts, wishes, strivings, etc.) directed toward satisfaction of the need.

negativism. Opposition to direction or manipulation, occasionally taking the form of specifically contrary behavior. Sometimes seen in the form of an *automatism* in *schizophrenic* states (qq.v.).

negrophilia. Love of Negroes.

negrophobia. Morbid dread of Negroes.

neolalia. *Neologistic* (q.v.) talk.

neologism. A word-condensation the meaning of which may be known only to the patient (e.g., "furt," to represent hurtful anal coitus in the language of a schizophrenic).

neonate. Newly born.

neophobia. Morbid dread of anything new.

neoplasm. A new-growth or tumor.

nepenthic. Inducing peace and forgetfulness.

+**nerves, nervous, nervous breakdown, nervous spells, etc.** Lay euphemisms used vaguely to describe almost any behavior disorder. These terms should never be used, other than in quotes from the patient, in psychiatric description or diagnosis.

neuralgia. Pain due to disease of peripheral nerves.

+**neurasthenia.** A euphemistic and psychiatrically obsolescent term for a vague group of symptoms consisting of muscular weakness or fatigability, inertia, petulant irritability, aversion to effort, variable aches and pains, and minor organic dysfunctions. At present the term has no connotation of organic disease of the nervous system.

neuritis. An organic disease in a nerve.

neuropsychiatrist. A physician who practices both neurology and psychiatry.

+**neuroses.** A group of behavior disorders representing suboptimal adaptations to biodynamic stress and conflict. Neuroses are characterized symptomatically by 1. *anxiety,* with its recurrent physiologic manifestations (v. *anxiety syndrome*), more or less covered 2, by various pervasive *defenses* and *fixations* such as *phobias, obsessions* or *compulsions,* or 3, by symbolic bodily expressions such as sensorimotor (*hysterical*) or organ-neurotic ("*psychosomatic*") dysfunctions (qq.v.). Generally, the history reveals previous sensitivities and maladaptations to frustration and conflict, exacerbation of neurotic symptomatology under duress, and partial recovery when stress is relieved either spontaneously or under therapy. For theoretic and practical purposes, neuroses are distinguished from *psychoses* by the criteria listed under the latter (q.v.), although all forms of transition occur.

neurosis, anxiety. See *anxiety neurosis.*

+**neurosis, conversion.** A *neurosis* (q.v.) characterized predominantly by dysfunctions of (a) sensation or motility (*hysteria*) or (b) one or more organsystems (*organ neurosis*). Frank anxiety or obsessive-compulsive defenses may be minimal, especially when the hysterical symptoms serve as adequate adaptations.

+**neurosis, obsessive-compulsive.**   A

neurosis characterized prominently by *obsessions* and *compulsions,* usually combined with *phobias.* When these are transgressed, an acute *anxiety syndrome* occurs (qq.v.).

neurosis, occupational. A neurosis, usually with *conversion symptoms* or *accident proneness* (qq.v.) occasioned by conflicts over maladaptations at work.

neurotigenic. Producing, or favoring the induction of a neurosis.

nexus. A bond or tie, usually unconscious, between previously experienced configurations of conations, affects, conceptions and acts.

nihilism. In a special psychiatric sense, the delusional denial of all existence.

✦Nirvana-fantasy. From the *Nirvana* of Buddhist theology, a state in which there is no desire, no affect, and no strife—only pervasive peace. Differs from *intra-uterine fantasy* (q.v.) in the sense that the latter may connote deeply regressive *maternal-cosmic reidentification* (q.v.) as well as sublime security.

noctambulism. Fuguelike walking or other activity at night; somnambulism.

non compos mentis. A legal term signifying that the subject is "of unsound mind," and therefore irresponsible in the conduct of his own affairs or those of others.

nosology. The naming and classification of diseases.

nosomania. Intensely *hypochondriacal* (q.v.) preoccupation with fears or convictions of being diseased.

nosophobia. Morbid dread of disease.

nostalgia. Sentimental longing for home or family; homesickness.

nostomania. Nostalgia of highly neurotic or psychotic degree; extreme homesickness.

noumenal. Refers to the doctrine that things or processes have an essence comprehensible only by "intellectual intuition," but not perceivable by the mere *phenomena* available to the senses. This extrascientific doctrine is inherent in much that is mystical in the study of behavior (v. Existentialism, Chapter 7).

nyctalopia. Impaired vision in dim light or at night.

nyctophobia. Morbid dread of darkness or night.

nymphomania. Morbidly incessant, almost insatiable heterosexual desire or activity in women.

nymphomania, inverted. Intense homosexual desire or activity in women.

nystagmus. Jerky oscillations of the eyeballs, lateral, vertical or (rarely) circular.

✦obsession. A persistent, conscious desire or idea, recognized as being more or less irrational by the subject, which usually impels *compulsive acts* on pain of *anxiety* (qq.v.) if they are not performed. Obsessions can often be analyzed as conscious reflections of unconscious conflictual wishes.

✦occupational therapy. Treatment by diverting the patient's energies into constructive recreational or manual pursuits satisfactory to him.

oclophobia. Morbid dread of crowds.

Oedipus complex. See *complex, Oedipus.*

oikofugic. Pertains to obsessive-compulsive itinerancy and wandering.

olfactophobia. Morbid dread of odors.

oligergasia. In psychobiology (A. Meyer) signifies the behavior of mental defectives.

oligophrenia. Intellectual deficiency.

oligophrenia, phenylpyruvic. A congenital metabolic disturbance characterized by muscular hypertonicity, motor disturbances and intellectual deficiency, apparently due to an inability to oxidize phenyl-alanine.

onanism. 1. Coitus interrupted for extra-vaginal ejaculation, as in the Biblical story of Onan. 2. Sometimes incorrectly used to signify masturbation.

oneirism. Day-dreaming, or trancelike dreaming.

oneirology. The study of dreams.

oneirophrenia. A fantasy-ridden form of schizophrenia presumably amenable to drug and/or convulsive therapy (Meduna).

oniomania. Obsessive-compulsive preoccupation with indiscriminate buying.

onomatomania. Morbid preoccupation with words or names.

onomatophobia. Morbid dread of names.

ontogeny. The study of the morphologic development of the individual.

onychophagia. Nail-biting.

ophidiophilia. Morbid fascination with snakes.

ophidiophobia. Morbid dread of snakes.

opiomania. Morphine addiction.

opisthotonos. Spastic arching of the back, as during tonic convulsions.

opsomania. Morbid craving for specific foods.

optic atrophy. Degeneration of the optic nerves, as caused by drugs or cerebral syphilis.

organ-erotism. In psychoanalytic theory, the investment (*cathexis*) of some body-part or organ-system with *libido* (q.v.), so that it is particularly cherished or valued.

organ-language. A term connoting the symbolic and communicative meaning of organ functions; e.g., vomiting as an expression of "disgust" over, and rejection of, some exceedingly unpleasant concept or experience.

organicist. In psychiatry, one who believes that all behavioral disorders are caused by organic disease.

organon. A comprehensive theoretic formulation of known facts.

+orgasm. The height of erotic pleasure, just preceding detumescence and relaxation. Generally refers to erotic sensations centered in the genitals, but orgastic sensations in the mouth, breast, anus or even skin (as in masturbatory-equivalent scratching) have been described.

+orientation. Awareness of place, time, circumstances and interpersonal relationships.

orientation, multiple. Coexistent but incompatible systems of orientation, sometimes seen in *schizophrenic delusions* (q.v.).

ornithophobia. Morbid dread of birds.

+orthopsychiatry. The study of the phenomena and dynamisms of the development of "normal" behavior, with emphasis on child psychiatry and "*mental hygiene*" (q.v.).

orthosympathetic nervous system. The thoraco-lumbar, *adrenergic* portion of the *sympathetic n.s.* (q.v.) which is generally catabolic in function and which is particularly active in the mobilization of energy to meet behavioral emergencies (Cannon).

osphresiophilia. Morbid fascination with odors.

osphresiophobia. Morbid dread of odors.

+overcompensation. 1. An adaptive process particularly stressed by Alfred Adler, whereby a person over-reacts to initial deficiencies, handicaps or inhibitions in some sphere of activity by becoming exceedingly adept in that field (e.g., Demosthenes, afflicted with an impediment of speech in his youth, strove for, and succeeded in reaching, the pinnacles of oratorical power). 2. In psychoanalytic theory, an excessive overplay of any defense mechanism; e.g., revealing over-politeness toward a disliked person; or compulsive *satyriasis* (q.v.) as a defense against unconscious homosexual tendencies.

+overdetermination. A process whereby a single behavior pattern becomes adaptive to many unconscious needs, thus rendering it particularly fixed and resistant to therapy. For instance, a *hysterical paralysis* (q.v.), of an arm may be a combat flier's initial reaction to a crash landing, but later the same symptom may also come to symbolize (a) an unconscious defense against his own mobilized aggressions, (b) a rationalized excuse for not returning to a hated civilian job, (c) expiation for a regressive dependence on a government pension, etc. In this sense, *overdetermination* parallels the process of *condensation* (q.v.) in the formation of verbal and dream symbols.

pack. In hydrotherapy, the wrapping of the body in several sheets wrung out in water at 60° F. (cold pack) or 130° F. (hot pack) generally for the purpose of calming excited or overactive patients.

paleopsychology. 1. The study of the behavior of primordial men. 2. Jung's concept of *racial* or *atavistic unconscious* in which remain traces of primitive human or even animal behavior.

+panic. Extreme anxiety, with blind flight or marked disorganization of behavior.

panphobia. Pervasive dread of everything.

papilledema. Swelling of the retinal end of the optic nerve observable through a retinoscope.

parageusia. Distortion of the sense of taste.

paralipophobia. Morbid dread of irresponsibility.

paralogia. False or perverted reasoning.

+paralysis agitans (Parkinson's disease). An organic disease of the brain, particularly of the basilar nuclei, caused by inflammation (encephalitis), drugs or senile changes, and characterized by progressive muscular dystonia, spasticity and tremor, disturbances in motor control (*festination, retropulsion,* dissociation of movement), masked facial expression and colorless voice, and sometimes by outbreaks of irrational rages and excitements.

paramimia. Inappropriate or perverted gesture and expression, not corresponding with the concurrent affect.

paramnesia. False memory, not recognized as such by the subject.

paranoia. See *psychosis, paranoiac.*

paranoia, alcoholic. Paranoid reactions in alcoholic patients, frequently characterized by unconscious attitudes of sexual and social inferiority, projected as delusions of neglect and mistreatment and, particularly, of unfaithfulness on the part of their marital partners. See *psychosis, paranoiac.*

paranoia litigans or **querulans.** Paranoid states characterized by resort to endless complaining and litigation on the part of the patient.

paranoid. Partaking of the phenomena or dynamics of *paranoia* (v. *psychoses, paranoiac*).

paranoid formula. In psychoanalytic theory, many paranoiac reactions are considered to be psychotic defenses against unconscious homosexuality in men, following a "mechanism" that may be paraphrased verbally as: "I *love* him," overreactively denied by, "No, I *hate* him," with the projected accompaniment "Therefore he hates and *persecutes* me" (Freud).

paraphasia. Distortion of speech.

paraphrasia. Incomplete, distorted, disorganized or circuitous grammatical structure in speech.

paraphrenia. A vague Kraepelinian term connoting a psychotic reaction other than *dementia praecox* or *manic depressive psychosis* (qq.v.).

paraplegia. Paralysis of the lower body and legs; *superior p.* designates paralysis of both shoulders and arms.

parapraxis. 1. Clumsy, inefficient or deviant manipulation. 2. In psychoanalysis, significant slips of speech or behavior.

parasexuality. Any deviated or perverse sexual behavior.

parasitophobia. Morbid dread of infestation.

✛parasympathetic nervous system. The *cranio-sacral, vagal, cholinergic* and generally anabolic and inhibitory portion of the *sympathetic nervous system* (q.v.).

parathymia. Inappropriateness of mood.

parathyroid glands. Endocrine organs located in the capsule of the thyroid gland. The parathyroid *hormone* (q.v.) influences the metabolism of calcium and phosphorus, and is a factor in the control of muscular tonicity. *Parathyroidectomized* animals (p. glands removed) develop protracted muscular spasms or *tetany.*

parenchyma. The essential and characteristic, as distinguished from the supporting or nutritive, tissues of an organ; e.g., the neurons of the brain as distinguished from the glia and blood vessels.

parergesia. In psychobiology (A. Meyer) a term referring to the characteristically "perverted" behavior of schizophrenic patients.

✛paresis (general paresis, general paralysis of the insane). An organic *psychosis* (q.v.) caused by syphilis of the brain, and generally characterized by affective instability with recurrent excitements, muscular tremors, speech disturbances, pathognomonic changes in the pupillary reactions and in the spinal fluid, and progressive behavioral deterioration.

Parkinsonism. See *paralysis agitans.*

parorexia. Perversion of appetite.

parosmia. Distortions of olfactory perception.

paroxysm. An episodic attack; or a sudden exacerbation of symptoms.

parthenogenesis. Reproduction from unfertilized ova.

parthenophobia. Morbid dread of virgins.

pathergesia. In psychobiology (A. Meyer) a behavior disorder caused by organic disease.

pathognomonic. Specifically diagnostic.

pathology. The study of organic and physiologic changes in disease.

pathophobia. Morbid dread of disease.

pavor diurnus. Tantrums of acute anxiety or fear occurring during the day; usually refers to such attacks in children.

pavor nocturnus. Night-terror; usually in children.

pcpt. Freud's abbreviation for perception, or the Conscious (Cs).

peccatiphobia. Morbid dread of transgressing.

pederasty. Anal coitus, especially with boys.

peniaphobia. Morbid dread of poverty.

penis-envy. In psychoanalytic theory, the unconscious longing of the female for male attributes, sometimes resulting in erotic inhibitions, general aggressivity and other neurotic masculine identifications.

Pentothal interview. See *narcosynthesis* and *Sodium Amytal.*

✚perception. The integration of sensory stimuli to form an image, the configuration and interpretation of which is influenced by past experiences.

persona. The mask or role a person more or less unconsciously assumes in his daily living, as distinguished from his inner character or *individuality* (C. Jung).

✚personality. Operationally, this term comprises the sum total of the unique behavior patterns of an individual, particularly these concerned in his social relationships.

personality, multiple. A term used by M. Prince to describe patients who assume various ostensibly distinct, and often contrasting, total behavior patterns ("personalities") at various times; and, while in one role, profess complete amnesia for the other.

personality, panels of. According to G. Draper, the anatomic, physiologic, psychologic and immunologic aspects of personality.

✚persuasion. In psychiatry a form of therapeutic influence, usually conceived as verbal, by which the patient's motivations, unconscious as well as conscious, are directed toward goals desired by the therapist.

petit mal. A minor form of *epilepsy* (q.v.).

phagomania. Insatiable eating.

phallus. Penis.

phantasy. An image, static or kinetic, composed of recombinations of past impressions and apperceptive interpretations generally fulfilling some wish. (See *test, projective, Thematic Apperception.*)

pharmacomania. Morbid preoccupation with the taking of many drugs; distinguished from *addiction* to a single drug.

pharmacophobia. Morbid dread of drugs.

pharmacothymia. Neurotic or temperamental avidity for drugs (Rado).

phasmophobia. Morbid dread of apparitions.

phenomenal. Refers to the sensory data of scientific *epistemology,* as distinguished from the *noumenal* approach (qq.v.).

-philia. A suffix indicating excessive interest in, love of, or susceptibility to some conation, concept or activity. The more common psychiatric terms with this etymologic structure, arranged according to their English referents, are these: Affinity for burial grounds, *taphophilia;* for death, *necrophilia;* for excreta, *coprophilia;* for injury, *traumatophilia;* for knowledge, *epistemophilia;* for looking, *scoptophilia, scopophilia;* for obscure places, *lygophilia;* for Negroes, *negrophilia;* for odors, *osphresiophilia;* for old people, *gerontophilia;* for plants, *dendrophilia;* for snakes, *ophidiophilia.*

phlegmatic. Slow, non-committal, calm, unexcitable. See *types, humoral.*

✚phobia. A morbid dread of an object, situation or act, generally derived from its unconsciously symbolic reference to an anxiety-ridden previous experience or series of experiences. Specific names, derived from Greek roots, for the almost infinite varieties of *phobias* are rapidly becoming obsolete, but the following is a partial list, arranged by the symbol feared, of many terms still found in the literature: Morbid dread of activity, *ergasiophobia;* of air, *aerophobia;* of animals, *zoophobia;* of apparitions, *phasmophobia;* of bees, *mellissophobia;* of birds, *ornithophobia;* of burial, *taphephobia;* of cats, *ailurophobia, galeophobia,* or *gatophobia;* of childbirth, *maieusiophobia;* of choking, *pnigophobia;* of climbing, *climacophobia;* of coitus, *cypridophobia;* of cold, *psychrophobia;* of color, *chromatophobia;* of constricted spaces, *claustrophobia;* of crossing water, *gephryophobia;* of crowds, *oclophobia;* of dampness, *hygrophobia;* of darkness or night, *nyctophobia;* of dawn, *eosophobia;* of death, *thanatophobia;* of dead bodies, *necrophobia;* of deformity, *dysmorphobia;* of depths, *bathophobia;* of dirt, *mysophobia;* of disease, *pathophobia, nosophobia;* of dogs, *cynophobia;* of drugs, *pharmacophobia;* of eating, *sitophobia;* of everything, *panphobia;* of evil spirits, *satanophobia;* of excreta, *coprophobia;* of contamination by excrement, *scatophobia;* of exhaustion, *kopophobia;* of fear, *phobophobia;* of felines, *ailurophobia;* of female genitalia, *eurotophobia;* of fire, *pyrophobia;* of fish, *ichthyophobia;* of food, *cibophobia;* of gaiety, *cherophobia;* of heat, *thermophobia;* of heights, *acrophobia;* of hell, *hadephobia, stygiophobia;* of infestation, *parasitophobia;* or injury, *traumatophobia;* of becoming insane, *lyssophobia;* of insanity, *maniaphobia;* of irresponsibility, *paralipophobia;* of justice, *dikephobia;* of lightning, *keraunophobia;* of loneliness, *eremiophobia;* of marriage, *gamophobia;* of materialism, *hyclophobia;* of micro-organisms, *bacillophobia;* of mirrors, *eisoptrophobia;* of giving birth to a monster, *teratophobia;* of movement, *kinesphobia;* of nakedness, *gymnophobia;* of names, *onomatophobia;* of Negroes, *negrophobia;* of anything new, *neophobia;* of odors, *olfactophobia, osphresiophobia;* of overworking, *ponophobia;* of pain, *algophobia;* of parasites, *parasitophobia;* of pleasure, *hedonophobia;* of pointed objects, *aichmophobia;* of poison, *iophobia;* of poverty, *peniaphobia;* of projectiles, *ballistophobia;* of punishment, *mastigophobia;* of red, *erythrophobia;* of responsibility, *hypengyophobia;* of right, *dextrophobia;* of seas, *thalassophobia;* of sermons, *homilophobia;* of sexuality, *genophobia;* of sinning, *hamartophobia, enisophobia;* of sitting, *thaassophobia;* of small inanimate objects, *acarophobia;* of snakes, *ophidiophobia;* of solitary places, *agoraphobia;* of sounds, *acousticophobia;* of (empty) spaces, *cenophobia;* of a specific place, *topophobia;* of spirits, *daemonophobia;* of standing and walking, *stasibasiphobia;* of stealing, *kleptophobia;* of storms, *brontophobia;* of strangers, *xenophobia;* of sunlight, *heliophobia;* of talking or stuttering, *laliophobia;* of thunder, *tonitrophobia;* of being touched, *haptephobia;* of touching, *aphephobia;* of transgressing, *peccatiphobia;* of trembling, *tremophobia;* of tuberculosis, *tuberculophobia, phthisophobia;* of vehicles, *amaxophobia;* of virgins, *parthenophobia;* of vocal sounds, *phonophobia;* of vomiting, *emetophobia;* of water, *hydrophobia;* of being weak, *asthenophobia;* of women, *gynephobia;* of writing, *graphophobia.*

photomania. Morbid affinity for light.

-phrenia. A suffix designating "mind."

phrenology. F. Gall's (1758–1828) obsolete doctrine, popularized by Spurzheim, that the "faculties of the mind" reside in specific regions of the cerebral cortex, and that these can therefore be determined by an examination of the skull.

phthenoid. See *type, Kretschmer.*

phthisophobia. Morbid dread of tuberculosis.

phyloanalysis. The metapsychology of Trigant Burrow, which deals primarily with the "partitive" and "dissipative" interplay between individual and group "tensions," as developed along evolutionary (*phyletic*) lines.

phylogenetic principle. C. Jung's term for the patterning of the individual Unconscious along the lines of the development of the race.

physiogenic. Originating in the functioning of the body.

physique. Body form. See *types.*

Pick's disease. Presenile organic degeneration of the cerebral cortex, most marked in the frontal lobes, causing aphasia, intellectual deterioration, irritability with affective instability, and rapidly progressive habit disintegration.

pithiatism. Forceful suggestion in the therapy of neuroses (Babinski).

plateau speech. Unitonal, colorless vocal speech.

✦pleasure-principle. In psychoanalytic theory, the seeking of release from libidinal tensions (giving pleasure) as distinguished from various manifestations of the *death-instinct or Thanatos* (such as the *repetition-compulsion* and *masochism,* qq.v.).

pleniloquence. Excessive, and especially redundant, talk.

pleonexia. Morbid acquisitiveness.

pleurothotonus. Spastic contractures of the body to one side.

plutomania. Morbid greediness for wealth.

pnigophobia. Morbid dread of choking.

poikilochromia. Adaptive changes in body color, e.g., as shown by a chameleon.

poikilothermia. Changes in body temperature in response to external influences; morbidly excessive in lesions of the hypothalamus.

poikilothymia. Excessive variability or swings in mood.

pollakiuria. Frequent or excessive urination.

polydipsia. Morbidly increased thirst.

polymorphous perverse sexuality. Diffuse, unchannelized, variable erotic interests and behavior, normal in infancy.

polyneuritis. Diffuse disease of the peripheral nerves.

polypnea. Morbidly deep or accelerated breathing.

ponophobia. Morbid dread of over-working.

porencephaly. Developmental or pathogenic cavitation of the brain.

poriomania. Incessant wanderlust.

pornographomania. Morbid preoccupation with obscene writing.

pornolagnia. An intense sexual preference for prostitutes.

post-hypnotic suggestion. See *hypnosis.*

potency. Sexual competency in coitus by the male.

power factor in intelligence. See *deterioration* and *intelligence.*

praxiology. The study of conduct.

preconscious. In psychoanalysis, unconscious concepts or images available to voluntary recall.

pregenital. In psychoanalysis, refers to phases of infantile development before the emergence or primacy of genital interests.

prehension. Grasping (whether physical *intellectual, emphatic* or *sympathetic,* qq.v.).

+prejudice. An intellectual set which unconsciously biases or distorts a subject's apperception and evaluation of later experiences according to his predetermined *attitudes* (q.v.).

presbyophrenia. The organic psychoses of later life (presenium), such as *Alzheimer's* or *Pick's disease,* or early arteriosclerotic *dementia* (qq.v.).

priapism. Morbidly frequent, excessive or continuous erection of the penis.

primal scene. A child's observation of coitus between its parents.

primary process. In early psychoanalytic theory, the relatively free expression of *libidinal tendencies* (q.v.), as distinguished from the inhibitions, fixations, channelizations and investments (*cathexes*) of energy comprising the *secondary process.*

prison psychosis. Refers to a wide variety of behavioral disorders (malingering, neuroses, psychoses) precipitated by the actual or anticipated stresses of imprisonment. See *Ganser syndrome.*

process psychosis. Bleuler's term for psychotic manifestations attributable to organic disease of the brain.

prodromata. Symptoms preceding and heralding a disease, behavior disorder, or an exacerbation of either.

prognosis. Prediction of the duration and course of a disease or behavior disorder.

+projection. An unconscious defense process whereby the subject attributes his own motivations, concepts or acts to others.

+prolonged sleep. Treatment of behavior disorders by continuous sleep (1 to 20 days) induced by drugs such as paradehyde or Amytal. *Dauerschlaf.*

proprioception. Sensory perceptions from muscles and joints, including vibratory sensibility.

propulsion. Accelerated forward staggering, as in *paralysis agitans.*

protopathic sensibility. Gross perception of deep pain and temperature, as differentiated from finer (*epicritic*) sensibility to touch, two-point discrimination, etc.

protophrenia. Profound physical, intellectual and social deterioration in young children subjected to severe affective deprivation (Bourne).

pseudocyesis. A state in which a female shows bodily changes suggestive of pregnancy (e.g., amenorrhea, morning vomiting, breast and abdominal enlargement) without being actually pregnant. Women with this form of *hysterical neuroses* (q.v.) may sincerely believe themselves to be pregnant.

pseudogeusia. Hallucinations of taste.

pseudologia fantastica. The insistent telling of elaborate and sometimes fantastically embellished stories by a subject, usually about himself; whether (a) with deliberate though irrational intent to deceive, (b) under partially resisted, but undeniable inner compulsion, or (c) as an evidence of delusional beliefs.

psychalgia. A vague term referring to "mental" pain or distress.

psychasthenia. An obsolescent term, generally indicating an *obsessive-compulsive-phobic* state (qq.v.) with impairment of initiative and energy.

psyche. Mind (q.v.).

psychiater. Obsolescent equivalent of psychiatrist.

+psychoanalysis. A psychologic system of research, theory and therapy, the broad outlines of which were propounded by Sigmund Freud (1856–1939). Cf. index for the multiple elaborations and implications of this theory.

+psychobiology. An eclectic system of behavior research, theory and therapy outlined by Adolf Meyer (1866–1944). See *reaction types* and index.

psychodiagnostics. In the special Rorschach sense, the grading and evaluation of the subject's performance on the ink-blot test or "Rorschach experiment." (See *test, projective,* Rorschach.)

psychodrama. J. L. Moreno's term for his diagnostic and therapeutic technique of having a subject verbalize or act out his inner conflicts in supervised relationships with other performers (*"auxiliary egos"*) who represent or symbolize persons important in his life.

psychology. Literally, the "study of mind," and therefore a term of many meanings; cf. index.

✦**psychology, analytic.** The metapsychology of Carl Jung, distinguished from Freudian psychoanalysis by various quasi-mystic concepts such as those of *anima, persona* and *racial unconscious* (qq.v.) by its rejection of orthodox analytic techniques and by its emphasis on didactic and inspirational guidance by the analyst.

✦**psychology, Gestalt.** A psychological system (Wertheimer, Koffka, Köhler, et al.) which rejects elemental stimulus-response (*reflex*) concepts of behavior, stresses the indivisible wholeness of perceptual configurations (*Gestalten*), and emphasizes the sudden "insightful" nature of learning as opposed to trial-and-error or automatic "association."

psychology, individual. The metapsychologic system of Alfred Adler, stressing particularly the concepts of *organ-inferiority, inferiority complex* and *overcompensation* (qq.v.).

psychology, topologic. The system of K. Lewin, emphasizing *boundaries* of delimitation, *valences* of attraction and repulsion, and *vectors* of directional forces acting between the organism and objects in its milieu (qq.v.).

psychometrics. The testing and measurement of various perceptive-integrative-manipulative abilities.

✦**psychoneurosis.** A term now generally used as equivalent to *neurosis* (q.v.) or sometimes as implying severe neuroses with larval or minimal psychotic tendencies or admixtures.

psychopathia sexualis. Aberrations of sexual behavior (Krafft-Ebing).

psychopathic personality. See *sociopathic personality.*

psychopathy. A severe behavior disorder.

✦**psychoses.** A group of grave disorders of behavior, most of which satisfy the legal criteria of *insanity* in that the patient is unable to care for himself and/or constitutes a danger to others. Psychoses, however, also fulfil one or more of the following *psychiatric* criteria: (1) Loss of contact with, or marked distortion of, socially accepted interpretations of reality (as shown in deviated perceptions, thinking disorders, hallucinations or delusions). (2) Severe and persistent disorders of affect (e.g., *manic* euphoria, *depressive* melancholia, or *schizophrenic* emotional blunting and lack of correspondence between affect and idea). (3) Marked *regression,* with (a) retreat from, or perversion of, social relationships (e.g., perverse passivity, dependency or aggressivity) or (b) habit reversions (e.g., open masturbation, soiling, etc.). (4) Personality disintegration, so that elementary erotic and hostile impulses or *automatisms* are released from control, and (5) (a) acute derangement of *perceptive-interpretative-manipulative* ("intellectual") capacities (as in toxic deliria) or (b) the permanent *deterioration* of such capacities (as in psychoses with organic cerebral disease).

✦**psychoses, depressive.** Psychoses variously characterized by melancholic fixation of mood, retardation of apperception and response, self-depreciatory preoccupations (ideas of inadequacy, of guilt and of being hated), morbid preoccupations with anticipated punishment, nihilistic fantasies ("all is hopeless," or "lost"), episodes of agitation, petulant demanding helplessness and regression, suicidal tendencies, and a marked *depressive physiologic syndrome* (q.v.) comprising insomnia, anorexia, loss of weight, sexual disturbances and various organic (especially gastro-intestinal) dysfunctions.

psychoses, functional. Generally refers to *psychoses* (q.v.) with no determinable organic etiology, e.g., mania, melancholia, paranoia and *schizophrenia.*

✦**psychoses, involutional.** Originally considered to be a definite syndrome characterized mainly by melancholia and agitation, generally progressing to *hebetude* and intellectual deterioration. Actually, psychoses occurring in the *involutional period* (q.v.) vary widely in etiology, clinical expression and prognosis.

✦**psychoses, manic.** A *psychosis* (q.v.) characterized by extreme *emotional lability* (though with superficially *euphoric* affect), *psychomotor hyper-activity* (uninhibited flow of free-associative speech and conduct), hypersensitivity to stimuli with marked distractability, and a tendency to unorganized delusions of *grandiosity*. Manic episodes are generally self-limited in duration; occasionally, they are apt to recur regularly (*cyclic mania*) or, more rarely, in alternation with periods of depression (*manic-depressive psychosis*). Rare cases of *chronic mania* (Schott) have been reported.

✛**psychoses, organic.** *Psychoses* (q.v.) in which pathologic changes in the body, especially in the central nervous system, are etiologically significant contributory factors, e.g.: psychoses with pellagra, chronic alcoholism, cerebral tumor, brain syphilis, etc. Organic psychoses are characterized by dementia and, generally, by impaired affective control.

✛**psychoses, paranoiac.** A relatively rare (about 4 per cent incidence) *psychosis* (q.v.) characterized by well-systematized, slowly progressive *delusions of influence, reference or persecution,* based on false premises and interpretations, but relatively logical and consistent, and accompanied by appropriate affect. Paranoia is distinguished from the *affective psychoses* and from *schizophrenia* in that in paranoia there is minimal affective distortion or personality disintegration; e.g., the paranoiac system is relatively isolated from the rest of the personality pattern (see *schizophrenia, paranoid*).

psychoses, puerperal. Loosely used for the widely variant psychotic states that may occur during pregnancy or after childbirth (*post-puerperal psychoses*).

psychoses, schizo-affective. Those characterized by almost equally prominent *schizophrenic* (q.v.) and *depressive* or *manic* features.

psychoses, schizophrenic. See *schizophrenia.*

✛**psychoses, senile.** Organic psychoses caused by senile degenerative or arteriosclerotic changes in the brain, and generally characterized by progressive dementia (*aphasic* defects, *amnesia* for recent events), habit deteriorations (e.g., loss of cultural interests, garrulity, hoarding, personal uncleanliness) and *regressions* to puerile affectivity (e.g., the petulant dependence and selfishness

of "second childhood"). See *Pick's* and *Alzheimer's disease.*

✛**psychosomatic medicine.** The study, theory and application of the dynamics of total behavior (*biodynamics*) in relation to the practice of medicine and its several specialities.

✛**psychotherapy.** The science and art of influencing behavior so as to make it (a) more efficient and satisfactory to the individual and (b) more compatible with social norms.

psychrophobia. Morbid dread of cold.

psychrotherapy. The therapeutic applications of cold, as in rubs or baths.

pubertas praecox. Premature genital maturation.

puerile. Childish.

puerperium. The period of pregnancy.

pupillary reflex. Changes in size of the pupil when adjusting to (a) changes in light intensity or (b) the distance of the object (*accommodation*).

pycnolepsy (*pyknolepsy*). Minor, mild epileptic seizures.

pygmalionism. Morbid attachment to one's own lifeless creations. [From Pygmalion, who fell in love with a statue he had carved and therefore beseeched Ovid to give her life as the beauteous Galatea. In one version of the fable, however, he then neglected her until she again turned to marble; in another, she disillusioned her creator by proving to be so harsh a shrew that Pygmalion longed for a return of her stony silence.]

pyrolagnia. Erotic excitation by starting or witnessing fires.

pyromania. A morbidly recurrent and pressing desire to start and witness fires.

pyrophobia. Morbid dread of fire.

quadriplegia. Paralysis of the arms and legs.

race. In anthropology, generally refers to the ethnic grouping of mankind into (a) Caucasians (Nordics, Alpines and Mediterraneans), (b) Mongoloids (including American Indians), (c) Negroids and possibly (d) the Australasians, each group showing wide variations and intermingling of anthropomorphic features. Other groupings of mankind as to ecology or language, (e.g., "Aryan") or especially with regard to "superiority" or "inferiority" in any respect, are generally the product of subjective *value—judgments or prejudices* (q.v.) and without scientific foundation.

rapport. An interpersonal relationship in which each participant feels a non-competitive sharing or compatibility of desires and goals.

rational. Referring to conscious reasoning, which itself is channeled mainly by unconscious determinants.

+rationalization. The conscious justification (usually on grounds of "reason," "logic" or social expediency) of attitudes, concepts and acts after these have already been determined by unconscious motivations.

reaction, all-or-none. In neurophysiology, the observation that single neurones (nerve elements) never discharge partially, but either completely or not at all. This concept has frequently been used in psychiatric thinking, but the analogy is spurious when applied to the complexities and intricate balances of total behavior.

+reaction-formation. In psychoanalytic theory, the process whereby conscious wishes, affects, ideation or behavior are made defensively contrary to rejected unconscious impulses; e.g., a father's overtly reactive cruelty to a daughter to whom, unconsciously, he is incestuously attracted.

+reaction-type. In psychobiology (A. Meyer), designates the predominant behavior pattern or *ergasia* of a psychiatric patient: i.e., *anergasia* (intellectually defective), *dysergasia* (toxic), *pathergasia* (organic), *holergasia* (psychotic), *meregasia* (neurotic part-reaction), *oligergasia* (feeble-minded), *parergasia* (schizophrenic) and *thymergasia* (affective psychoses).

+reality-principle. In psychoanalytic theory, the modification of the expression of unconscious libidinal drives (*Eros* or *pleasure-principle*) or of the death-instincts (*Thanatos* or the *Nirvana-principle*) by rational consideration of the requirements of "reality."

recessive. The effaced effects of the non-dominant one of a pair of *allelic genes* (q.v.) on hereditary characteristics; i.e., a hereditary influence which remains dormant or hidden in the presence of the dominant determinant.

recidivism. The recurrence of delinquency or criminality despite treatment or punishment.

reciprocal induction. In Pavlovian reflexology, a postulated neural process whereby a focus of cortical excitation is automatically surrounded by a sphere of counterposed inhibition, which is in turn limited by a larger sphere of induced excitation, and so on to involve large concentric regions of the brain.

reefers. Popular term for cigarettes containing marihuana.

+reference, delusion of. A fixed, irrational belief that one is the object of the thoughts and actions of others.

+reflex. In neurophysiology, a sensorimotor neural pathway. Cf. *conditioning* and Index for other connotations of the term.

reflex, conditioned, equivalent phase. In Pavlovian reflexology, a *conditioned reflex* in which strong and weak conditional stimuli produce equal effects. See *conditioning.*

reflex, conditioned, inhibitory. In Pavlovian reflexology, a *conditioned reflex* that prevents the glandular or motor expression of an *excitatory reflex* established earlier. See *conditioning* and *reciprocal induction.*

reflex, conditioned, paradoxical phase. In Pavlovian reflexology, a *conditioned reflex* so altered that a weaker signal produces stronger effects than in the original conditional stimulus.

reflex, conditioned, ultraparadoxical phase. In Pavlovian reflexology, a conditioned reflex so altered that a positive conditional stimulus produces negative effects.

+regression. 1. The resumption, under stress, of earlier and experientially more satisfactory modes of behavior. 2. In psychoanalytic theory, the return to infantile phases of libidinal organization: i.e., *narcissistic, oral* or *anal* (qq. v.).

rejuvenation. A term formerly employed to designate the effects of vasectomy (Steinach operation) or testicular implants in temporarily restoring potency in men.

relapse. The recurrence of an illness after partial or complete recovery.

remission. Partial or complete amelioration of the symptoms of an illness or behavior disorder, with or without permanent recovery.

repetition-compulsion. See *compulsion, repetition.*

replacement. The substitution of favorable conations, concepts and activities for unfavorable ones removed or altered spontaneously or by therapy.

+repression. The automatic and unconsciously defensive process of banishing dangerous desires, affects or ideas, singly or together, from awareness to the *unconscious;* distinguished from *suppression* in which the control exercised is seemingly deliberate and conscious.

✦resistance. In psychiatric, and especially psychoanalytic, therapy the reluctance (mainly unconscious) of the patient to relinquish accustomed patterns of thinking, feeling and acting, however neurotic, in favor of new and untried modes of adaptation. In psychoanalytic theory, *resistance* often has the more limited meaning of the *Ego's* refusal to accept insight into the *Unconscious,* as shown by the patient's covert rejection of interpretation or the development of a *negative transference* (qq.v.).

riddance-principle, or -reflex. Automatic activity to purge the body of noxious agents, as in coughing, scratching, vomiting, defecation (S. Rado).

sadism. Pleasure, often directly erotic, in inflicting pain or other suffering on human beings or animals; cf. Index.

sapphism. Intense female homosexuality.

satanophobia. Morbid dread of evil spirits.

satyriasis. Morbidly intense heterosexuality and venery in men.

scatophagy. The ingestion of bodily excrements.

scatophobia. Morbid dread of contamination by excrement.

Schilder's disease. A disease of the young caused by degeneration of the central white matter (neural tracts) of the brain, and manifested by progressive blindness and dementia.

schizoid. Partaking of the nature of schizophrenic behavior.

✦schizophrenia. A group of variable *psychotic* (q.v.) syndromes characterized predominantly by: 1. General blunting and distortion of *affect,* especially in relation to professed ideational content and interpersonal relationships. 2. Bizarre perceptual and category formations and thinking disturbances, loosely organized into fantastic *delusional* systems, and sometimes projected as *hallucinatory* experiences. 3. Regression to primitive forms of *narcissistic,* erotic or aggressive expression, and 4.

Disintegration of behavior with the appearance of *stereotypies* and motor *automatisms* (qq.v.). For the various clinical forms of schizophrenia, see below.

schizophrenia, ambulatory. A term loosely used by Zilboorg, apparently to mean schizophrenic behavior under circumstances which do not lead to the patient's permanent incarceration.

✦schizophrenia, catatonic. A form of *schizophrenia* (q.v.) characterized by motor disturbances (*catalepsy, flexibilitas cerea, negativism, mannerisms*), stupors or acute outbreaks of hallucinatory excitement, and occasional periods of *remission* (qq.v.).

✦schizophrenia, hebephrenic. A highly variable form of *schizophrenia* (q.v.) particularly characterized by early onset, insidious distortion and blunting of affect, inconstant hallucinosis and fragmentary delusional formations, the development of symbolic mannerisms and stereotypies, and progressive deterioration of personal and social habits (Kahlbaum, Kraepelin).

✦schizophrenia, latent. Schizoid or schizophrenic tendencies likely to find overt expression under unfavorable stress.

schizophrenia, oneiric. See *oneirophrenia.*

✦schizophrenia, paranoid. A form of *schizophrenia* (q.v.) in which delusions of reference and influence are prominent; distinguished from *paranoia* in that (a) the delusions are highly fantastic, logically bizarre and poorly systematized, and (b) other schizophrenic criteria (affect distortion, pervasive behavioral disintegration, etc.) are also present. See *psychoses, paranoiac.*

✦schizophrenia, process. A term sometimes used to designate schizophrenic "dementia" in which organic changes in the brain are found (or are postulated) to be important etiologic factors.

✦schizophrenia, pseudoneurotic. Ambulatory schizophrenia underlying severe hysterical, somatic, obsessive-compulsive-phobic, or character neuroses (P. Hoch, S. Rado).

✦schizophrenic deterioration. Disintegration of habit patterns and disuse of intellectual capacities consequent on schizophrenic contraction of interests and deviations or perversions of behavior; however, except in so-called *process* (organic) *schizophrenia,* there is no demonstrable loss of basic abilities.

schizothymia. Affective distortion or noncorrespondence with apparent ideational content.

scopolagnia; scopophilia, scoptophilia. Erotic pleasure in looking, sometimes leading to compulsive *voyeurism.*

scotoma. Blind spot.

+screen-memory. 1. A relatively acceptable memory recalled in place of one charged (*cathected*) with greater anxiety. 2. A retrospective illusion.

secondary process. See *primary process.*

self-abuse. Lay term for masturbation, significantly connoting guilty fear of the consequences.

semeiotic. Specifically symptomatic or indicative of an illness.

senile psychoses. See *psychoses, deterioration* and *senile.*

sensorium. Awareness of the configurations of time, place and person in their proper anamnestic setting.

sentiment. An *attitude* charged with strong or pervasive *affect* (qq.v.).

shell-shock. A misleading term used in World War I for cases now known to have comprised almost every form of neurotic and psychotic (as well as a small minority—about 5 per cent—of traumatic) behavior disorders. The term should be limited to the neurologic after-effects of actual concussion from shell explosions (*blast injury*); or, preferably, abandoned altogether.

shibboleth. A pass-word, often meaningless in itself, which identifies its user as belonging to a group with a common but restricted ideology. [From the Hebrew word, "shibboleth," meaning an ear of corn, used as a watch-word by the Gileadites to identify fugitive Ephraimites who pronounced it "sibboleth."]

+shock-treatment. The subjection of psychiatric patients to convulsive doses of Metrazol, carbon dioxide or insulin, or to electric current passed through the brain. Cf. Index.

sibling. Strictly, a full brother or sister not a twin of the subject; generally, any other child in the family.

signal, sign, symbol. Respectively more complex and elaborate representations of an earlier experiential configuration, referring to some conative, affective or conceptual component of the original experience. See Chapter 13.

sitophobia. Morbid dread of eating.

sixty-nine. Mutual simultaneous fellatio (from the graphic representation 69).

skoptsy. Masochistic self - castration. (From the Russian Skopts, who practice religious castration and flagellation.)

+sociopath; sociopathic personality. Generally refers to an individual who is not readily classifiable as predominantly intellectually defective, *autoplastically* (q.v.) *neurotic,* or definitely *psychotic* (qq.v.), but whose behavior is characterized by recurrently episodic impulsivity, irresponsibility, lack of emotional control, and inadequate or unstable educational, marital, occupational and other social adaptations. Psychopaths are prone to come into conflict with police or other social authorities—a tendency used by some to distinguish them from a group of *"neurotic characters"* who keep their eccentricities and aberrations (e.g., prejudices, excessive religiosity, *obsessive-compulsive-phobic* behavior, etc.) within the bounds of law and custom. Formerly *psychopathic personality.*

Sodium Amytal, Pentothal sodium. Barbiturate drugs which, when injected intravenously in 5 to 10 per cent solution, in doses of from 0.2 to 0.5 Gm., induce a state of somnolence and relaxation during which previously repressed impulses, affects and concepts may appear in the partly clouded consciousness of the subject. See *narcosynthesis.*

sodomy. Sexual intercourse with animals; *bestiality.*

solipsism. The doctrine that any organism, including man, can "know" only itself and its own conceptions of the universe.

soma. Pertaining to the tissues of the body; (a) as distinguished from the genetic *germ-plasm* (ovum and sperm) and (b) as spuriously contrasted with the *psyche* or *mind* (q.v.).

somnambulism. Walking in a state of sleep, trance or *fugue* (q.v.).

somnifacient. Inducing sleep.

sophistry. A spurious concept or argument.

soporific. Calming or sleep-inducing.

spasmophilia. Susceptible to excessive or prolonged muscular contractions.

spasmus nutans. Rhythmic nodding and *nystagmus* (eye-jerking) in young infants.

speech disorders. See *aphasia.*

split personality. See *personality, multiple.*

spurious pregnancy. See *pseudocyesis.*

stasibasiphobia. Morbid dread of standing or walking.

status epilepticus. See *epileptic status.*

stereognosis. The ability to recognize the size, shape and weight of objects through muscle and joint sensibility.

stereotypy. Cyclic repetitiousness of thought, speech (*verbigeration*) or behavior.

stigmata, hysterical. Absence of corneal or pharyngeal sensitivity, formerly thought to be characteristic of hysterical states.

stigmata of degeneration. Physical features (e.g., projecting ears, cranial malformations) erroneously thought by Lombroso to indicate "constitutional" *psychopathy* or *criminality* (qq.v.).

strephosymbolia. Reversed perception of sensory configurations, as though in a mirror (Orton).

stupor. Mute, confused, unresponsiveness; not with extreme physical prostration as in *coma.*

stygiophobia. Morbid dread of hell.

subconscious. A term generally comprising the *co-, fore-* and *unconscious* (qq.v.); not used in formal psychoanalytic theory.

+sublimation. A "normal" process of deviating unconscious and essentially selfish motivations into socially acceptable services or creative activities. See Index.

+substitution. The replacement of conations, affects, concepts or acts by others with a lesser charge of anxiety.

succubus. A female demon which perverts a man's behavior by sexual influences.

+suggestion. A process of gestural or verbal communication by which one person may use another's evaluations of him (*transference relations,* q.v.) to channelize the other's behavior into desired patterns.

+superego or **Superego.** In psychoanalytic theory, that portion or function of the personality which (a) as *conscience,* prohibits the Ego from direct forms of instinct-expression and thereby prompts the Ego to utilize various *defense mechanisms* against unconscious *Id* impulses, and (b) as *Ego-ideal,* channelizes behavior along patterns similar to those of individuals with whom the subject wishes to *identify*

(i.e., whose advantages he unconsciously desires).

+suppression. The conscious subjugation and control of impulses, ideas, affects and acts felt to be dangerous.

+symbol. The more or less remotely displaced representation of an experience in imagery. Cf. Chapter 13.

+sympathetic nervous system. That portion of the nervous system that innervates the organs and glands of the body, as distinguished from the *peripheral nerves* which innervate the muscles and sense organs. The *s.n.s.* is usually divided functionally into the *orthosympathetic n.s.* (generally catabolic) and the *parasympathetic n.s.* (generally anabolic) (qq.v.).

sympathy. A compatibility of desire or affect between two persons; distinguished from *empathy* by the intuitive nature of sympathy and its relative independence from superficial intellectual formulations.

symptom. Any overt manifestation of a disease or behavior disorder, as distinguished from the specific meaning of *diagnostic sign,* which must be elicited by special test.

syncope. Fainting.

syndrome. A group of behavioral phenomena integrated by the functional patterns of an organism; especially as elicited under adaptive stress (e.g., *anxiety syndrome*) or by organic disease (e.g., diabetic syndrome). More narrowly, a configuration of symptoms.

synergy. Coordination; harmonious movement.

synesthesia. The transliteration of stimuli in different sensory modalities; e.g., certain tones may seem "blue" to the subject, designs may "feel" hot or cold; or certain words may carry an intrinsic sense of color (*verbochromia*).

synthesis, distributive. In psychobiology, the guided reintegration of a patient's reaction-patterns (as *distributively analyzed*) into more satisfactory total behavior (Diethelm, Muncie).

syntonic. Harmonious.

syntropy. In psychobiology (A. Meyer), the satisfactory integration of individual and social behavior.

tabes (locomotor ataxia). Syphilis of the central nervous system mainly localized in the spinal cord, causing loss of deep sensibility, motor incoordination, painful paresthesia, optic atrophy and acute, episodic disturbances of organ functions (*tabetic crises*).

taboo, tabu. A strict social prohibition. (The term is derived from certain religious customs of Polynesian tribes.)

tachylogia. Rapid, garrulous speech.

tachypnea. Rapid respiration.

talion principle. In psychoanalytic theory, the concept or fear that all injury, actual or intended, will be punished in kind; i.e., in *retaliation* or *retribution*.

taphophilia. Morbid preoccupation with, or attraction to, burial grounds.

taphophobia. Morbid dread of burial.

tarantism. A form of hysterical dancing, "epidemics" of which spread through Europe in the Middle Ages.

taxonomy. The classificatory branch or phase of a science.

teleology. The study of purposes as causations.

telepathy. The concept of direct communication among living persons without the intermediation of any form of speech, and over any obstacle of time, space or distance.

teratophobia. Morbid dread of fathering or giving birth to a monster.

✦test. Any controlled or standardized situation for investigating the behavior patterns of a subject. Tests frequently referred to in the literature are here grouped as to the field of behavior tested :

intelligence, (*q.v.*), *tests of:*

CATTELL INFANT INTELLIGENCE SCALE. Performance levels for infants from 2 to 30 months of age. Scored like the *Stanford-Binet* (q.v.).

KUHLMAN INTELLIGENCE TEST. Stresses performance over verbal facility and is therefore more accurate in the presence of language difficulties than is the *Stanford-Binet* (q.v.). Measures also rate of development (P.A.), speed and accuracy.

OTIS SELF-ADMINISTERING. Four alternate forms for rough estimate of average perceptive-integrative capacity, especially as to speed and alertness.

✦STANFORD - BINET (*revised*). Test items are arranged in *year levels* from two to superior adult. The level at which the subject passes all items is the *basal year;* his total score is his *mental age;* this divided by his chronological age (up to 16) is his *intelligence quotient* (q.v.). Test results are most accurate for children, but not reliable for adults

unless contingently interpreted. The "normal" range is from 90 to 109; other ranges are: 0–24, idiot; 25–49, imbecile (both requiring custodial care); 50–69, moron, requiring special extramural supervision; 70–79, borderline; 80–89, dull normal; 110–124, superior; 125–139, very superior; 140, maximal. Wide ranges of performance and failures in abstract items may indicate *organic deterioration.*

✦WECHSLER-BELLEVUE INTELLIGENCE SCALE. A verbal and performance test standardized on adults, which investigates information, comprehension, arithmetical measoning, digit memory, similarities, configurational grasp, visual completion and object assembly; or, as an alternate test, the subject's vocabulary. Subtests are weighted for speed and accuracy, and differentially graded. I.Q. as in the Stanford-Binet, but more reliable in estimating average intelligence in adults.

intelligence, deterioration (*q.v.*) *tests of:*

BABCOCK-LEVY (REVISED FORM). Tests vocabulary, general information, symbol substitution and copying designs for correctness, speed and accuracy. Scored as an index between vocabulary norm (*expectancy*) and efficiency on other performance scales. Indicates aphasic or categorical disintegration in organic deteriorative states.

CATEGORY TEST. The subject arranges a wide variety of jumbled objects into groups or "categories" of his own choosing, and is graded for proficiency in "*abstract*" as distinguished from "*concrete*" behavior (K. Goldstein).

VIGOTSKY TEST (HANFMANN - KASANIN). The subject is asked to group small wooden blocks differing in size, shape, color and weight into any arrangements he selects, and is graded on the speed, accuracy and type of his "category" formations. Impaired capacity for abstraction may reveal organic cerebral disease, whereas deviated or bizarre categories may indicate schizophrenic thinking (N. Cameron).

WELLS MEMORY TEST. Tests remote and recent anamnestic memory, and speed and accuracy of associative retention and recall.

personality (*q.v.*) *tests of:*

ALLPORT-VERNON STUDY OF VALUES. A self-administered series of 45 items with alternative answers which are graded as indicating the subject's predominant values in life according to the Spranger "personality types" (see *types, Spranger*).

BERNREUTER PERSONALITY INVENTORY. A series of form questions answered by "Yes," "No," and "?" on the basis of which the subject is graded by percentile rank as to *neuroticism, self-sufficiency, introversion* and *dominance*. Like all such tests, the replies really indicate only the subject's *professed* attitudes under the circumstances of the examination.

KENT - ROSANOFF WORD - ASSOCIATION TEST. The subject associates to a list of 100 stimulus-words, and is graded on speed, content of reply and emotional reaction, as presumably influenced by his unconscious ideational - affective "complexes."

projective tests:
These study the subject's "projected" imagery, static or kinetic, in response to standard stimuli (v. *projection*). The most frequently used are these:

✦RORSCHACH PSYCHODIAGNOSTIC EXPERIMENT. The subject describes what he sees on a series of 10 standard cards showing large, almost symmetrical inkblots, 5 black-and-white and 5 colored. His answers are graded as to form (F), movement (M), color (C) and other criteria as to whole field-perception (W), detail organization (D or d), "color shock," chiaroscuro effects (K), banal (P) or original (O) content, etc. Scoring indicates personality patterns (e.g., "*pedantry*," q.v.), special interests and (less reliably) general intelligence; in addition the patient's performance may reveal deviations of affect, and neurotic or psychotic tendencies. The administration and evaluation of the Rorschach test requires special training and skill, else its reported results may be seriously misleading.

SZONDI TEST. The subject's expressed preferences among a series of photographs is held to be psychiatrically diagnostic; highly dubious rationale and reliability.

✦THEMATIC APPERCEPTION TEST. The subject is shown 20 photographs of various dramatic scenes and is asked to tell a story about each. These stories may then be analyzed (1) as to their *themes* of opposed motivations and frustrations (Morgan and Murray), or

(2) their symbolic significance as to the subject's unconscious conflicts and their verbal content of various expressions, words, or phrases indicating underlying anxiety, doubt or depression as opposed to wishfully defensive fantasy patterns (Masserman and Balken). The evaluation of this test, too, requires extensive psychiatric training and special experience on the part of the examiner.

vocational aptitude, *tests of:*
MINNESOTA MECHANICAL ASSEMBLY TEST. The subject assembles 33 mechanical devices, and is graded for speed and accuracy.

PSYCHOLOGICAL EXAMINATION FOR COLLEGE FRESHMAN, AMERICAN COUNCIL ON EDUCATION. A comprehensive test for information and various abilities. Well standardized and validated for the prediction of scholastic success.

SEASHORE MEASURE OF MUSICAL ABILITY. Tests of appreciation of loudness, time, timbre, rhythm and tonal memory for sounds produced by standardized phonograph records. Tests musical apperception, but *not* creative or technical talent.

STANFORD SCIENTIFIC APTITUDE TEST. A paper-and-pencil test for knowledge of physical and chemical principles, mathematical ability, mechanical visualization, patterns, etc. Useful at the high-school level.

STRONG VOCATIONAL INTEREST INVENTORY. The subject indicates his preferences among 400 vocational pursuits and part-activities listed on a blank which is compared with standard norms to determine his predominant interests. Separate blanks for men and women.

tetany.   Intense, sustained muscular contractions.

tetraplegia.   Paralysis of the arms and legs; *quadriplegia.*

thaassophobia.   Morbid dread of sitting.

thalassophobia.   Morbid dread of open water, as lake or sea.

thanatomania.   Incessant impulse to suicide.

thanatophobia.   Morbid dread of death.

Thanatos or death-instinct.   In older psychoanalytic theory, a group of "instinctive" tendencies variously labelled *sado-masochistic, aggressive, repetition-compulsive,* etc., which seemingly outweigh the libidinal *pleasure-principle* (qq.v.) and appear to lead the organism toward self-destruction, senescence and death. The concept of Thanatos is, however, rapidly becoming obsolescent cf. Index).

thaumaturgy. The employment of magic symbols and maneuvers.

theatre, therapeutic. In Moreno's *psychodrama* (q.v.) the stage setting for the mimetic therapy.

✦therapy. In psychiatry, the science, techniques and art of exerting a favorable influence on behavior disorders by every ethical means available. Cf. *psychotherapy* and Index.

thermophobia. Morbid dread of heat.

thymonoic. In psychobiology (Muncie), thought processes determined or strongly influenced by deviations in mood.

tic. A minor, unconscious, repetitious gesture or muscular movement; a *habit-spasm.*

tic douloureux. Severe facial pain caused by disease of the fifth cranial nerve.

tonitrophobia. Morbid dread of thunder.

tonus. State of muscular tension; tonicity.

topography, mental. The concept that the "psyche" or "mind" is divisible into layers, regions or structures.

topophobia. Morbid dread of a specific place.

torpillage. The infliction of physical pain in the treatment of behavior disorders.

torsion-spasm. Spasmodic twisting of neck or body.

torticollis. Maintained torsion of the neck.

total push. A method of therapy of behavior disorders eclectically formulated, in which every available means is energetically utilized in the treatment (A. Myerson).

totem. A symbol for the protective or ruling spirit of a group.

toxic. Pertaining to *noxious* (injurious, poisonous) substances or processes.

trait. A specific, characteristic, or relatively constant behavior-pattern.

✦transference. 1. In general, the attribution (transfer) of desires, feelings and relationships, originally experienced by the subject with regard to his parents and siblings, onto other persons who, in the subject's residual unconscious attitudes, are assigned parental or other familial roles in his later life. 2.

More specifically in psychoanalytic therapy, the unconscious attitude of the patient toward the analyst and the role in which the latter is fantasied, e.g., maternal, rivalrous, erotic, etc.

transference, counter-. In psychoanalysis, the unconscious attitudes of the analyst toward his patient.

transference, negative. Resistant or hostile attitudes of the patient toward the analyst.

transference, positive. A seemingly favorable (though perhaps neurotically overdependent, passive or erotic) attitude of the patient toward the analyst.

transposition. A defensive process of isolating guilt-ridden conations, affects and behavior-patterns and interchanging them with others less charged with anxiety (e.g., a mother incestuously attached to her son and jealous of her daughter may be compulsively aggressive toward the son and over-indulgent to the girl).

trauma. An injury, physical or otherwise, which is disruptive to the optimal adaptations of the organism.

traumatophilia. A seeming avidity for injury; e.g., *accident-proneness* (q.v.).

traumatophobia. Morbid dread of injury.

tremophobia. Morbid dread of trembling.

tremor. Rapid, small-amplitude muscular shaking or trembling.

tribade. A female homosexual who plays the male role.

trichotillomania. Incessant pulling of the hair.

tuberculophobia. Morbid dread of tuberculosis.

tumescence. Congestion and swelling.

twilight state. Semi - consciousness, sometimes with automatic or *fugue*-like (q.v.) activity. May be induced by hypnosis or by drugs.

twins, fraternal. From separate ova and sperms; therefore may be very different in hereditary characteristics.

twins, identical. From one ovum and sperm; therefore must be identical in hereditary characteristics.

twins, Siamese. Anatomically joined.

✦types of character, personality or physique. The various classifications are legion, but the following are most often referred to in the literature: *Draper, G.:* The hereditary characteristics of an

individual (*biotype* as derived from *genotype*), further modified by environment (*phenotype*).
Galenic-Hippocratic (*humoral*).
1. CHOLERIC. (Dominated by "yellow bile"): mercurial, irritable, impulsive.
2. MELANCHOLIC. (Dominated by "black bile"): brooding, emotional depressive.
3. PHLEGMATIC. (Dominated by "phlegm"): slow, apathetic, stolid.
4. SANGUINE. (Dominated by "strong blood"): impulsive, active, optimistic.
Hippocratic.
1. HABITUS APOPLECTICUS. Thick-set, heavy body-build, susceptible to apoplexy.
2. HABITUS PHTHISICUS. Tall, slender, angular body-build, susceptible to pulmonary disease.
Jaensch, E. R.
1. B, Basedow, or *integrated constitution*, characterized by a capacity for voluntary control of *eidetic imagery* (q.v.), a tendency to hyperthyroidism, relatively stable emotional organization and a typical end-capillary structure (W. Jaensch).
2. T, *tetanic* or *unintegrated constitution*, distinguished by lesser control of imagery, low blood calcium, hypersensitivity to stimuli and dissociated personality reactions. Recent work indicates that the Jaensch typology, especially that concerned with its racial implications, has very little scientific validity.
✦*Jung, C.*
1. INTROVERTED. Self-concerned, ruminative, remote, imaginative, inclined to schizoid behavior (Kretschmer).
2. EXTRAVERTED. Objective, sensitive to external affairs, emotionally labile, active, energetic; inclined to manic-depressive disorders (Kretschmer).
Jung also speaks of
3. FEELING TYPES, with labile and sensitive affect, and
4. INTUITIVE TYPES, markedly influenced by their unconscious racial and personal heritage.
✦*Kretschmer, E.*
1. ASTHENIC OR LEPTOSOMIC. A body type characterized by leanness, underweight, flat chest and underdeveloped muscular system, especially marked in the phthinoid subgroup; prone to *schizothymia* (q.v.).
2. ATHLETIC. Characterized by robust

skeletal and muscular development; generally schizothymic.
3. DYSPLASTIC. A group of "body-types" which show wide anthropometric deviations from the other three types, and which also tend to "schizothymia."
4. PYKNIC. Short, stocky, large body cavities, bradycephalic; inclined to *cyclothymia* (q.v.).
Meyer, A. PSYCHOBIOLOGIC or ERGASTIC types. See *reaction types.*
psychoanalytic character types. See character, anal-, oral-, and genital-.
Rosanoff, A. F.
1. ANTISOCIAL. Tending to *psychopathy* or *criminality.*
2. CYCLOTHYMIC, subtyped as (a) *manic*, (b) *depressive*, (c) *irrascible*, (d) *unstable*—all tending to affective disorders.
3. AUTISTIC (constricted in interests, introspective) tending to *schizoid* reactions.
4. EPILEPTIC (impulsive, stubborn, aggressive).
Rostan and Sigaud.
1. CEREBRAL. A body type supposedly dominated by the central nervous system.
2. DIGESTIVE. Corresponds to Kretschmer's *pyknic.*
3. RESPIRATORY. Characterized by a well-developed heart, lungs and respiratory system; corresponds to *athletic.*
Spranger, E.
A typology based on the intellectual interests and social values of the individual, i.e.: 1. THEORETICAL; 2. ECONOMIC; 3. POLITICAL; 4. AESTHETIC; 5. SOCIAL and 6. RELIGIOUS.
✦*Sheldon, W.*
1. ECTOMORPHIC. A "body type" characterized by predominant development of the ectoderm (epidermis, sense organs and central nervous system), hence sensitive and hyperreactive.
2. ENDOMORPHIC. Predominant endoderm derivatives (mainly gastrointestinal, and organic), hence interest in nutritive living.
3. MESOMORPHIC. (Predominantly skeletal and muscular), hence active and energetic. All persons are classified as a mixture of these fundamental "types," graded as to predominance on a scale of 1 to 7.
Stockard, C. R.:
1. "LATERAL" as distinguished from
2. "LINEAR" body-types.
Viola, G.:

1. MICROSPLANCHNIC. A "body-type" with small viscera and well-developed soma, as distinguished from
2. MACROSPLANCHNIC. Corresponding to the *pyknic* (cf. Kretschmer).
3. NORMOSPLANCHNIC or EUMORPHIC designates a normal, intermediate or optimal "body type."

ululation. Incessant, compulsive sobbing or crying.

uncinate fit. Episodic olfactory or gustatory hallucinations and chewing movements attributed to lesions of the uncinate gyrus of the brain.

✦unconscious. In general, any behavioral process of which the subject is not directly aware. In addition, *unconscious* has many meanings as variously used in the literature, ranging from *stuporous* to vaguely mystic connotations of *atavistic* communality (Jung, Miller).

✦Unconscious. In psychoanalytic topography, that portion of the *psyche* which comprises the *Id* instincts, plus those large parts of the *Ego* (adaptive) and *Superego* (self-directive) portions of the personality which are in contact with the Id, and the functions of which are not available to direct awareness *consciousness*) or immediate recall and introspection (*preconscious*).

✦undoing. A defensive reversal of an anxiety-ridden act.

uranism. A rare term for homosexuality.

✦Ur-defenses (-delusions, -illusions). Irrational but indestructible faiths in one's own (1) physical powers, (2) supposed friends and (3) magic concepts and practices.

urethral phase. In psychoanalytic theory, that phase of libidinal development in which the child's erotic activities center about the urinary functions of his phallus.

urolagnia. Morbid fascination with urine.

ursymbol. A primitive, relatively stable representation of some pervasive human association; for instance, monuments associated with phallic ideas, or caves symbolizing maternal femininity.

vaginismus. Spastic contraction of the vagina before or during intercourse.

vegetative nervous system. An old term for the *sympathetic nervous system* (q.v.).

verbigeration. Stereotyped repetition of words or sentences.

vertigo. Dizziness, usually with faintness.

voyeurism. Erotic pleasure in clandestine peeping.

Weltschmerz. Pervasive, socially - projected brooding or melancholy.

womb-phantasy. An unconscious desire to return to the complete passivity, security and peace of the womb. See *Nirvana-fantasy.*

✦working-through. 1. In general, an active reexploration of a problem situation until satisfactory solutions or adaptations are found and firmly established. 2. In psychoanalysis, the tracing of a symbolism to its "deepest" unconscious sources.

xenophobia. Morbid dread of strangers.

yen sleep. Morphine addict's term for withdrawal stupor.

zoanthropy. Animal-like behavior.

zoophobia. Morbid dread of animals.

zoosadism. Erotic pleasure in cruelty to animals.

Index of names

Index of subjects

Page numbers in **boldface type** represent principal discussions.